The Hot Springs Mammoth Site: A Decade of Field and
Laboratory Research in Paleontology, Geology, and
Paleoecology. Produced by The Mammoth Site of Hot Springs,
South Dakota, Inc., 1800 Highway 18-Truck Route, Hot
Springs, South Dakota 57747-0606.

Edited by Larry D. Agenbroad and Jim I. Mead

Produced in MS Word 5.0© by Finn Agenbroad and Maxine
Campbell and into Pagemaker© by Maxine Campbell

Printed in Rapid City, South Dakota by Fenske Printing, Inc.

ISBN 0-9624750-6-8

THE HOT SPRINGS MAMMOTH SITE:

A Decade of Field and Laboratory Research in Paleontology, Geology, and Paleoecology

Larry D. Agenbroad and Jim I. Mead
Editors

To: Phil Anderson, Les Ferguson, Don Collogan, and Eddie Clay, plus the past and present Board of Directors, staff and crew members whose efforts and foresight helped preserve and exhibit this deposit to the people of the Black Hills region, South Dakota, the Nation, and the world.

Table of Contents

PART I
Introduction, History, and Natural Setting

PART II
Paleoecology and Paleontology

PART III
Site Significance, Development and Future

List of Figures

List of Tables

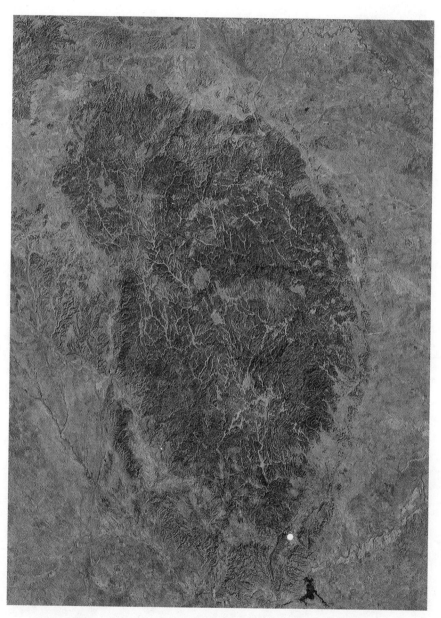

Frontspiece: A satellite image of the Black Hills Uplift.
The Mammoth Site is indicated by the white dot in
the southeastern portion of the Hills.

PART I:

INTRODUCTION, HISTORY, AND NATURAL SETTING

PART I: INTRODUCTION, HISTORY AND NATURAL SETTING

FORWARD

By way of introduction, it should be pointed out that this volume is not the final word on the Mammoth Site of Hot Springs, South Dakota. It should be viewed as an indepth progress report at the end of ten field seasons of excavation and research. The final story that Hot Springs has to tell is still in the future—probably more than an additional ten field seasons away. What is to be set down in the pages that follow is a summary of what we know today, the knowledge we have accumulated in the past ten field seasons, with some indications of where we think the future investigations may lead.

A volume, at this point in time, is needed to allow the professional, and layreader a glimpse of the deposit and what it tells us. Even more importantly, it will also show what we are currently unable to interpret, from the existing database. That, in turn, helps set the focus on questions to be answered, theories and working models to be tested, and procedural adjustments for the forthcoming (future) field seasons.

Authors for each chapter, or section of a chapter, have been noted in the table of contents and in the chapter headings. This volume is composed of investigation results from a number of cooperating, interdisciplinary researchers.

INTRODUCTION

The Mammoth Site of Hot Springs, South Dakota represents a natural trap of Pleistocene fauna. This locality became the site of death, decomposition, and depositional entombment of the attritional accumulation of the remains of a large, local population of Columbian mammoth (*Mammuthus columbi*).

The Hot Springs Mammoth Site is located within the city limits of Hot Springs, South Dakota (Figure 1). Discovery of the Hot Springs Mammoth Site was accidental; during earth-moving operations of the initial phase of construction for a housing development on the south side of Hot Springs, South Dakota, bulldozers and graders exposed teeth, tusks, skulls, and postcranial skeletal elements of mammoth.

Two weeks of salvage excavations and stabilization were done in 1974. Ten days of testing in the summer of 1975 proved the site to be paleontologically significant, and formal excavations were undertaken at the site during the summers of 1976, 1977, 1978, 1979, and 1983, followed by excavations in 1986, 1987, 1988, 1989, and 1990. In those field seasons, the general extent, content, and makeup of the site and its geologic history were outlined and refined. It soon became evident that the deposit represents a unique trap for a large population of Late Pleistocene mammoth.

Preservation of the deposit can be attributed to the unselfish foresight of the landowner–contractor, Phil Anderson, who gave us up to three years to test and evaluate the bone bed; and to Les Ferguson, who became the first president of a newly formed Board of Directors, for the mammoth Site of Hot Springs, South Dakota. Phil ultimately sold the land containing most of the site to the Board of Directors, who began efforts to preserve the locality for posterity.

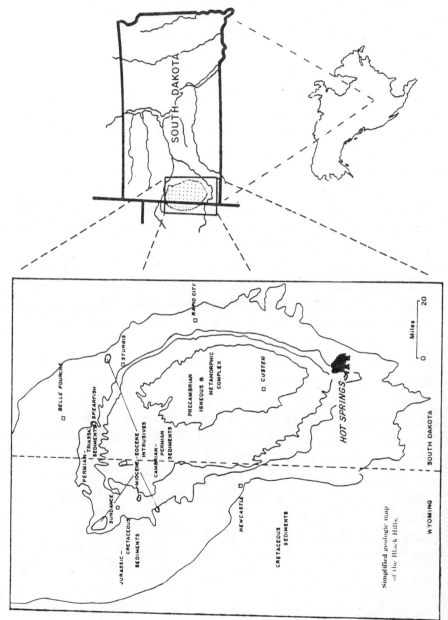

Figure 1. A location map for the Mammoth Site of Hot Springs, South Dakota.

3

Chapter 1

A BRIEF HISTORY OF
THE HOT SPRINGS MAMMOTH SITE

Larry D. Agenbroad

The site was discovered, accidentally, in June of 1974. Discovery was the result of the modification of a local topographic high within an area being developed by a local Hot Springs contractor, Phil Anderson. This hill was being cut down, with the excavated portion being used as fill in other areas of the development. The heavy equipment operator, George (Porky) Hanson, noted a number of large bones protruding from the ground after one pass of his equipment. He put some of those bone fragments in his pickup and was mentioning them to his family at mealtime. His son, Dan, went quickly to the site, and near dusk found two fragments of the same tooth of a mammoth. Recognizing the importance of this discovery, he guarded the site for a period of nearly two weeks while Phil Anderson attempted to get professional evaluation and assessment of the site. The site was turned down, for a variety of reasons, by three agencies within the state of South Dakota. It was also examined and turned down by Charles Jones, of Chadron State College, in Nebraska.

At the time of discovery I was in southeastern Arizona, as co-director of an excavation at the Lehner Ranch Site, a famous mammoth kill-site, where at least 13 Columbian mammoth had been killed, butchered, and consumed by Paleoindian hunters, the Clovis people (Haury *et al.* 1959). That site was closed for the season at the end of June, and several of the crew members and I were transferring to the panhandle of Nebraska where we were to begin a field season of excavation at a paleoindian bison kill, the Hudson-Meng Site (Agenbroad 1978b). Our date of rendezvous and initiation of the season's excavation was set for July 5. I arrived in the area July 2, to

4

Figure 2. The discovery skull of 1974.

find a message stating: "They have elephants in Hot Springs, South Dakota and want you to come have a look." On July 3, I visited the Hot Springs locality (Figure 2) and could estimate 4 to 6 individual animals based on the exposed material. Phil Anderson and Dan Hanson had already put plaster jackets on an articulated hind leg that had been partially exposed by heavy equipment. Numerous ribs, scapulae, vertebra and unidentified elements, which were partially exposed, were observed.

Phil asked me what did I think should be done with the bones. My response was that I had a large crew beginning excavation at the bison kill on the 5th of July and that I would be unable to personally be present at Hot Springs. I would, however, send a portion of my crew—who had just been working on the mammoth kill-site in Arizona—to Hot Springs, under the direction of Jim Mead. Those individuals would spend ten days stabilizing, mapping, excavating and removing, and backfilling over bone-rich areas so that we might return when the bison-kill was finished for the season. Phil said there were plenty of areas that he could be working on within the development, and that he could allow us 2-3 years to test the bone deposit to see if it had scientific potential.

Jim spent the first 10 days of the 1974 Hudson-Meng field season commuting to Hot Springs from our field camp with several members of the crew. They stabilized, mapped, salvaged and backfilled over portions of between 6 and 8 individual mammoth. McColley's Chapel in the Hills funeral home provided a grave canopy (Figure 3) as a shade for the crew. Dan Hanson and some of his associates kept night guard on the excavations during this interval.

It was apparent from the 10-day salvage period in July of 1974, and several weekend test excavations later in the fall that the locality deserved a more intensive test period. I began to write grant proposals, seeking funds for a small scale field excavation in the summer of 1975. Having placed an asterisk on the final budget figure of the proposals, reviewers were guided to a notation stating I would rather receive a portion of the funds requested than a complete denial of funds. The result was an award of $500 from the Penrose Grant of

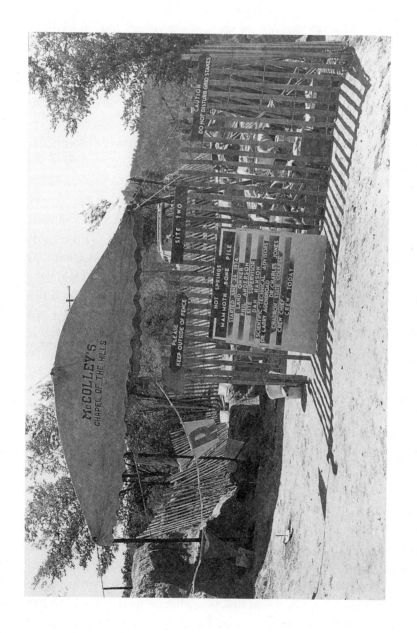

Figure 3. A grave canopy (for shade) over the site in 1974

7

the Geological Society of America.

After the Hudson-Meng field session of 1975, I asked for ten volunteers to work for ten days at the mammoth site in Hot Springs. All I could offer was a tent camp on-site, and I would feed the crew at a local cafe, plus we could use shower facilities in the National Guard armory.

Our efforts indicated a very thick bone concentration in the northeastern portion of the deposit. We had numerous elements exposed—some with pedestals for field casting and removal. On the last day (Saturday) of the volunteer test season one of the crew called me over and said, "I think I've got a skull!" I looked and said, "Yes, you have the nuchal crest, detail it, lets cast it and get it ready for removal, we've got seven hours left." A little later I was called back to the same specimen when she called out, "I've got the orbits!" My response was to the effect that the skull would probably be broken at the alveoli (tusk sockets) and to hurry and detail it so we could cast it as we had only five hours left. Again, shortly thereafter, I was called back to the specimen by Barb calling, "I've got the alveoli!" Upon examination, I said, "The tusks will probably be missing, detail it, cast it, and lets get a move on, we've only got four and one-half hours left." The next call (which I anticipated) was, "I've got ivory!" And sure enough, not only ivory but full ivory in a skull sitting in near-life position on the very margin of the eastern portion of the sinkhole (Figure 4).

At that point, the shut-down schedule for the excavation was no longer practical. We decided to extend our activity until this specimen was taken care of. Many of the crew had to register on Monday morning, for colleges and universities in the local area, and at more distant locations. We held a "council of war" and decided that all who could do so would be first in line for registration and then skip school until Wednesday, or until we had the skull taken care of—whichever came first.

That evening, sitting on a backdirt pile eating a cookie, I was admiring the newly exposed skull in the life-like position in which it was deposited and buried. While doing so, a full moon rose over

Figure 4. The 1975 skull, in life position, with the mandible only slightly misplaced.

Battle Mountain, to the east, and moonlight flooded across the skull. My thoughts were, "How many thousand years has it been since moonlight was in this animal's eyes?" We had yet to place the deposit in a chronologic framework.

That specimen and renewed grant writing activity provided funding for the 1976 field season, from Earthwatch and the National Geographic Society.

The 1976 field season produced such a large concentration of bone and ivory near the location of the 1975 skull that a temporary building was constructed over a portion of the bone bed, rather than backfill, or cast and remove bone. It was also during this season that Phil Anderson asked me what he should do with this site and its bones. My reply was that since he was the landowner, I would do whatever he wanted, but that my opinion was that the bone would never look better than it did right there in the ground—where it was deposited. I said, "If you want me to remove the bone and truck it to a museum, I'd do so, but that an *in situ* exhibit for mammoth bones such as are present here would be unique in North America, if not in the world." It was from this conversation that the concept that has now materialized—that *in situ* exhibit of the mammoth bone bed was born. It was also at that time that the initial Mammoth Site of Hot Springs South Dakota was formed, with Les Ferguson as the president. This group served as volunteer guards, guides, and talent to promote the site, its value, and the purchase of the land on which the site was located. It should also be noted, as a matter of record, that Phil sold the land containing the majority of the site, to the Mammoth Site group, at his cost.

Now, unless it appears that from that point on, all was a succession of tranquil, easy steps in the progression to the present facility, a few items should be mentioned, for the record. We began having a series of complaints from at least two residents who had just moved into the development. They did not want the site, crew, visitors, etc. in their neighborhood, and requested that we, "dig it up and haul it away." In fact, I've spent more time in city council meetings in Hot Springs, South Dakota, than all the other communities I've ever lived

10

in. Then it was decided the city <u>must</u> have an alleyway, which went through the northern portion of the site (they hadn't had one for 270 million years, but it was deemed <u>essential</u> that one be emplaced in 1979). I agreed to do the earthwork, so that we could salvage the faunal remains, and test deeply below the alley (Figure 5). We did not know if we would ever be able to go below the alley in the future.

Space in which to store bones that were cast and removed from the site was always a problem. Various board members stored casts in their garages, the local power company stored casts in some of their buildings, etc. Finally, in 1979 we put all the casts in the basement of a ranch house near Cheyenne River, on one of the board members' farm. The casts were then locked at the basement door, and again at the ground-entry door. During the winter, we got a call asking if the Mammoth Site was missing any bones. The immediate answer was, "No," since they were presumed to be in safe storage. Some of the board members went to the farm, found the locks had been forced and all the bones were missing! It seems two unemployed miners just happened to be trying to sell the Mammoth Site bones, after having, "accidentally" found them in, "an unlocked, abandoned" building. After that adventure the bones were transferred to the upper floor of the Minnekahta Mall, in Hot Springs. They stayed there until space was purchased, on-site, for their storage and stabilization.

After the 1979 season, I informed the board of directors for the Hot Springs Mammoth Site that my crew would not return until we had a decision, from the board, as to the ultimate disposition of the bone bed—whether it would be removed, or a permanent structure placed over the site. The rationale behind this statement was that we had proven the value and extent of this unique paleontological repository and that it was not in the best interest of the bone bed to keep exposing, mapping and backfilling incremental portions of the site. Thus, we initiated a self-imposed moratorium on further excavation, until a decision was forwarded by the board of directors.

In the fall of 1982, I received a telephone call stating the site

Figure 5. Deep testing below the alley right-of-way, 1979.

would have a structure over it by 1983 season. I initiated grant proposals, received a positive response from the granting agencies and
then received a phone call from the newly elected board president
telling me not to come as they had decided not to erect a building.
My response was, "We have been funded and will be there for the
month of July 1983, to test one of the areas," (southwest portion) of
the site we had not seen since the 1974 backfill, to see if bone were
as abundant there as in the 1975-79 excavations. In retaliation for
not heeding the presidential "order," we were denied use of the Hot
Springs High School facilities that year.

That was the year we found the giant short-faced bear (*Arctodus
simus*) among the mammoth bones (Agenbroad and Mead 1986). At
the close of the season, we again initiated a self-imposed moratorium on further excavation, due to fund solicitation and the construction of Phase I of the present facility. On September 21, 1985, the
building was dedicated and excavation began, again, in the summer
of 1986.

Figure 6 depicts the intervals of exploration, excavation, and
moratorium at the site is a graph of percentage of total bone recovered per season since 1974. It can be noted that there is a marked
reduction in bone recovery percentage in the post-building phase. It
may be expressed in these terms: the 1974 through 1983 seasons
were exploratory in nature—an attempt to find the limits of the bone
bed and test for the abundance of faunal material within various sectors of the deposit. With the construction of the building over the
site, we spent the 1986 season exhuming the backfilled areas of previous seasons, and at that point in time began a change from
the"exploration phase" to the "exhibit phase" in the methodology of
excavating the site.

The 1986 season was the first season within the new building.
For once, we could "laugh at Mother Nature" as far as negative
weather conditions were concerned. That "blessing" brought its own
problems in high humidity and heat within the building. Most of the
1986 season was spent exhuming old excavations that had been backfilled, for protection, prior to the construction of the present build-

13

ing. Since that season, the excavations have concentrated on slower, exhibit-style excavations within a controlled environment. Some testing has taken place because we still do not know the exact configuration of the most productive bone bed. Not having to combat rain and hail in open excavations has allowed a more liesurely pace of excavation. The building has also allowed a permanent preservation crew year-round access to the bone bed—not just the field excavation period—for stabilization and preservation of bone, *in situ*, for exhibit.

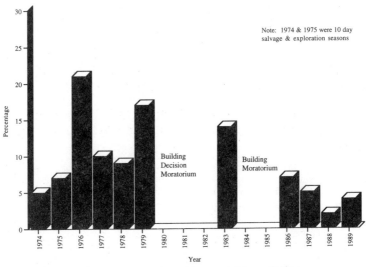

Figure 6. Percentage of total bone yield per field season.

On Friday afternoon, the 20th of October, 1989, ground was broken for Phase II of the building. This expansion provided educational exhibits, and a retail area. As revenue is available we anticipate additional expansion, for laboratory space, bone storage facilities, bone preparation laboratories, a theatre/auditorium, a library, and quarters for visiting researchers—not just for the Mammoth Site, but throughout the Southern Black Hills region. Increased educational endeavors, in the classrooms, at the site, and via television are planned for K-12 curriculum, as well as college and university students and faculty, and the general public.

14

Chapter 2

GEOLOGY, HYDROLOGY, AND EXCAVATION
OF THE SITE

Larry D. Agenbroad

Location and Physiographic Setting

The Hot Springs Mammoth Site is located within the city limits of Hot Springs, South Dakota. An extension of existing streets would place the locality near the intersection of Nineteenth Street and Evanston Avenue, in the southern portion of the city.

Located in Red Valley, a topographic low eroded in the Spearfish Shale, which encircles the Black Hills interior, the site is a local topographic high. The small hill on which it is located is due, in fact, to the relative resistance to erosion of the sediments containing the fauna, as opposed to the less resistant Spearfish Shale. The site remains as an example of reversed topographic expression, the sedimentary fill of a former sinkhole having become the top of a small hill by differential erosion. To the east and southeast, prominent ridges of resistant sandstones are exposed. To the north, northwest, and southwest, hills formed of limestones and older sedimentary units rise in response to the anticlinal structure of the Black Hills (Figure 1).

Origin

Solution and removal of gypsum and anhydrite from underlying formations, particularly the Minnelusa Formation, resulted in post-solution collapse. The collapse caused breccia pipes to be formed above the collapse areas, and such pipes extend upward to the modern surface, penetrating as much as 300 meters (Laury 1980) of overlying sediments. The Hot Springs Mammoth Site was formed in one of these breccia pipes (Figure 7).

15

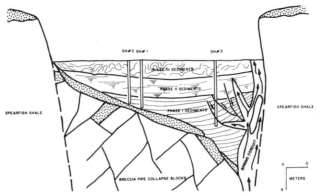

Figure 7. A schematic of the physical character of the sinkhole hydraulics and sedimentary fill.

Interpretation of the results of years of excavation at the site has revealed that the accumulation and preservation of mammoth remains was accomplished by a natural trap in the form of a karst depression containing a spring fed pond. Excavations exposing portions of the walls of this ancient sinkhole reveal an elliptical depression (Figure 8) in the Permo-Triassic Spearfish Shale. Where exposed, the walls vary in slope from 60° from the horizontal, to overhanging. Drill holes provided by the South Dakota Geological Survey indicate the sinkhole fill to be a lense-shaped deposit, ±14 m thick in the southwest portion to ±21 m in the northeastern portion. The sinkhole fill consists of laminated fine grained materials, ranging from clay to course sand. These deposits represent reworking and sorting of decomposed wall rock and terrace gravels. The energy, and agency, for such reworking was furnished by artesian springs emerging from the northeastern portion of the depression. A pond environment was created by the spring effluent, resulting in laminated fine-grained deposits. Three phases of sedimentation are recognized (Laury 1980). The initial phase consisted of a coarse grained unit representing, in part, the reworking of material from the initial collapse of sinkhole walls, carrying overlying terrace gravels from the ancestral Fall River. The second phase of sedimentation is represented by well-laminated sands and silts. The final phase is characterized as more clay-rich and silt-rich, and is heavily bioturbated (by mammoth). This final phase is considered to represent a low energy, shallow water deposit —essentially a mud hole, or wallow created as spring effluent diminished, or was diverted to the deepening channel of Fall River. Mammoth remains and tracks occur in all the sedimentary phases.

16

The environment of deposits and the nature of the sediments being deposited have preserved even the most delicate bones, such as
hyoids, from the mammoth carcasses. Fish skeletons have been faithfully preserved in the low energy portion of the sinkhole fill.

Excavations through the 1989 field season have disturbed less
than 25% of the site. These excavations have revealed the remains
of at least 43 Columbian mammoth. It is estimated that at least this
number still remain in the undisturbed portions of the site.

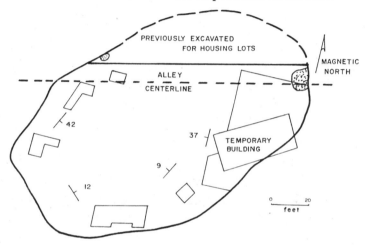

Figure 8. A plan map of the sinkhole, as known in 1976.

HYDROGEOLOGY

Regional Hydrogeology

The Black Hills uplift is classed as a domal mountain mass caused
by the intrusion of granites into overlying Paleozoic sedimentary units.
The result and land form is an elliptical area (Figure 1) of anticlinal
folding whose crest has been eroded, exposing an elevated crystalline igneous core, surrounded by a metamorphic envelope, in turn
surrounded by tilted sedimentary units dipping outward from the core,
in all directions. In the northern Black Hills, much later, Tertiary
igneous intrusives are very localized features.

With an elevated, crystalline core exposed in the center of the uplift, surficial drainage is radial, away from the core. The major surface streams flow north to the Belle Fouche River, or south, and east to the Cheyenne River (Gries and Crooks 1968). These drainages emerge from the uplift through a series of water gaps which break the cuestas ringing the Hills. From the core, surface water migrates across tilted Upper Cambrian to Cretaceous sedimentary units. Of particular importance is their encounter with a series of Pennsylvanian and Mississippian limestones (Table 1).

Table 1. The geologic section near Hot Springs.

Period	Litholgic unit
Quaternary	Terrace/pediment sands and gravels
Tertiary	White River Group
Cretaceous	Pierre Shale Niobrara Formation Greenhorn Formation Graneros Group Fall River (Dakota?) Sandstone Lakota Formation
Jurassic	Morrison Formation Unkpapa Sandstone Sundance Formation
Triassic	Spearfish Shale
Permian	Minnekahata Limestone Opeche Formation
Pennsylvanian	Minnelusa Formation
Mississipian	Pahasapa Limestone

Crossing these limestones, there are significant water losses, especially in the Pahasapa (Madison) Limestone (Gries and Crooks 1968). This region is also an area of major sinkhole development, and hosts many of the major cavern systems such as Wind Cave, and Jewel Cave. Water entering the limestones becomes part of an artesian system due to the penetration into the inclined carbonates, and the presence of overlying impermeable formations (Gries and Crooks 1968), usually in the upper Minnelusa Formation, to just beneath the

Minnekahta Limestone. These areas are often the loci of large resurgent springs such as Cascade Spring, Hot Springs, and Martin Valley (Buffalo Gap) Spring, in the southern Black Hills, and as a series of spring fed lakes, such as Coxes Lake, near Spearfish in the northern Hills. Often, these springs cause, or are present in breccia pipes and sinkholes formed in surficial deposits such as the Spearfish Shale, or even the Sundance Sandstone.

Local Hydrogeology

The Mammoth Site of Hot Springs represents a paleohydrogeologic natural trap which enticed mammoth to their death and incorporated their remains in the sedimentary fill of the feature.

In addition to the physical formation of the breccia pipe and resulting karst feature, a critical factor in producing an animal trap from what would otherwise be just another sinkhole was the presence of an artesian spring. Groundwater in the Minnelusa Formation utilized the conduit formed by the breccia pipe, forming the spring. Spring effluent created a standing body of water within the steep-walled sink. The presence of a pool of water served as the attraction for mammoth, which were apparently abundant in the southern Black Hills at the time, based on the large number of individuals whose remains are incorporated in the sediments that ultimately filled the sinkhole.

Artesian and thermal springs (Table 2) are not uncommon in the Black Hills Uplift. The snowpack and runoff are able to infiltrate into limestones, dolomites, and sandstones, which are dipping from the uplifted crystalline core. The hydraulic gradient of these aquifers and confining beds produces sufficient piezometric conditions to generate artesian springs wherever structural features, such as faults, or breccia pipes, allow water to penetrate overlying formations.

Table 2. Thermal Springs within the Red Valley (Race Track) of the Black Hills, South Dakota (Rahn and Gries 1973)

Locality	Spring	Discharge (cfs)	Temperature (Fahrenheit)
Hot Springs	Evans	22.92	87
Hot Springs	Cold Brook	.66	
Hot Springs	Hot Brook	1.98	75
Cascade	Cascade	22.55	67
Buffalo Gap	Beaver Creek	8.56	64
Crow Creek	Coxes Lake	17.47	52
(Spearfish)	Mirror Lake	17.47	

Water Supply

The principal water supply for the Mammoth Site pond was through marginal artesian springs. Conduits 1 and 2 (Figure 8), are present along the pond-fill/Spearfish contact, and others probably exist. Conduit 2 spring vents and their limited areal extent (<1 m^2) suggest very low energy and very low volume discharge. Conduit 1 was the dominant water source. Highly turbulent water issued from Conduit 1 feeders, and so doing eroded and deepened the pond floor, induced slope failure in adjacent pond strata and sinkhole walls (Figure 8). Sediment grain size, sorting quality, and stratigraphic section thickness are diminished toward the southwest, away from Conduit 1. In contrast, such facies changes are lacking around Conduit 2.

Peripheral to Conduit 1 mammoths undoubtedly contributed to sediment disruption. Preliminary investigations suggest more of them have been trapped in or near the Conduit 1 area than elsewhere in the site, attesting to the treacherous substrate conditions. (Agenbroad and Laury 1979; Laury this volume)

Water Depth

The water level within the sinkhole pond was probably controlled by the elevation of the hydrostatic head within the artesian-pressured groundwater system in combination with surface leakage over a sill or through capping Terrace IV gravels. Water-level fluctuation during pond filling is unknown, but several estimates of pond depths have been possible.

Mammoth tracks, which are locally common in the laminated pond sediments, have been used to provide an independent estimate of water depths. Using an average maximum shoulder height of 4.3 m for Columbian mammoths (Osborn 1942), water depths of 4 to 5 m seem plausible for the central pond, supporting the other evidence (Agenbroad and Laury 1979; Laury this volume).

Pond-Water Temperature

Several factors strongly suggest that the Mammoth Site pond was being fed by heated springs, possibly even related to the geothermal system that feeds Evans Plunge in downtown Hot Springs and nearby Cascade Springs. Estimates of water temperature derived from invertebrate remains and fish fossils from the sedimentary fill further substantiate thermal water. It is estimated the water temperature was approximately 35°C (95°F) (Agenbroad and Laury 1979; Laury 1980, 1990, this volume). Mead *et al.* (this volume) suggest water temperatures in the range of 40°-35°C.

Fossil Springs and Black Hills Cave Hydrology

Geomorphic evidence in the form of fossil spring mounds and carbonate (tuffa) encrustations and benches along Fall River and Cascade Creek attest to higher water tables and piezometric surfaces in the late Pleistocene and Holocene. A group of fossil spring mounds, including the one containing the Mammoth Site are present at a surficial elevation of 1070 to 1115 m (3500 to 3650 ft) above sea level. This discharge level, dated by the mammoth site at 26,000 yr B.P., indicates: a) higher artesian head in the confined aquifer; b) higher elevation of the ground surface adjacent to the site; higher elevation of the bed of Fall River at that time.

There is some support for higher artesian head in the late Pleistocene. Snowpack and precipitation would have been greater, due to the stationary cold front concomitant with the ice front at the position of the present Missouri River. Increased precipitation and snow pack would equate to increased surface runoff, therefore increased infiltration where those streams run across the limestones described above. Cooler temperatures would result in less evaporation and possibly, less transpiration, making more water available for recharge. Palmer (personal communication) has evidence of a ± 50 foot higher elevation of pools in Wind Cave at approximately the time the sink-hole at the Mammoth Site was an effective trap. The tuffa terraces, etc., along Fall River and Cascade Creek are positioned ± 50 feet above modern stream level.

Wind Cave water levels may not directly relate to artesian springs in Hot Springs, since it appears to be more directly related to the Buffalo Gap spring (Bakalowicz *et al.* 1987). It is considered by Rahn and Gries (1973) that Jewel Cave ground water is the source of resurgent springs such as Cascade Springs at the southern tip of the Black Hills. This indicates the Hot Springs effluents—fossil and modern—were tied to the regional artesian system (Figure 9), and that cave water level chronologies also are reflected by the hydrogeology of resurgent springs, down dip, and to the elevated tuffa deposits along modern water gap streams in the Southern Black Hills.

If we take an average peizometric surface for spring discharge as 1097m (3600 ft) elevation at 26,000 yr B.P. as indicated by the dates from the Mammoth Site, that also is indicative of a higher base level for Fall River, and the floor of the Racetrack Valley (Spearfish Formation surface elevation) in the immediate vicinity of the Mammoth Site.

The Mammoth Site is situated on the 1088 m (3570 ft) contour, above sealevel. The current geomorphic situation is one of reverse (inverse) topography. The sedimentary fill of an ancient sinkhole containing an artesian spring is now the crest of a small hill on the southern outskirts of the city. It is possible the sinkhole was located at the crest of a small, local rise in the ancient topography, just as some modern sinkholes are. Even with that possibility, using the 1088 m (3570 ft) contour as a guide, the present drainage (to the

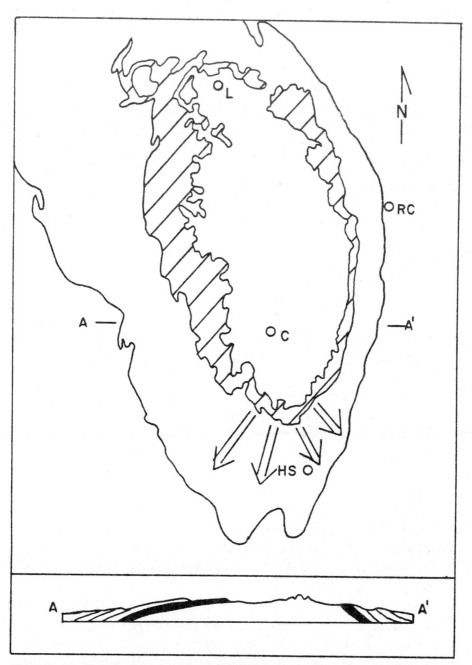

Figure 9. Regional hydrologic character of the Mammoth Site. The shaded area (cross-hatched in plan; black in cross-section A-A') gives a feeling of the porous, permeable limestones receiving precipitation and infiltration generating the artesian system in the Southern Black Hilla. Arrows indicate ground water flow directions. (HS=Hot Springs, C=Custer, RC=Rapid City, L=Lead).

23

south of the Mammoth Site) has been degraded ± 43 m (140 ft) in the past 26,000 years. This amounts to approximately one-tenth of a foot of surficial denudation per year, to give the present topography. That figure combined with the erodability of the Spearfish Shale, is easily within reason.

The relative cohesion of the reworked Spearfish Shale sediments within the sinkhole fill is greater than that of the original Spearfish material, resulting in differential erosion of the original versus reworked sediment. This resulted in a topographic reversal, not just at the Mammoth Site, but at several other fossil spring locations within the city limits. Water availability in the area was not a deciding factor in whether or not a sinkhole became a faunal trap, as the area is well watered by spring discharge at the present itme, and presumably was similarly watered in the past. Correlation of spring mound location and elevations indicates the land surface ca. 26,000 years ago was at or near 1097 m (3600 ft) above sea level in the southern part of the city, at least in the vicinity of the springs. The valley floor may have been at a slightly lower elevation, although the terraces of the ancestral Fall River, give mute evidence of a higher elevation for both surface and ground water. Of even more importance, the piezometric surface for the Minnelusa Formation artesian aquifer appears to have fluctuated through time (Bakalowicz *et al.* 1987). If dated water levels in Wind Cave are extrapolated to the Hot Springs vicinity, assuming an elevation difference of ca. 15 m (50 ft) in surficial (outcrop) elevation the hydraulic gradient would be sufficient to provide a pressure surface at ± the 1066-1097 m (3500-3600 ft) contour elevation in Hot Springs.

EXCAVATION OF THE SITE

Methodology
Excavation of the site followed standard archaeological and paleontological techniques as applied at Murray Springs (Hemmings 1970) and Lehner Ranch (Haury *et al.* 1959), Arizona; Boney Springs, Missouri (Saunders 1977); and Hudson-Meng, Nebraska (Agenbroad

24

1978b). Bones were mapped *in situ*, both vertically and horizontally, as encountered in the fill. Horizontal provenance was obtained with a string grid and transferred to metric graph paper. A vertical datum gave levels on individual bones. A level was taken on the central portion of the bone except in instances in which one end was vertically much higher or lower.

Remains were mapped, field-numbered, and stabilized in place, or removed and taken to the laboratory for further stabilization, reconstruction, and identification. A portion of the remains was left *in situ* after excavation, for subsequent development of the site. Each season saw the inventory of individual mammoth expanded at the near exclusion of all other species of megafauna. Invertebrates were recovered, such as ostracods, gastropods, and pelecypods (Mead 1978; Mead *et al.* this volume). Microvertebrate remains were recovered in screen wash of the spring conduit excavations (Bjork 1978). Pollen and macroflora were absent from the deposit, apparently having been leached by the thermal waters of the spring.

In addition to hand tools, a backhoe/front-end loader was used in trenching, removal of overburden, and backfill operations. A contracted power shovel gave us greater depth penetration for trenches cut for stratigraphic information under the alley right-of-way. The South Dakota Geological Survey provided a truck-mounted drill rig to give us three test holes in the fall of 1978. The information from those holes provided data on the total depth and configuration of the sedimentary fill within the karst depression.

CHRONOLOGY

An estimate of 20,000 yr B.P. was assigned to the site on the basis of the faunal remains in association with the mammoth. Although the wolf and coyote are historically extant, the presence of Pleistocene bear, camel, antelope, and shrub-ox indicate the probability of Late Pleistocene deposits, possibly terminal Pleistocene, as all three generally became extinct at the end of the Wisconsin glaciation.

Several attempts were made to obtain a bone collagen date from scrap mammoth bone from the site. In each attempt, there was insufficient collagen recovery to allow dating of this fraction. Alternately, bone apatite was used as a datable bone fraction. The first results, from scrap bone throughout the excavation to that time, gave a date of 21,000 ± 700 yr B.P. (Gx-5356-A). During the following field season expendible bone from a stratigraphic horizon within the excavation was accumulated and submitted for a more controlled age determination. The date of 26,075 + 975 -790 yr B.P. (Gx-5895-A) on bone apatite from a stratigraphic horizon approximately one half of the fill depth gives a chronologic base. Because the dated fraction is bone apatite, the date should be considered minimal.

Four additional dates were run on bone carbonate and bone apatite under a variety of laboratory conditions (Table 3; Figure 10; H. Haas, SMU, personal communication). The average of the four SMU dates is 25,657 ± 840 yr B.P.; the average of the five dates on apatite and apatite fractions is 22,549 ± 773 yr B.P.; the average of all six radiocarbon dates is 24,950 ± 839 yr B.P. Whether one considers the averages noted above, or the apatite date from the one stratigraphic horizon, it appears 25,000 to 26,000 B.P. closely approximates the period of entrapment at the Hot Springs Mammoth Site.

Table 3. Radiocarbon dates from the Hot Springs Mammoth Site.

Lab #	Material dated	yr B.P. C-14 date	Notes
GX-5356-A	bone apatite, composite sample	21,000±700	
GX-5895-A	bone apatite, 1 stratigraphic horiz.	26,075±975/-790	
SMU-837	Carbonate fraction from bone	36,960±1170	
SMU-838	Apatite fraction	25,640±320	
SMU-863	heated apatite fraction	20,770±350	(765° C)
SMU-865	heated apatite fraction	19,260±1520	(920° C)
	Avg. all dates	24,950±839	
	Avg. apatite	22,549±773	

A uranium series date was conducted by Curtis McKinney of Southern Methodist University. He dated the tooth enamel from one tooth plate from the site. His analysis (L. McKinney, personal communication) dates the deposit at 128,966 yr B.P. This antiquity seems incompatible with the radiocarbon dates for the site. It is possible that uranium rich groundwaters may have altered the accuracy of this technique.

In an attempt to reconcile the dating disparity, a thermoluminescence (TL) date is currently in process. This date, directly from one of the upper Phase II sediments of the western portion of the site should help clarify the relative magnitude of the age of the deposits and the included fauna.

Currently, a ± 26,000 yr B.P. timeframe has been considered to approximate the time the sinkhole was actively trapping mammoths.

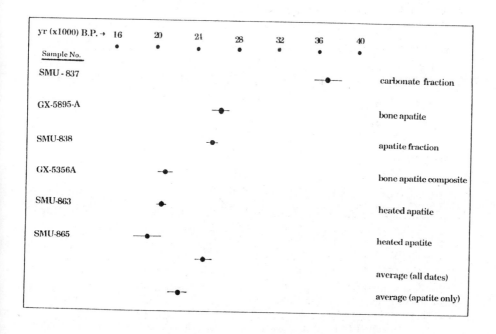

Figure 10. A graphic presentation of the absolute dates from the Mammoth Site. The dot is the accepted age; the bars are standard deviations (see Table 3).

Chapter 3

PALEOENVIRONMENT OF
THE HOT SPRINGS MAMMOTH SITE

Robert L. Laury

The mammoth-bearing laminated sediments which constitute the Mammoth Site fill a steep-walled sinkhole which formed at least 26,000 years ago. Collapse over a solution breccia pipe formed the depression. Artesian water issuing principally from an energetic spring on the northeast margin of the sink quickly established a lake and thereafter maintained an energy gradient which affected sediment dispersal. Sediments were supplied to the pond by storm runoff from proximal uplands and by spring erosion of sinkhole walls. Three successive and gradational phases of sedimentation are recognized in the sinkhole: (1) relatively rapid deposition of poorly sorted gravels and sands as predominantly subaqueous talus accumulations adjacent to near-vertical sinkhole walls, and coeval sedimentation of micrograded sands and silts in the central pond area; (2) slowing of sedimentation rates and widespread deposition of finer grained, rhythmically laminated, but not varved, sands and clayey silts; and progressive but fairly rapid reduction in spring discharge and water depth, terminating pond sedimentation; (3)erosional downcutting by major streams in the area and the synchronous decline of regional groundwater tables likely triggered the original collapse event and, ultimately, terminated spring discharge to the sinkhole.

Paleontological and other indirect evidence strongly suggest that the sinkhole pond was fed by heated springs which maintained a year-round temperature of at least 35°C (95°F). Although warm water may have attracted a variety of megafauna to the sinkhole, mammoths were almost exclusively trapped there. Mammoths were entrapped intermittently throughout sedimentation phases I and II, a

28

time period estimated as several hundred years. When in the water, mammoths deformed pond strata and generated several types of sedimentation events. Pond depths probably did not exceed 4 to 5 m except in the spring conduit area.

INTRODUCTION

The great concentration and abundance of mammoth remains (*Mammuthus columbi*) as well as their manner of entrapment makes the Mammoth Site of Hot Springs, South Dakota, paleontologically unique within the New World. The trap and burial place for the mammoths was a spring-fed pond which occupied an oval-shaped (approximately 25 by 50 m), steep-walled sinkhole (Agenbroad *et al.* 1978a; Laury *et al.* 1978; Agenbroad and Laury 1979; Laury 1980).

Sinkholes or dolines are common landforms which can develop or be filled under widely varying conditions (Jennings 1971; Bloom 1978). However, detailed sedimentological studies of these interesting features are rare (see e.g. Hall 1976; Laury 1980). Extensive trenching and core drilling in the Hot Springs site and reconnaissance coring in several modern Black Hills sink ponds provided a model for sedimentation in this little known terrestrial lacustrine setting. Fossil sinkhole deposits of the Hot Springs type (but not necessarily mammoth-bearing!) are probably fairly common in the Black Hills and similar geologic settings, but they are physiographically inconspicuous and generally go unnoticed. The objectives of this report are (1) to provide a synopsis of the genesis and sedimentary history of filling of the Hot Springs sinkhole, and (2) to relate these events to the Quaternary geomorphological evolution of this part of South Dakota.

GEOLOGICAL SETTING

The Hot Springs site is situated in a grass-covered valley of the southern Black Hills. Termed the Red Valley or "racetrack" (Darton 1901), this lowland is underlain by weakly indurated red siltstone of

29

the Spearfish Formation (Permian and Triassic age) and encircles the entire anticlinal Black Hills Uplift (Figure 11). The low-relief, undulating, Spearfish surface is a karst terrain. The terrain is classified as *subjacent karst* (Martin 1965; Jennings 1971) in that most of the Spearfish landscape was not produced by solution attack of its own strata; rather it is the consequence of extensive ground water dissolution and removal of up to 70 m of anhydrite from the Minnelusa Formation (Permian), stratigraphically 60 m beneath the Spearfish Formation (Bowles and Braddock 1963: 91).

Post-solution collapse within the Minnelusa initiated upward stoping and the development of cylindrical breccia pipes up to 75 m in diameter which locally penetrate over 300 m into Lower Cretaceous formations. Vertical collapse within these breccia pipes has produced numerous steep-walled sinkholes in the Black Hills since mid- to late Tertiary time (post-Laramide uplifting) (Gable and Hatton 1983; Osterkamp *et al.* 1987). The Mammoth Site at Hot Springs occupies one of these sinks.

From 3 to 6 m (depending on site location) of the upper part of the sinkhole fill sediment and adjacent wallrock were removed by excavation prior to investigation of the site. Where walls of the sinkhole have been observed, all have been very steep with no measured dips of less than 60° (Figure 12). Although the structural attitude of the fill strata is locally very complex (e.g. in the northeast portion), they tend to dip centrally and become horizontal near the center of the depression. Deep core drilling at three sites indicates that the floor of the original sink is markedly spoon-shaped with the deepest part at the northeast end of the site. Original (pre-excavation) thickness of the sinkhole fill ranged from a minimum of 14 m at the southwest end to a minimum of 20 m in the northeast, near spring conduit 1.

The land surface immediately adjacent to the Mammoth Site is situated 70 m above the Fall River, a tributary of the Cheyenne River (Figure 11), and is within Fall River Terrace IV (Figure 13). Gravels of Terrace IV were deposited on a surface bevelled on the Spearfish Formation. The history of the Mammoth Site sinkhole is intimately

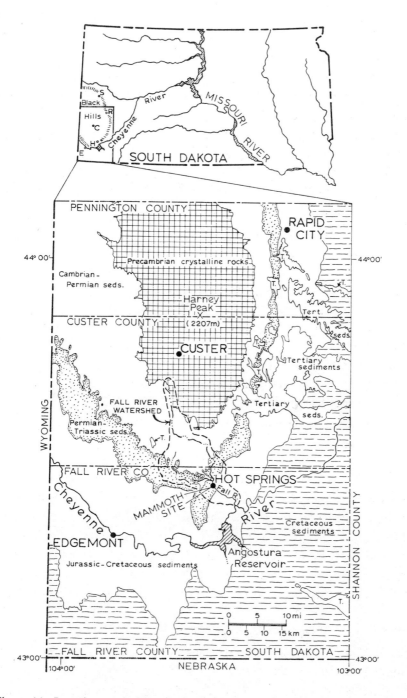

Figure 11. Location map of Hot Springs Mammoth Site sinkhole, southwestern
South Dakota. T, Tertiary sediments.

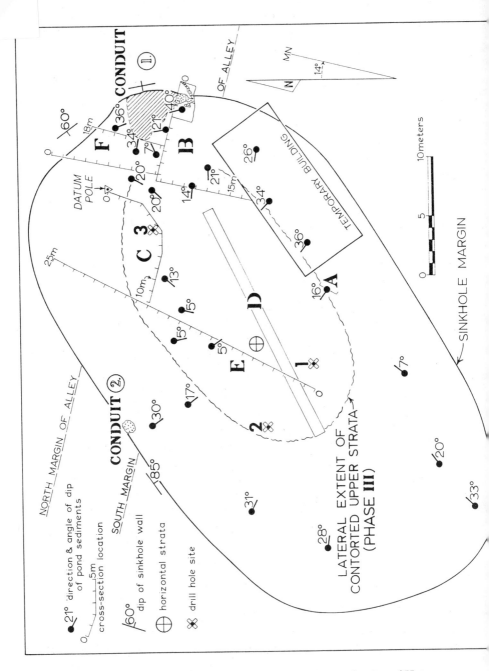

Figure 12. Map of Mammoth Site sinkhole, located on south edge of Hot Springs, South Dakota. Bedrock adjacent to present sinkhole margin is Spearfish Formation (Permo-Triassic) red siltstone. A fixed vertical reference point, the 0.0 m level for all cross sections, is located on the datum pole. A through H are excavated vertical cross-sections.

related to the late Quaternary behavior of the ancestral Fall River. Fall River terrace development has been studied by Kempton (1980, 1981).

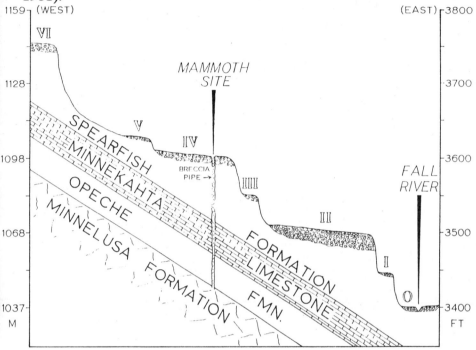

Figure 13. Simplified geologic and physiographic setting of the Mammoth Site sinkhole. Terrace O is the present floodplain of the Fall River. City of Hot Springs is built on all 6 terraces of the ancestral Fall River. Bedrock geology after Wolcott (1967). Horizontal distance not drawn to scale.

SINKHOLE SEDIMENTS

Three different but gradational episodes of sedimentation have been documented within the Mammoth Site deposits and are summarized in Figure 14. The oldest sediments in the sinkhole, phase I, consist of marginally accumulated, poorly sorted gravels of the laminated and micrograded sands and silts of the central sinkhole. Phase II sediments are comprised predominantly of rhythmically depos-

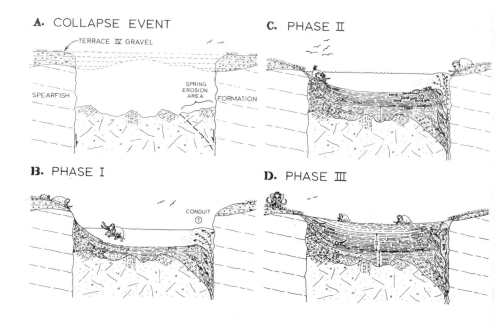

A. COLLAPSE EVENT

TERRACE IV GRAVEL

SPEARFISH

SPRING EROSION AREA

FORMATION

B. PHASE I

CONDUIT ①

C. PHASE II

D. PHASE III

Figure 14. Sequence of events in history of Mammoth Site sinkhole. Cross-sections are simplified northward views.

    A. Sinkhole as it may have appeared immediately after formation of breccia pipe and ground surface collapse. Steep to overhanging walls are typical of such features. Ancestral Fall River had abandoned Terrace IV prior to collapse.

    B. End of phase I sedimentation, a period of rapid wall erosion and pond sedimentation. Most of marginal gravels were deposited during phase I.

    C. Near end of phase II sedimentation. More time was involved during this period, and more mammoths were trapped. Sedimentation rates had slowed considerably from thoseof phase I.

    D. Late phase III time. Water tables had dropped following continued Fall River entrenchment, spring discharge to the sinkhole virtually ceased, and the pond was reduced to a mudpuddle. Where depression floor was still water saturated, mammoth/megafauna bioturbation was pervasive. No mammoths were trapped during phase III. Finally, subaerial deposition of slope-derived colluvium concluded this last phase of sinkhole sedimentation.

ited, thinly laminated sands and silts. Lower (earlier) phase III sediments are more thinly laminated, finer grained, and more areally restricted than phase II strata. The youngest sinkhole sediments studied (later phase III) are poorly stratified, very poorly sorted mudstones.

A radiocarbon date of 26,075 + 975/-790 yr B.P. (GX-5895-A) obtained from the apatite fraction of mammoth bones is presently the absolute date for the Mammoth Site. Collagen has been selectively leached from all bones and could not therefore be dated. Because of the problems inherent in dating bone apatite, the date must be considered a minimum. The dated bones were collected from upper phase II strata.

PHASE I SEDIMENTATION

Exposures and deep coring confirm that phase I sediments were deposited subaqueously in a sinkhole, at least 14 m deep, whose walls at many localities were initially near vertical. The depression floor was uneven, being underlain by a jumble of randomly oriented collapse blocks of Spearfish siltstone and terrace gravel. In map view the sink and fill are oval-shaped with the long axis (50 m) oriented northeast-southwest (Figure 12). The wallrock exposed in the sinkhole after the collapse event consisted of red Spearfish siltstone capped by several meters of Fall River Terrace IV gravels. Remnants of the latter are preserved in outcrops adjacent to the site. The nearby Terrace IV deposits seen in Figures 15 and 16 are clearly truncated by the steep wall of another sinkhole which, on the basis of its geomorphic position and sedimentary history of filling, is hypothesized to be essentially synchronous in time of formation with the Mammoth Site sink. A preliminary examination of a soil developed on the fill sediments of the second sinkhole suggests that the soil has an antiquity commensurate with the presumed age of the Mammoth Site (Heber D. Lessig 1978, pers. comm.).

Phase I sedimentation began with the marginal introduction of gravel-rich colluvium. This produced along most of the sinkhole walls steeply dipping (28 to 34°), poorly stratified, gravel talus deposits. Locally, these water-laid gravels were partially or completely removed by layer slumping and/or springwater erosion. The gravels are grain supported but very poorly sorted, are weakly indurated, show no imbrication, and tend to fine upwards. Mean clast sizes range from 8 to 10 cm (cobbles) in older phase I strata to 0.5 to 1.0 cm (pebbles) in the younger talus debris. However, boulders up to 0.75 m have been observed in the older talus. Phase I gravels comprise mostly subangular to subrounded clasts of micritic Permian Minnekahta Limestone (64%), other Paleozoic limestones (16%), and fine-grained sandstone of the Jurassic Sundance Formation (12%). Pebbles of vein quarts (Precambrian), chert (from Paleozoic limestones and dolostones), rock gypsum (Spearfish Formation), and Jurassic belemnite fragments are less common but identifiable constituents. Lithologically and texturally the sinkhole gravels are identical only to those found in Fall River Terrace IV (Kempton 1980).

Figure 15. Outcrop approximately 65 m east of Mammoth Site, on north side of alley. Photograph taken to the northeast showing remnant of Fall River Terrace IV gravels overlying Spearfish Formation siltstone. Base of gravel is at top of vertical, 1 m tape. Spearfish is massive. Large clasts of Spearfish are preserved in the Terrace IV gravel. To the right (east) of the darker gravel and Spearfish siltstone is the near vertical contact with a sinkhole and its sediment fill. See Figure 16 for details.

These data, plus the preservation locally along the sinkhole margin of intact (slump) blocks of the same gravels, confirm the existence of this terrace deposit prior to the sinkhole-forming collapse event.

Earlier phase I talus gravels grade upward and laterally (toward the sinkhole center) into finer grained and better stratified sediments. Cores from drill holes 1 and 2 (Figure 12) show that a pond setting existed from the onset of post-collapse sedimentation. While poorly stratified gravels were accumulating along the sinkhole periphery, rhythmically intercalated, clayey silt and silty sand (size nomenclature after Picard 1971) were being deposited in delicate, thin laminae (1 to 3 mm thick) in the central pond area. The laminae are commonly micrograded and varve-like, sand-silt couplets up to 1.0 cm in aggregate thickness (Figure 17). Cross-stratification has not been observed in these or any other of the pond sediments. It is postulated that the laminated fine sediment of the central pond was deposited by small-scale turbidity currents (dilute graded suspensions) or by settling from uniform suspensions, many of which were generated during gravel introduction. Thin layers of coarse sand or fine gravel are rare (<5%) constituents of phase I central pond strata. The introduction of sediment gravity flows during later phase I time (see later discussion) represents the only real departure from the generally fine-grained/laminated nature of the central pond sediments.

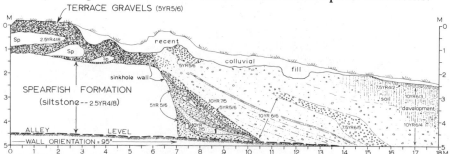

Figure 16. Stratigraphic section measured on south-facing wall of outcrop in Figure 15. Remnant of Fall River Terrace IV gravel rests on eroded Spearfish Formation bedrock. Both are truncated by steep sinkhole wall. Large detrital clasts of Spearfish siltstone (Sp) are incorporated in the terrace gravels. Sinkhole formation and fill are believed coeval with Mammoth Site sinkhole. This sinkhole has not been excavated.

Mineralogically, phase I finer grained sediments are virtually identical to those of succeeding phases II and III. Components from the Spearfish and Sundance formations are readily recognized in the pond sands and silts. Table 4 summarizes petrographic modal analyses of the pond sediments and shows that the latter are quartzose, calcareous, and glauconite-bearing. The marine Sundance Formation (Jurassic) supplied quartz, glauconite, kaolinite, substantial illite, and abundant invertebrate skeletal fragments. The Triassic Spearfish Formation, a terrestrial deposit deficient in fossils and glauconite, supplied silt-size euhedral dolomite rhombs, muscovite, and montmorillonite. Thus data on the compositional makeup of both the gravels and fines of the sinkhole deposits indicate that most of the sediments that infilled the sinkhole were derived from surface runoff and accompanying erosion of the terrace gravels and Spearfish siltstone which were exposed subaerially in uplands adjacent to the pond. Subaqueous erosion of the pond wall by vigorous conduit 1 spring discharge also supplied some material.

Figure 17. Micrograded, phase I central pond laminae. Coarser (lighter) parts of coarse-tail-graded couplets are silty very fine sand, finer parts are clayey silts. Silt laminae vary in color from gray to pink. Drill hole 2 (core 5), 0.5 m above base of sinkhole fill.

Phase I comprises the lower 5 m of central pond fill, or about one-third of the total sinkhole sediment thickness. These oldest pond sediments, which have been studied in deep drill cores (holes 1 and 2, Figure 12) and in deep trenches (Figure 18), are in the lowermost 2 to 3 m commonly reddish brown in color (Munsell colors 2.5YR 4/4-5 YR 5/4), a pigmentation inherited from the (2.5YR 4/6) Spearfish siltstone. The reddish color is restricted to the more clay-rich silt laminae but may be abruptly replaced in succeeding clayey silt laminae by colors ranging from weak red (2.5YR 5/2) to brown (7.5YR 5/2), pinkish gray (7.5YR 6/2), or gray (10YR 6/1). The sediments of several modern water-filled sinks within the Spearfish red siltstone were studied to determine the preservability of the red pigment in those particular environments. Cores taken in Mirror and Coxes lakes (located in the northern Black Hills 14.5 km northwest of Spearfish, South Dakota) indicate that the red color of the clayey silt carried into the ponds is generally altered at or within a few cm below the sediment-water interface to a gray color. The color change is produced by the chemical reduction of ferric iron within the hematitic pigment to ferrous iron. Because of the high sulfate (SO_4) content of the spring waters that feed these and most of the other sink ponds of the Black Hills (Gott and Schnabel 1963), sulfate-reducing bacteria are active in the near-surface aquatic sediment realm. The bacteria noticeably generate highly reactive hydrogen sulfide gas (H_2S) and create a low Eh environment favorable for the ferric (Fe^{+++}) iron reduction (Berner 1971). Because the color change takes place rapidly (probably within one year), the preservation of red-pigmented clays is possible only where they are buried below the near-surface reaction zone.

Thus the upward decrease in the number of red laminae within phase I of the Mammoth Site central pond facies suggests a parallel decrease in sedimentation rates within the sink. A similar vertical change in sedimentary history is expressed within the coarser pond-margin units in that they show an upward fining, improved stratification, and loss of red-pigmented strata.

Post-depositional modification and/or disruption of the early pond

Table 4. Summaries of modal analyses

Sample	Grain analysis (>0.02 mm)								Clay minerals (<0.002 mm)*			
	Quartz	Chert	Feldspar	Detrital carbonate	Rock fragments	Glau-conite	Mica	Heavy minerals	Montmorillonite	2m Muscovite	Illite	Kaolinite
Pond sediments (fines, conduit sands)	80.4	1.5	4.7	8.1	3.3	0.7	0.9	0.4	Abund.	Abund.	Common	Abund.
Spearfish Fm. (Siltstone wall rock)	70.1	0.6	5.7	18.0	0.6	—	4.4	0.6	Abund.	Abund.	Rare	Rare
Sandstone boulder, pond gravels	NOT ANALYZED								Rare	Rare	Abund.	Abund.
Sundance Fm. (sandstone)									Rare	Rare	Abund.	Abund.

* Clay mineral abundances: dominant (>75%), abundant (15-75%), common (5-15%), rare (0-5%).

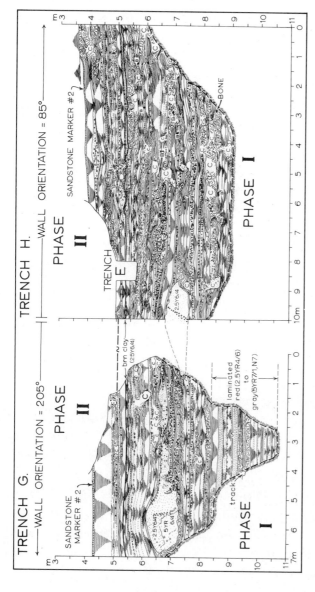

Figure 18. Sections G and H (Figure 12). These are the deepest measured sections in the Mammoth Site and exhibit the thickest phase I sections. Section G faces southeast, H faces north. Section G has deepest penetration into central pond fill. The base of the section is estimated to be within 1 m of the floor of the sinkhole. Several sandy/gravelly debris flows or grain flows are preserved as discontinuous lense-shaped sedimentation units up to 1 m thick. As their occurrence coincides with the stratal appearance of mammoth track (localized convolute zones, C), it is likely that the debris flows were mammoth induced. Bone occurrences, B.

41

sediments is both common and important. Trace fossils were observed and take the form of small, well defined, vertical, straight to U-shaped infilled burrows, which rarely extend more than 1.0 cm below the sediment-water interface (Figure 19). Average burrow diameter is 1 to 3 mm, but horizontal burrow traces with diameters of 1.0 cm are also present. Most are believed to be the products of infaunal aquatic detritus feeders (probably oligochaete worms). The worm traces were intermittently produced throughout most of the pond's existence.

Microfaulting, sediment gravity flows, and contorted stratification are additional types of post-depositional disturbance documented in phase I pond sediments. The microfaults, which are gravitationally induced normal faults with displacements of only millimeters or a few centimeters, are seen mostly to the west of conduit 1. They are very late phenomena formed after sinkhole infilling by compactional readjustments of the strata following the overburden loading and dewatering of the sediments. Larger scale faults found in close proximity to conduit 1 are related to spring activity in that area and will be discussed later.

In contrast to microfaulting, mass flows and contorted stratification are large-scale features that were contemporaneous with phase I pond sedimentation. Field-constructed stratigraphic cross-sections E and F (Figures 12, 20, 21), which show the older marginally deposited sediments, suggest the following sequence of events: (1) Deposition of gravels as subaqueous, angle-of-repose (28-34°) shear surfaces within the gravel talus (Figures 20, 21). (2)Subaqueous sediment gravity flows thus generated during the latter sediment disruption deposited the massive pebbly mudstones (probably debris flows) seen in sections E and F (Figures 20, 21), and the thick, sandy/gravelly debris flows or grain flows of sections G and H (Figure 18). (3) The slide masses disrupted laminated sediments producing contorted or convolute laminae. (4) Sedimentation of laminated silts and sands on progressively lesser slopes (<25°), with occasional disruption and development of contorted strata.

Sediment gravity flow deposits are observed only in later phase I

Figure 19. Moderately bioturbated phase II strata. Burrows (1 to 3 mm diameter) were probably produced by aquatic earthworms (oligochaetes). Section F, 7.0 m position, 10 cm above sandstone marker no. 2.)

pond fill and are contemporary with the earliest occurrences of mammoth tracks and bones in the sinkhole strata. It is therefore suggested and very logical that the foundering of mammoths initiated sediment gravity flows within the steeply inclined, metastable pond sediments. The apparent absence of comparable debris flows in younger Mammoth Site pond sediments is probably due to the substantial reduction of marginal pond-floor slopes and to a greater cohesiveness (and decreased metastability) of the finer slope materials, the latter being commensurate with slower sedimentation rates during phase II time.

Water Supply

The principal supply of water for the sinkhole pond was apparently through artesian springs issuing upward and penetrating the debris-laden floor along the outer wall of the breccia pipe. Spring

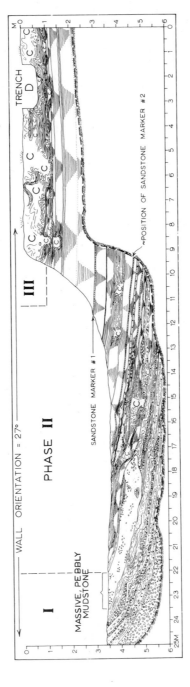

Figure 20. Section E (Figure 12), showing all three phases of pond sedimentation. Geographic and structural center of sinkhole is near 6 to 7 m positions. Base of sinkhole is 10.8 m below 0.0 datum at the sink center. Convolute (C) zones vary from smaller, more localized mammoth tracks to massively disturbed zones, as seen in phase III. Mammoth tracks are scarce but present in phase I and II strata; they dominate in phase III. Massive, pebbly mudstone is a late phase I subaqueous debris flow deposit. Exposed wall was dug by backhoe and faces northwest. Contact of pone fill and sinkhole wall (Spearfish Formation) is approximately 2 m to the left (north) of section wall (see Figure 11).

44

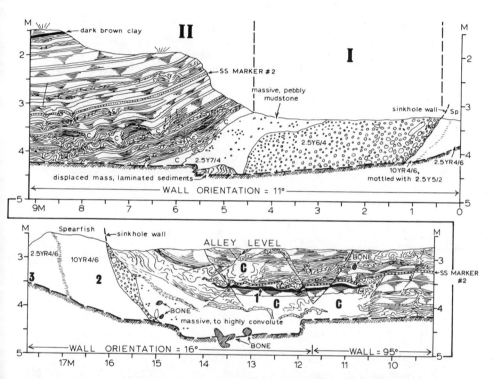

Figure 21. Section F (Figure 12). Sketch shows two subparallel walls (0 to 9 m facing east, and 11.7 to 17.7 m, facing west) which intersect the same steeply dipping sinkhole wall. These two faces are joined by a short, north-facing wall (9 to 11.7 m). Wall 11.7 + m clearly shows a greater sediment/pond-floor instability related to its juxtaposition to conduit 1. Note the nearly complete removal, probably due to slumping, of phase I gravels from the same wall. Mammoth bone abundance increases noticeably near conduit 1. Red (2.5 YR 4/6) Spearfish wall rock (siltstone) has been locally altered (hydrated) by pond-water infiltration to dark yellowish brown (10 YR 4/6). C. convolute zones. 1, 2, 3, selected sample sites. Sedimentation phases I and II are distinguished on less disturbed 0 to 9 m wall.

45

Figure 22. Photo to the east of the west-facing wall (12 to 17.5 m) of section F. Spearfish/pond-fill contact is at top of vertical 1 m tape. Note disturbed laminae in section face, and the mammoth bones in the foreground on the excavation floor.

feeders are preserved as branching and anastomosing mazes of predominantly sand-filled cracks and pipes. Two such complexes, conduits 1 and 2 (Figure 12), have been discovered along the pond-fill/Spearfish contact, and others may well be unearthed later. The small sizes and numbers of conduit 2 spring orifices and their overall restricted areal extent (1 m^2) suggest very low energy and low volume water discharge from that area. Conduit 1, however, was clearly larger and more energetic (Figure 23). From earliest phase I through early phase III time highly turbulent water issued from conduit 1 feeders; this spring discharge eroded and deepened the pond floor, induced slope failure in adjacent pond strata, and noticeably affected sedimentary facies over much of the pond.

The conduit 1 complex established a nearly funnel-shaped, steep-

Figure 23a. Spring conduit 1, northeast margin of Mammoth Site sinkhole. A. View to north of main area of conduit 1 spring discharge (outlined). Water discharged through numerous, irregularly shaped feeder pipes and cracks which are now filled with light colored, moderately sorted, friable, and sometimes cross-bedded (Figure 18B) very fine- to medium-grained sand and darker large clasts (collapse blocks) of Spearfish siltstone and laminated pond sediments. Spearfish wallrock (Sp) adjacent to the discharge area (to the right or east) is extensively scour-pocked and is eroded into vertical and overhanging walls. Mammoth bones (B) are common. Most pond-fill strata around the conduit 1 complex are disturbved by slimping or flowage. Section F (Figure 21) was measured on other side of wall in upper left of photo.

Figure 23b. Cross-stratification in spring conduit sand (light area), as seen in horizontal section through part of conduit 1 complex. The conduit sands sharply truncate darker, earlier deposited, crenulated, laminated pond sediments (phase II). The latter were subsequently partially bleached (recuction of ferric to ferrous iron oxidation states) by the spring water.

walled depression (35° + slopes), about 20 m² in surface area. Water turbulence there was locally capable of moving and abrading pebble- and cobble-sized clasts (including mammoth bones) down to sand- size grains. The sands filling conduit 1 feeders are predominantly quartose, very fine to fine-grained, poorly to moderately sorted, shite (N8 to 2.5Y 8/2), and uncemented. Grain sorting is better in the conduit sands than in all other sink-fill sediments (Figure 24). Be- cause of the tumbling/ball mill mechanical abrasion of clasts in this high energy spring area, the more durable grains are commonly well rounded and frosted.

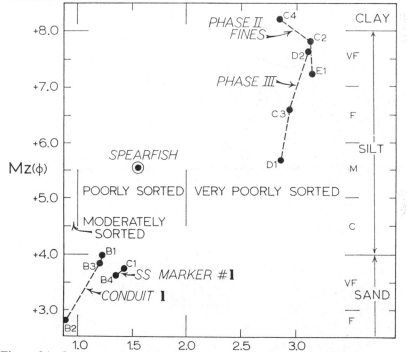

Figure 24. Summary plot of Graphic Mean (Mz) versus Inclusive Graphic Stan- dard Deviation (σ¹) (Folk 1974) for pond fill and wallrock (Spearfish Formation) sediments. Sandstone marker no. 1 is typical of phase II sands. Phase III sedi- ments are overall slightly finer grained (Mz = 6.0 phi).

Small-scale cross-stratification is locally well developed in the larger conduit 1 feeder pipes (Figure 23b).

Pond strata peripheral to conduit 1 attain dip angles of up to 40° into that area and show great structural complexity (Figures 12, 21, 25). Highly convoluted zones, water expulsion structures, and downslope-inclined flow folds are common, and are in turn offset by numerous gravity faults which moved centripetally into the spring discharge area as wedge-shaped graben blocks and rotational slump masses. Vertical displacements along some faults approach 1 m. Although plastically deformed strata can be seen elsewhere in the sink fill, faulting of this magnitude and abundance is confined to the region around spring conduit 1, and was probably induced by pervasive spring water penetration and vigorous undermining (oversteepening) of the adjacent pond sediments. More mammoths appear to have been trapped in or near the conduit 1 area than elsewhere in the site, attesting to the treacherous pond-floor conditions there. As in the case of the sediment gravity flows, it is logical to assume that the mammoths themselves also contributed to conduit 1 sediment disruption.

Sedimentation throughout the Mammoth Site pond appears to have been affected by conduit 1 activity. In tracing phase II and III strata southwestward away from conduit 1 into the central sinkhole pond the following changes are observed: (1) an overall reduction in mean grain size (Mz) in both sand and silt units, (2) a decrease in sediment sorting quality (o^1), and (3) a reduction in stratigraphic section thickness. A diminution in spring discharge turbulence away from conduit 1 can account for the above changes. In contrast, low-energy water discharge from conduit 2 had no visible effect on pond sediment facies.

Water Depth

Because of the generally impermeable and unfractured nature of the Spearfish wallrock of the sinkhole, the water level of the pond was probably regulated by either overflow over a surface sill, percolation through Spearfish-capping Terrace IV gravels, and/or by the elevation of the hydrostatic head within the artesian-pressured groundwater system. The actual amount of water-level fluctuation during

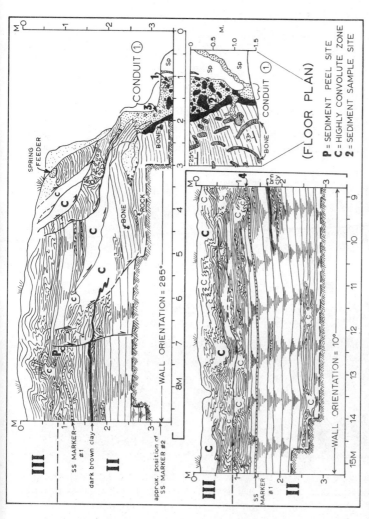

Figure 25. Section B (Figure 12), showing sediment deformation and spring erosion related to mammoth megabioturbation and spring erosion, respectively. Wall 0 to 8.8 m faces south and adjoins wall 8.8 to 15.2 m which faces east. Smaller convolute zones (c) are commonly individual mammoth footprints (shown well in east-facing wall). Phase III strata were almost totally convoluted by megafauna when the pond had shrunk to a muddy waterhole. Conduit 1 has eroded both Spearfish wallrock (Sp) and early deposited pond sediments. A small segment of horizontal floor excavation is shown (it attaches to the 0 to 3 m wall): mammoth rib bones, lying on north-dipping bedding planes of pond strata, are elongated downslope. P, site of sediment peel. 1 to 4, selected sample sites.

51

sinkhole infilling is unknown. However, several estimates of pond water depths have been possible.

The most accurate figures for water depths were derived by calculating the topographic relief of several carefully mapped pond marker strata. The construction of elevation-calibrated, highly detailed sketches of the walls of numerous backhoe trenches permitted recognition and correlation through much of the pond fill of several distinctive sand and clay units (Figures 18, 20, 21, 25, 27). Each marker bed or lithologically traceable sedimentation unit was considered to be isochronous. The absolute or total relief of each unit, as measured between its lowermost pond position and its contact with the sinkhole wall, was directly equated with water depth. Since reliable estimates of sediment compaction could not be made, depth figures must be considered a minimum. Using the above technique, water depths in the central pond area of at least 4 to 5 m have been

Figure 26. Thinly laminated phase II sands and silts. Unit in bracket is sandstone marker no. 1. Non-graded and distribution-graded laminae are dominant stratification styles shown. Section B, 11.0 m position (Figure 25).

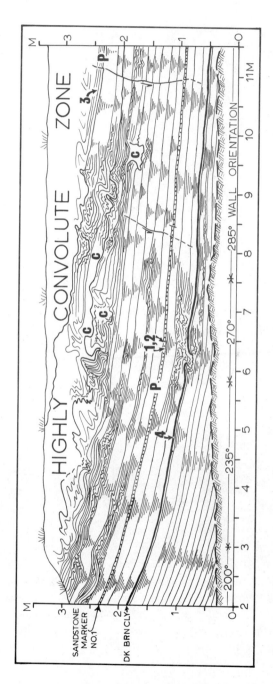

Figure 27. Section C (Figure 12), a curved outcrop facing generally north. A. A short stratigraphic section showing transition between upper phase II and lower phase III strata. The boundary varies from 1.0 to 1.5m above sandstone marker no. 1, and is denoted by the development of pervasive convolution of the pond strata. Localized zones of convolution (c) are believed to be individual footprints of mammoths; and stratal disturbance of phase III was likewise probably mammoth-induced. P, sediment peel area. 1,2,3, and 4 are selected sediment sample sites, Sample 4 is from dark brown clay marker bed.

Figure 28. Photo taken between 9.0 to 10.5 m horizontal position in section C, (Figure 27). Transition from phase II to phase III pond strata, shown approximately 0.25 m above the level line, is abnormally abrupt here. Phase II sediments are very well laminated, but are locally disrupted by mammoth tracks (T). Sandstone marker no. 1 is located at arrow.

Figure 29a. Mammoth footprints in Mammoth Site pond strata.
    A. Vertical cross-section through mammoth track present in well laminated phase II strata. Ruler is 15 cm (6 in.). Track is one of two shown in section E (Figure 20) at the same stratigraphic level, approximately 1 m below sandstone marker no. 1 and between 10.5 and 12.5 m positions. Near geographic center of site. View northeast.

calculated for late phase I time. Insufficient exposures precluded accurate water-depth assessment for older phase I strata. Water depths appeared to progressively decrease during phase II and phase III pond sedimentation, but the pond setting did not completely disappear until late phase III time.

Figure 29b. Horizontal slice through east-dipping, phase II laminated pond strata showing localized disturbance produced by mammoth track. The upturned, elongated anticlinal structure in the right-center of photo is commonly present on one side of a footprint—perhaps on the side where foot is coming up and moving forward. Section B (Figure 25).

Mammoth Tracks

An independent estimate of water depths has been possible through the use of mammoth footprints. Numerous cross-sections and plan views of mammoth tracks have been observed in the laminated pond sediments (see Figures 20, 22, 27, 28, 29). Measurements of track cross-sections indicate: (1) track diameter and depth of sediment disturbance below the pond floor, as measured in the shallower pond areas, have an average maximum of 0.1 to 0.35 m; (2) the depth of the actual surface depression of the track is generally one-fourth of the sediment-disturbance depth; (3) disturbed laminae beneath the surface depression are completely microconvoluted, and (4) laminae immediately adjacent to the tracks may be sharply downwarped, or downwarped on one side and upturned on the other (possibly where a foot was being lifted and moved forward), or microconvoluted in 1- to 10-cm-thick zones (bounded above and below by undisturbed laminae) which extend sub-horizontally several meters away from the tracks.

The density of occurrence of mammoth tracks, their depth of disturbance below the sediment-water interface, and their geographic location in the sink pond are clues to water depth. High track density and deep (normal) tracks imply relatively shallow water; conversely, low track density and consistently shallow tracks would suggest either the presence of only a few, small mammoths or deeper water where only the largest adults could lightly touch the pond floor. The scarcity of juvenile mammoths in the Mammoth Site support the latter hypothesis for the origin of shallow tracks.

Phase I and younger strata were nearly completely exposed in a very deep trench dug in 1979 in the central pond area (Figure 20). Here, commencing in later phase I strata and moving upward through phase II strata, observed tracks are very scarce and shallow. Track density and track depth increase as these stratigraphic units are traced laterally toward the pond margin. Thus, using an average maximum shoulder height of 4.3 m for Columbian mammoths (Osborn 1942), water depths of 4 to 5 m seem plausible for the central pond, corroborating the other evidence.

PHASE II SEDIMENTATION

Five meters of sediment were deposited in the Mammoth Site sinkhole during phase II time. Aside from the aforementioned complexities in proximity to spring conduit 1, phase II sediments consist of a rhythmic succession of relatively undisturbed, thinly laminated sands and silts, with individual genetic units being widely traceable through much of the central sinkhole (Figure 27). The overall finer grain size and thinner and more numerous sedimentation units of phase II in contrast with those of phase I suggest that phase II sedimentation was slower and encompassed more time. Thus, the observation that more mammoths appear to have been trapped in phase II sediments than in phase I might merely be an expression of a longer time period for entrapment during the phase II interval of sedimentation. Silt laminae are more abundant than sand laminae in phase II sediments. These sediments have a composite mean grain size of 6 phi (medium silt), slightly finer than the mean (5.5 phi) for the Spearfish siltstone wallrock of the sinkhole. Pure clays are lacking; but thin beds (up to 2.0 cm thick) of fine gravel are not uncommon occurrences in lower phase II strata, especially along the pond periphery. Sedimentation unit thicknesses average 1 mm for the clayey silts and 2 to 3 mm for the very fine sands.

In the central pond area there are no conspicuous trends in the vertical or lateral distribution of types of sedimentary structures within phase II sediments. Slightly less than one-half of these strata have thin, parallel, non-graded laminae with generally sharp lower and upper contacts. The remaining phase II strata exhibit either micro-grading, bioturbation, or small-scale mechanical deformation—all in subequal amounts and randomly intercalated with the parallel laminae.

Depositional processes responsible for the above phase II sedimentary structures are shown in Table 5. Graded sedimentation units in phase II strata are thin, 5 to 7 mm thick, with distribution grading (Figure 26) being more common than coarse-tail grading. The reverse is more characteristic of phase I graded laminae where, apparently, steeper pond-floor slopes resulted in higher concentration flows (and more coarse-tail grading) (Figure 20). The absence of Bouma C zones in the turbidites can be attributed to the small flow sizes and short distances of sediment transport.

Sheet (surface) runoff from eroding uplands adjacent to the sinkhole would have entered the less dense pond water as thin hyperpycnal inflows (density underflows), thus creating marginal turbidity currents which could have easily reached the central pond area. In addi-

Table 5. Phase II depositional processes

Process	Resultant sedimentary structure
Uniform suspension	Thin, nongraded silty clay laminae
Dilute graded suspension (for example, turbidity current)	Micro-distribution-graded laminae
Higher concentration density (turbidity) current	Coarse-tail-graded laminae
Low-energy fluidized flow	Crinkly silty sand laminae (2 to 3 mm amplitude), and microconvolute laminae (0.5- to 1.0 cm-thick layers)

Note: Most of these interpretations are after Middleton and Hampton (1973).

tion, dilute graded suspensions are believed to have been dispersed westerly from conduit 1 following major slump/disturbance events there. Finally, the effect of mammoth disturbance of the unconsolidated pond substrate on the generation of the above processes must have been substantial.

Organic-rich and/or silt-free clay laminae, which are usually associated with "winter" layers of classical varves (Ashley 1975), are conspicuously lacking in the pond sediments of the Mammoth Site. Six different types and stratigraphic levels of pond sediments (phase I through phase III) were analyzed for total organic carbon content using a Leco Carbon Analyzer. All samples showed a consistently very low organic carbon level with a measured range of 0.15 to 0.19%. Also the same and additional pond samples produced no pollen. The following three causes probably inhibited organic carbon/pollen preservation in the sink pond: (1) oxidation and destruction of organics at the sediment-water interface, (2) post-depositional metabolic consumption of the organics by sulfate-reducing bacteria within the top few centimeters of the pond sediments, and (3) the lack of a seasonal freeze-over of the pond surface and/or a sustained period of quiescence in pond sedimentation when fine organic matter could finally settle and become concentrated in distinct laminae. Consequently, a seasonality or a more precise absolute chronology of sedimentation and mammoth entrapment events has unfortunately not been possible to establish.

PHASE III SEDIMENTATION

At least 4 m of sediment were deposited in the Mammoth Site sinkhole during this, the final phase of sedimentation. The sequence of events during phase III was probably as follows: (1) progressive and fairly rapid reduction of spring water discharge, pond water level, and pond surface area; (2) extreme disturbance of the remaining pond sediments, and cessation of the sink as a megafauna trap; (3) termination of the aquatic environment, and initiation of the final colluviation of the sinkhole.

Final Pond Sedimentation

The oldest phase III sediments occupy a much reduced portion of the Mammoth Site sinkhole (Figure 12). Maximum dips of the floor along the pond margin lessened from about 15° at the beginning of phase III time to less than 5° toward the end. Phase III pond strata are mostly thin laminated (1 mm average thickness) clayey silts; sand laminae are thinner and less numerous than those of phase II strata. The mean grain size (Mz) of phase III sediments is about 6.65 phi—somewhat finer than that of phase II strata (6.0 phi) (Figure 24).

The sand-poor, rhythmically intercalated light (more silt-rich) and dark (more clay-rich) laminae that characterize most of the phase III strata (Figure 30) are superficially similar to the "microvarves" of Glacial Lake Hitchcock, Massachusetts (Ashley 1975, p. 308). And like the Lake Hitchcock sediments, the varve-like phase III laminae were probably deposited in a sediment-starved, shallowing basin. However, the dark/light phase III couplets are less uniform in appearance than the microvarves and are of dubious seasonal significance. Instead, deposition of phase III strata probably resulted from repeated but random water muddying or from pond-margin runoff events, the latter being less intense than those of phase II or earlier time. Spring water discharge from conduit 1, although greatly reduced, was nonetheless sufficient to maintain a southwestward decreasing energy gradient. Also, slumping was still active around the main spring feeders (Figure 25).

Figure 30. Thinly laminated, sand-poor phase III pond strata. The sandier laminae are thicker and darkly iron-stained (from more recent groundwater infiltration). Clayey silts dominate. Laminae are structurally similar to "microvarves" described by Ashley (1975: 308). Worm bioturbation is sparse, but present at numerous levels. Section C, 12.0 m position, 1.5 m above sandstone marker no. 1.

Most Recent Events

The end of the pond depositional environment within the Mammoth Site is denoted by large-scale disruption of phase III and peripherally exposed, saturated phase II sediments. Deformed pond strata, varying from large-scale convolutions (up to 0.5 m in amplitude) and upward-erupting water-escape structures to nearly completely churned and homogenized sediment stratification, are seen in the tops of all of the shallower trench sections which reach the central pond area—sections A to F (Figure 12). There is an upward and fairly rapidly increasing frequency of occurrence of well defined mammoth footprints within phase III sediments and a gradation of these tracks into the highly convolute zone (Figures 20, 25, 27). It is therefore hypothesized that the massive phase III sediment disturbance was wholly mammoth produced. The extreme track density, the restricted area, and the lack of any entrapped megafauna clearly reflect that the sinkhole pond had been reduced to a mudpuddle.

The post-pond record of sedimentation in the Mammoth Site sinkhole is very fragmentary. Much of the estimated 3 m of this latest phase III material was removed by natural erosion and land leveling prior to formal excavation of the site. Preserved remnants of late phase III sink fill show that earlier phase III laminated pond strata are overlain by subaerially deposited colluvium. The latter consist of very poorly sorted, poorly stratified reddish gravels and yellowish brown, sandy to pebbly mudstones. These were probably the last sediments deposited in the Mammoth Site sinkhole.

In summary, the concluding (phase III) sedimentation within the Mammoth Site sinkhole records a transition from aquatic to subaerial depositional conditions. Sediments had either accumulated to the level of a static water table (potentiometric surface), or the latter had begun to drop, very likely in response to renewed erosional downcutting of the ancestral Fall River. Fall River incisement and development of terraces III and II, respectively 15 and 30 m below the level of the Mammoth Site (Figure 13), probably commenced during phase III time and effectively diverted groundwater from the sinkhole.

DISCUSSION

Water Temperature
Several factors strongly suggest, albeit indirectly, that the Mam-

moth Site pond was being fed by thermal springs, possibly very much like those at Evans Plunge in downtown Hot Springs, South Dakota. The absence from the pond sediments of diatoms, traces of rooted higher plants, or significant populations of indigenous aquatic invertebrates or vertebrates is best explained by assuming a year-round, abnormally warm pond-water temperature.

Diatoms are completely absent in the Mammoth Site pond sediments as are unequivocal root traces or the remains of indigenous rooted aquatic plants. In contrast these floral types are abundant and well preserved in similarly fine-grained sediments of the two small, spring-fed, cold water (circa 15°C, 59°F), modern ponds (Coxes and Mirror lakes) which were studied in the northern Black Hills (Figure 31). Because of pervasive root disturbance, delicate sediment lamination cannot be preserved in the vegetated part of these cold-water lacustrine settings. Optimum productivity temperatures for diatoms and higher plants are below 30°C, and temperatures in excess of 35 to 40°C (95 to 104°F) are generally lethal (Brock and Brock 1971; Patrick 1974; Brock 1978).

Aside from the earlier mentioned worm burrows, the only other indigenous faunal elements thus far recovered, despite extensive screening efforts, are a few small gastropods, a small bivalve, some ostracods, and several minnow-size vertebrae. Thus preservation of the biota in the pond sediments is not at issue, as these well preserved, delicate skeletal remains attest. The upper temperature limit for freshwater invertebrates is about 47°C, and for vertebrates (fish and frogs) it is 38°C (Brock and Brock 1971). It is therefore suggested that the low invertebrate/vertebrate faunal diversity and abundance within the Mammoth Site sinkhole pond were caused by the presence of significantly elevated water temperatures, an estimated 35 to 38°C, and the lack of seasonally changing thermal regimes (Lehmkuhl 1974), rather than by nutrient or oxygen depletion.

Annelid worms inhabiting the somewhat cooler, insulating bottom sediments of the pond could survive the warm water habitat. They were probably oligochaetes (aquatic earthworms) which derive their nutrition from the ingestion of bacteria (Brinkhurst and

Cook 1974). Thus, a reduced supply of organic matter or a lethal buildup of bacterially produced H_2S would eliminate both the bacterial and oligochaete populations. Bacterial activity and worm bioturbation were undoubtedly at peaks when mammoth carcasses were decaying in the water, but were considerably reduced during periods of rapid sediment influx.

Figure 31. Mirror Lake, 9 mi (15 km) northwest of Spearfish, South Dakota, in the northern Black Hills. A spring-fed lake, approximately 5.4 m deep, situated on the Spearfish Formation, with easily erodible, poorly vegetated, subaerially exposed, marginal siltstone uplands. Subaerial slope configurations, slope materials, water depth, and spring feeding are similar to those envisioned for the mammoth Site sinkhole during phases I and II.

Limited numbers of delicate microvertebrate/invertebrate skeletal remains that were contemporaneous with, but exotic to the pond setting are present and well preserved in the Mammoth Site pond strata. Thus, the paucity of indigenous skeletal material in these sediments is apparently real and cannot be attributed to removal by post-depositional diagenetic or weathering processes. It is important to note that the few above-mentioned organisms that apparently did survive the pond conditions were recovered only in the southwestern portion of the Mammoth Site. This may reflect a slight southwest-trending cooling gradient in the pond away from the hot-water input at conduit 1.

In conclusion, paleontological evidence or lack thereof supports the existence of a sinkhole pond that was continuously warm during its existence with an ambient water temperature of at least 35°C (95°F). In addition to the aforementioned biological controls, the thermal spring water would have (1) kept the pond from freezing, (2) enhanced the development of sediment laminae, (3) minimized or eliminated seasonality in stratification (i.e., true varves), (4) increased settling rates of suspended sediment two-fold over typical cold-water (15°C) ponds of the area (thus permitting preservation of more and thinner laminae in any given time period), (5) accelerated carcass disarticulation, (6) selectively dissolved the collagen from the mammoth bones (Olsson *et al.* 1974), (7) supported a year-round flora on heated ground marginal to the pond, and (8) preferentially attracted large number of megafauna to the site.

Sedimentation Rates

What was the duration of sedimentation in the Mammoth Site sinkhole? Unfortunately, the lack of suitable radiocarbon-datable material in the site has made it difficult to provide much more than speculation in answer to this question. In view of the warm-water hypothesis and the foregoing discussions on pond laminae, the existence of true varves or other laminae of seasonal significance seems doubtful. Instead, laminae in the pond fill simply represent sedimentation events, whether they be generated by storm runoff from adjacent uplands, megafaunal activities, periodic surges or erosion/ slumping in spring conduit 1 area, eluvial (aeolian) contribution, or other processes not yet identified.

Sedimentation rates can be calculated from Mirror Lake (Figure 31), a modern pond which is comparable in size, wallrock material, and many of the sedimentation processes to that envisioned for the Mammoth Site sink. This spring-fed pond, developed on the Spearfish Formation in the northern Black Hills, has had an average sedimentation rate of circa 50 mm/yr over the past 40 years (Black Hills Conservancy Sub-District 1973, p. 109). If, for the sake of comparison the 14 m of Mammoth Site sediments were deposited at the same rate, filling of the sinkhole would have taken 280 years after the initial collapse event. Independently, estimates of 175 to 700 years were calculated for the sinkhole filling. These latter numbers are based on using 10 to 20 sedimentation events per year and an average laminae thickness (usually a sand-silt couplet) of 2 to 4 mm for each sedimentation event.

The above duration figures are reasonable approximations for the Mammoth Site. They accordingly suggest that mammoth entrapment in the sink pond may have averaged as little as one individual every 1.25 to 5 years (assuming a total of 100 mammoths). This is also taking into consideration the fact that mammoths were not being trapped during the final 25 to 30% (phase III) of the sinkhole's history. The stratigraphic occurrence of both the mammoth tracks and the invariably associated bones provide clear evidence that mammoth entrapment was not catastrophic. Rather, individuals or very small groups of probably less than 5 mammoths were being trapped quite sporadically. One can thus conclude that mammoths were either (1) regular but infrequent visitors to the sink pond, (2) overly cautious about entering the water, and/or (3) much more adept at extricating themselves from the sink pond than formerly perceived.

CONCLUSIONS

The sequence of events summarizing the beginning, infilling, and end of the Mammoth Site sinkhole is shown in Figure 14. Prior to the development of the sink the late Quaternary landscape of the southern Black Hills was much less dissected than now. Streams, however, had already commenced incising a high, widespread, gravel-veneered, pre-Pleistocene White River/Ogallala (?) surface (Kempton 1980). And by the time the Mammoth Site sinkhole appeared, several new, relatively small stream terraces, including Terrace IV, had been formed by the ancestral Fall River. A declining regional water table, which presumably accompanied the steady downcutting of the Fall River, likely triggered numerous breccia pipe collapse events and thus created the Mammoth Site sinkhole (Figure 13). The Fall River did not have access to the newly formed depression. Nonetheless, the effective water table of the area was still elevated, and artesian-pressured springs quickly entered the sinkhole from the underlying breccia pipe. A pond setting was thus established, partially filling the steep-walled sink to an estimated depth of at least 4 to 5 m.

Sediment input and filling of the pond was rapid at first (phase I, Figure 14B) and progressively slower thereafter (phases II and III, Figures 14C, D). Sediment was principally supplied from rainfall or animal erosion of subaerially exposed sinkhole walls and adjacent uplands, and secondarily from the energetic spring, conduit 1, which occupied the northeastern margin of the sink. Conduit 1 discharge was sufficiently vigorous to (1) locally erode and deepen the floor of the depression, (2) create highly metastable pond-floor substrates around spring orifices, and (3) establish a nearly pond-wide energy gradient which noticeably affected fine sediment distribution. Spring upwelling finally ceased as did the pond setting during phase III time (Figure 14D). Continued downcutting by the nearby Fall River doubless altered the groundwater regime and terminated spring discharge to the sinkhole. Just when the latter happened is not known. The bone radiocarbon date of circa 26,000 yr B.P. from the older sediments of the sink fill place the site in the Wisconsinan Stage (Birkeland *et al.* 1971). Based on a comparison with several physically analogous modern sinkhole ponds in the Black Hills and an understanding of sedimentation processes operative in the Mammoth Site, sedimentation rates have been estimated for the latter; they suggest that the Mammoth Site sink could have been infilled in 175 to 700 years.

Finally, the Mammoth Site sinkhole appears to have been somewhat unique in that it was being fed by geothermally heated waters, and also in that it was a highly effective, almost exclusively mammoth-selective megafaunal trap. A continuous supply of warm (at least 35°C) water severely curtailed indigenous pond life, but may have attracted megafauna, especially in winter months. The frequency of mammoth entrapment may have been as low as one individual every 1 to 5 years. The mammoths not only contributed directly to the filling of the pond, but also had a substantive effect on pond sedimentation processes and sediment stratification.

ACKNOWLEDGEMENTS

Funding for the investigation has been provided primarily by the National Geographic Society and the Center for Field Research, Belmont, Massachusetts. Larry D. Agenbroad has been the principal investigator and a most valued colleague on the Mammoth Site project. The Institute for the Study of Earth and Man (Southern Methodist University) and the Chadron State College Research Institute have also generously funded the study. I am grateful to the South Dakota Geological Survey for the invaluable core drilling in the site and continued support of the project. Organic carbon analyses of the sinkhole samples were contributed by Sunmark Exploration Company (Dallas). Pamela D. Kempton supplied critical data on the Fall River terrace deposits of the region. J. I. Mead and N. W. MacLeod have painstakingly searched for microbiota in the sediments. P. R. Bjork and Mead supplied data on the microvertebrates, and D. A. Brown on the phytoliths. Barb L. Dutrow assisted the author in drafting and in mammoth/elephant-related questions. Discussions with D. C. Thorstenson on the geochemistry of the Mammoth Site have been very stimulating. Finally, I am deeply indebted to the townspeople of Hot Springs, South Dakota, who have unselfishly contributed their time and services; Carten Billups and Don Collogan are especially recognized for their invaluable geological and material assistance, respectively.

Chapter 4

TERRACES, SOLUTION COLLAPSE EVENTS, AND LATE QUATERNARY HISTORY OF THE FALL RIVER, HOT SPRINGS AREA, FALL RIVER AND CUSTER COUNTIES, SOUTH DAKOTA

Pamela D. Kempton and Robert L. Laury

INTRODUCTION

Terraces in the Hot Springs area of South Dakota record an unusual association with collapse events that have occurred as a result of incisement of the Fall River. In addition, terrace form, composition, and sequence of development have provided significant information regarding the Cenozoic evolution of the southern Black Hills (Kempton 1980; Laury and Kempton 1980; Kempton 1981).

The Mammoth Site of Hot Springs is certainly one of the more exceptional collapse features studied in the region. Detailed examination by Laury (1980) of the sediments of the site has shown a genetic stratigraphic association with terrace gravels of the ancestral Fall River. And with a minimum radiometric age for the site of about 26,000 yr B.P., time constraints on the evolutionary history of the Fall River watershed can be established. Through a systematic geomorphological/sedimentological analysis of Fall River terraces it has been possible to (1) determine the sequence of terrace development within the Fall River drainage basin; (2) locate within this sequence the events leading to formation of the Hot Springs Mammoth Site; and (3) integrate the history of the Fall River watershed with late Cenozoic development of the Black Hills. Study units are shown in Figure 32.

GEOLOGIC SETTING

The Black Hills comprise a fault-bounded structure in the northern Great Plains region which experienced both Laramide (late Cretaceous to Eocene) and post-Laramide (Neogene-Miocene and Pliocene, into early Pleistocene) block faulting and uplift (Gries 1983). Wrench-style deformation is believed responsible for the structural fabric of the Black Hills (Maughan and Perry 1987; and Brown and Brown 1987). The deformation resulted in the differential vertical displacement of rectangular basement blocks moving along bounding NE- and NW-trending orthogonal fracture systems (Maughan and Perry 1987).

Although information is lacking specifically for the Black Hills, studies elsewhere in the Rocky Mountains suggest that the Laramide orogeny was followed by a period of quiescence (early to middle Oligocene), during which time widespread erosion surfaces were formed (Madole *et al.* 1987). Post-orogenic uplift commenced in the Rocky Mountains in late Oligocene and fragmented and displaced these surfaces, producing most of the relief seen today. This mostly Neogene epeirogenic uplift was episodic and probably associated with the East Pacific Rise (Gable and Hatton 1983; Swinehart *et al.* 1985). The entire realm of the northern Great Plains (including the Black Hills) was affected, with uplift decreasing from west to east. Over the past 10 my 100 to 500 m of uplift have taken place along the eastern margin of the province, with Plio-Pleistocene uplift accounting for one-fourth to one-half of these amounts (Osterkamp *et al.* 1987: 169).

The physiography of the Black Hills is the product of erosion of two nearly flat-topped, uplifted blocks; the eastern block trends nearly north, the western block more northwest (Noble 1952; Eardley 1962). Structurally, the western flank is the result of narrow, monoclinal flexures in the sedimentary units overlying faulted basement; the eastern flank, consisting of broader, curving monoclines, has been described by Lisenbee (1978, 1985) as a partial dome. The resulting structure consists of a Precambrian core flanked by upturned sedimentary rocks that range in age from Cambrian to Cretaceous (Darton 1901; Fillman 1929; Plumley 1948). Erosion of these formations has produced four distinct geomorphic divisions (Figure 32). The rugged topography of the Precambrian core forms the central unit. It consists of highly folded schists and quartzites intruded by Precambrian granites and pegmatites and by Tertiary dikes, stocks, and laccoliths of Laramide age. Surrounding the core is an asymmetrical ring of Paleozoic limestones and dolomites. They are exposed in a broad plateau on the west flank where dips are gentle, but form a sequence of parallel hogbacks on the east where dips are somewhat steeper. Rimming the Paleozoic limestones is the "race track" (Darton 1901), a strike valley eroded in the soft, red silts and gypsum units of the Spearfish Formation (Permo-Triassic). It is bounded stratigraphically below by the Permian Minnekahta Limestone and above by resistant upper Jurassic/lower Cretaceous sandstones and siltstones. These relatively resistant clastic units, which describe the fourth geomorphic unit, form a second set of hogback ridges on the eastern flank of the Black Hills. Stratigraphically above these resistant sandstones are the upper Cretaceous shales forming much of the plains regions to the east and west. In many places these soft sedimentary rocks are overlain by flat-lying Tertiary sediments—the most notable of which form the Big Badlands of western South Dakota. Tertiary sediments also occur in the Black Hills (Fillman 1929; Darton 1901), but their ages are not well documented (Plumley 1948). It has been suggested (Harksen and Macdonald 1969; Harksen 1974) that these Tertiary deposits represent remnants of an extensive blanket of sediment which nearly covered the Black Hills—presumably the product of the post-Laramide quiescent period (Madole *et al.* 1987). The deposits have now largely been eroded away during subsequent uplift of the Black Hills; however, this event of downcutting is recorded in a system of Quaternary terraces located along many of the present-day stream valleys which drain the Black Hills.

The Fall River exhibits remnants of 6 to 8 previous levels of stream flow located 6 to 150 m above the present stream bed. Located on the south edge of the Black Hills, the drainage basin encom-

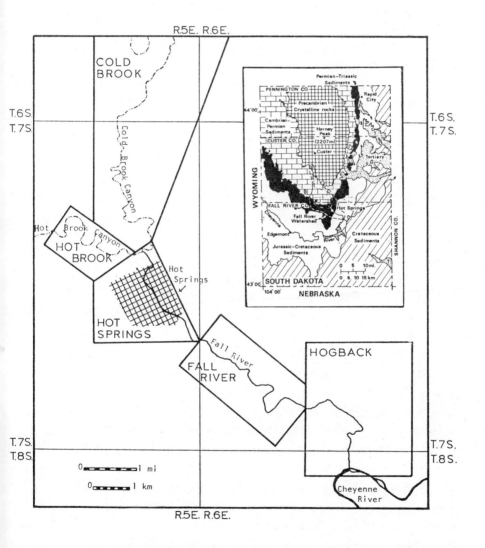

Figure 32. Location of Fall River drainage segments considered in gravel analyses. Inset shows location of Fall River watershed and general geology of the Black Hills.

passes portions of all the geomorphic units described. There are also deposits of gravel which have been mapped by Wolcott (1967) as the Tertiary White River Formation and which may represent remnants of the blanket of sediment hypothesized by Harksen (1974). Thus, the sediments incorporated by the Fall River into its alluvial deposits potentially sampled material ranging from Precambrian crystalline rocks to poorly consolidated Tertiary alluvium.

FALL RIVER DRAINAGE BASIN DESCRIPTION

Although the Fall River itself has a total length of only 13.5 km, it drains an area of approximately 415 square kilometers through its two principal tributaries, Hot Brook and Cold Brook. Hot Brook is a subsequent stream flowing generally parallel to the strike of the relatively nonresistant Permo-Triassic sediments; the Fall River and its remaining tributary, Cold Brook, are essentially consequent streams. The drainage has apparently been superimposed on the present structural grain by erosion through a preexisting surface since channels are commonly established across the strikes of beds and structures. This situation appears to be characteristic of Black Hills drainage in general. The significance of the superimposed nature of the drainage and the surface upon which it formed will be elaborated later.

The watershed of the Fall River is elongate and slightly pear-shaped-narrowing toward the head rather than toward the mouth. The maximum relief, the difference of the highest point on the divide from the lowest point in the drainage, is 860 m. The overall steepness of the drainage basin can be approximated by the relief ratio which is the maximum basin relief divided by the horizontal distance along the longest dimension of the basin parallel to the principal drainage line (Schumm 1956); for the Fall River watershed it is 0.026.

Although the determinant of a particular drainage basin shape is poorly understood, Schumm (1956) has implied that drainages tend to become more elongate as the relief ratio increases. Comparing the shapes of the drainages described by the two tributaries (Figure

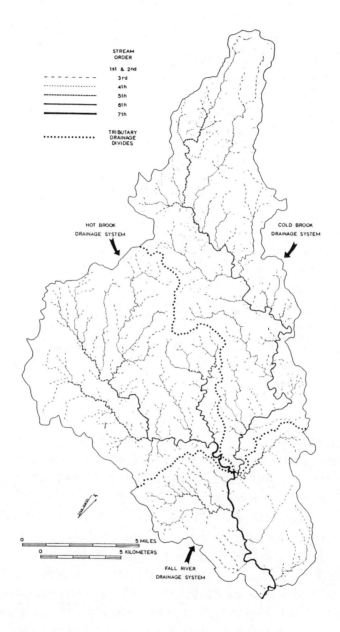

Figure 33. Drainage network of the Fall River watershed.

73

33), it becomes apparent that Hot Brook is nearly circular while Cold Brook is strikingly elongate. However, the two drainages have identical relief ratios, 0.024. But Schumm's hypothesis was based on drainages existing in different climates and on different bedrock types. For interrelated drainages in a state of dynamic equilibrium, the length of streams must adjust to compensate for the relief available. This may produce similar relief ratios for different shapes when other conditions such as bedrock and climate are similar. In the case of the Fall River watershed, the elongate shape of the Cold Brook drainage may be a consequence of its orientation parallel to the initial radial drainage inferred for the Black Hills during its early history (Todd 1902). The widening of the drainage toward the mouth may then be a function of the fact that farther out from the center of the dome-like uplift, the area to be drained increases. More equant drainages are then added to the main channel to compensate for the increased area.

Detailed drainage basin analyses were not feasible for the Fall River watershed since the topographic maps available do not all have the same contour interval. This poses a significant problem since it has been shown by numerous authors (Schumm 1956; Morisawa 1957; Carlston 1963; and Gregory and Walling 1973) that in order to obtain useful information on the character of a drainage basin, it is necessary to consider the entire drainage system, not just the blueline drainage network. This means that a drainage line is shown wherever a "V" in a contour line indicates a channel. The difference in contour interval would, therefore, indicate different numbers of channels for the same area. Channels that would be labeled first and second order streams on maps of one scale may not even be apparent on another. Thus, only minimum values for drainage basin descriptors can be calculated; these minimum values have been evaluated and are summarized in Table 6.

Although more qualitative than the above approach, a more fruitful observation involves the difference between bedrock geology underlying the two tributaries of the Fall River. Cold Brook trends NNW having much the same orientation as the Fall River; above its junction with Hot Brook, it drains Paleozoic units and Precambrian crys-

Table 6. Heights of terraces above Fall River stream bed.

Segment	Distance from mouth ((km)	Height (m) T1	Height (m) T2	Height (m) T3	Height (m) T4	Height (m) T5	Height (m) T6	Height (m) T6
	0.2	14-20						
HOG	1.6	0-20	24-30	40-49	67-73	94	131	
BACK	3.2	15-24	30-41	46-61				
						88		
	4.8		30-37					
	5.6				61-76			
FALL	6.4			37-52	67-76			
RIVER	7.2			34-43	52-61			
	8.9					73	104-116	140-146
	9.7			29-38				
	10.5			18-30				
HOT	10.9			15-30	55-58			
SPRINGS	12.2			37		61	98	
	13.5		6-15	21	43			
	14.5		9	15				
HOT	15.8		3-6	18-30				
BROOK	16.9			17-29	32-38			
	18.2			24-37	40-50	61		
	14.5		15	24-37	58			
	15.8			21-27				
	16.9			15-24	46-49			
	17.2					58		
	17.9			15-21				
	18.2			18-27				
	18.3		3-9	21				
	19.3			12	18-30			
COLD	19.5							
BROOK	19.8			21	34	46-49		
	20.3		11-17					
	20.4		9	18	37	52		
	21.4			8-17	27	38-46		
	21.6							82
	21.7							113-123
	21.9							98
	22.5						46	
	24.0						15	

talline core. Hot Brook, heading approximately west, encounters upper Paleozoic carbonates and Mesozoic clastics, but does not drain crystalline core material. However, as will be described in detail later, terrace deposits in Cold Brook and Hot Brook Canyons contain comparable percentages of crystalline core material. A logical suggestion is that in the past the area drained by Hot Brook extended to the central core, but evidence for this has not been observed. An alternate hypothesis, and the one favored here, recalls that erosion during the Tertiary produced a broad blanket of sediment which covered most of the Black Hills (Harksen 1974); most of the Paleozoic and Mesozoic formations were covered by sediment and only the exposed lower Paleozoic and Precambrian crystalline rocks served as potential source material. Subsequent erosion of this crystalline-rich pediment gravel is believed to have supplied abundant core lithologies even to those drainages which do not presently sample the Precambrian core.

PREVIOUS STUDIES

The Cenozoic deposits of the Black Hills have received only minor and sporadic attention (Darton 1901; Todd 1902; Cook 1922; Wanless 1923; Darton and Paige 1925; Fillman 1929; Plumley 1948; Schultz and Stout 1948; Wolcott 1967; Harksen and Macdonald 1969). Detailed stratigraphic studies of the Tertiary Badlands sediments east of the Black Hills were made by Ward (1922) and Wanless (1923), but their work was not correlated to the deposits within the physiographic limits of the Black Hills.

Fillman (1929) completed the first such detailed study. Focusing predominantly on the Cenozoic deposits of the northern Black Hills, she was able to define three principal terraces: the Mountain Meadow, the Rapid and the Sturgis.

The Mountain Meadow surface, considered to be the oldest of the three, is described by Fillman as occurring widely distributed in the Precambrian interior basin, on the western edge of the Paleozoic limestone plateau and on the outlying Great Plains on flat-topped divides and interstream areas. The surface is buried under younger sediments out on the plains. Fillman states that the age of the surface is fixed by the vertebrate fossils reported in the gravels which lie upon it—five mid-Oligocene forms like those commonly found in the White River beds in the Big Badlands. She also reports that the Mountain Meadow surface occurs anywhere from 60 to 275 m above the present stream bed for the various drainages throughout the Hills which she investigated. Compositionally, the gravels capping the

Mountain Meadow surface are dominantly siliceous gravels derived from the Precambrian core formations.

Younger than the Mountain Meadow surface are the Rapid and Sturgis terraces. Both are characterized by well-formed, flat-topped surfaces which occur at relatively consistent elevations above and parallel to the present-day stream courses—approximately 30 m for the Rapid and 15 m for the Sturgis. Their distribution is less extensive than the Mountain Meadow surface, extending from the edge of the limestone plateau out onto the plains on interstream divides.

The gravels capping the Rapid surface may be as much as 9 to 12 m thick, but are commonly around 5 m. The composition of the gravels appears to be indistinguishable from that of the Mountain Meadow (Fillman 1929)—being high in Precambrian igneous and metamorphic clasts, quartz, chert and a small percentage of locally derived material.

Although occurring on a smaller scale, the younger Sturgis terrace is similar to the Rapid in form and composition. It forms level surfaces parallel to the present stream and is predominantly composed of porphyry, quartz and quartzite clasts, although the amount of younger sedimentary material is greater than in the older terraces.

Plumley (1948), in a detailed sedimentological study of three eastern flank drainages, Rapid Creek, Bear Butte Creek and Battle Creek, made the only other attempt to integrate the Cenozoic deposits of the Black Hills into a logical sequence of development. His work demonstrates that many of the surfaces defined by Fillman as the Mountain Meadow are actually the Rapid or the Sturgis; thus, the 'Mountain Meadow' as defined by Fillman is not representative of a single erosion event, but rather is a composite of several cycles of erosion. In addition, the Rapid terrace identified by Plumley occurs approximately 55 to 70 m above the present stream. This is in direct contrast to the 30 m elevation specified by Fillman as characteristic for the same terrace. The Sturgis terrace also occurs anywhere from 5 to 15 m higher than the 15 m datum given by Fillman.

Plumley (1948: 535) also points out that Fillman's age of mid-Oligocene for the Mountain Meadow surface should be suspect. Her conclusion regarding the age of the Mountain Meadow is based on the work of Darton (1901) who specifically states: "All of the White River beds have yielded fossil bones of various kinds which are typical of the White River group....(Mid-Oligocene fossils) were obtained in beds high up on the flanks of the Black Hills west of Fairburn" (p.543). Since Fillman did not establish that these beds were equivalent to gravels capping the Mountain Meadow surface, her statement about a mid-Oligocene age for the Mountain Meadow surface is not justified. Based on evidence from Meyerhoff and Olmstead (1937) and Fenneman (1931), Plumley (1948) contends that the Mountain Meadow surface was more likely produced by degradation during Miocene and Pliocene time. Similar age constraints have also been suggested by Schultz and Stout (1948), Frye and Leonard (1957, 1959), Harksen and Macdonald (1969), and Harksen (1974). The discovery of a bone identified as an early Pliocene camelid astragalus (Green and Gries 1963) in gravels capping the Mountain Meadow surface south of Rapid City lends further credence to a Pliocene age of formation.

DESCRIPTION OF FALL RIVER TERRACES

Terraces were mapped from the junction of the Fall River with the Cheyenne to their upstream termini along both Cold Brook and Hot Brook. Six and possibly as many as eight distinct former levels of stream flow exist (represented as T_1 to T_8, Figures 34-38). Although it has been suggested that the term terrace be reserved for a topographic form having a flat surface (calling the deposit alluvium, gravel, fill, etc.; Ritter 1986), for the sake of simplicity the term terrace shall be used here for all deposits representing a former, higher level of stream flow. Terraces T_1 and T_4 typically form well-developed, planar surfaces easily located on aerial photographs. Terraces older than T_4 are largely eroded and dissected—having poorly defined boundaries with sparse gravels remaining as the only evidences for the former stream levels.

Technically, terraces may be either erosional or depositional in origin. It has been suggested that these distinct modes of formation can be distinguished on the basis of the spatial relationships of terrace levels. Paired terraces, those which have level surfaces at equal elevations on opposing sides of the stream valley, are depositional in origin; unpaired terraces, those having surfaces which alternate in elevation from one side of the valley to the other, are erosional. It has, however, been pointed out by Ritter (1967) that unpaired terraces may also be depositional if the entrenchment between two episodes of valley filling occurs at the valley sides rather than along the valley axis.

The terraces of the Fall River are in most cases of erosional origin. They are characterized by planar surfaces which bevel inclined bedrock strata, and are unpaired and discontinuous in areal extent. Although the surfaces are planar, they are not strictly horizontal. Rather, they possess components of slope both toward the present stream valley and in a downstream direction. In addition, except where terraces have formed in association with collapse events, deposits are best described as thin veneers of sediment (less than 2 m thick). These characteristics have commonly been documented for terraces of degradational or erosional origin (Stricklin 1961; Ritter 1986)—that is, terraces which are the product of continuous lateral planation and simultaneous very slow downcutting, as opposed to strictly vertical entrenchment interrupted by periodic standstills and alluviation (aggradation).

There are, however, exceptions to these generalities. Paired terraces do occur at the confluence of two tributaries where there is substantial increase in sediment load delivered to the trunk stream (see Figures 34, 35, 36, and 37). The response to such an increase is primarily to steepen the stream gradient by localized deposition of the load in excess of the stream's capacity (Mackin 1948; Lane 1955). Deposits are also somewhat thicker in the younger terraces, T_1 and T_2, where they have formed on the soft Cretaceous shales located outside the last hogback ridge; thicknesses of as much as 3 m are observed. This condition may be explained if the areal restriction of these thicker deposits to shale bedrock is considered. The less ero-

HOGBACK

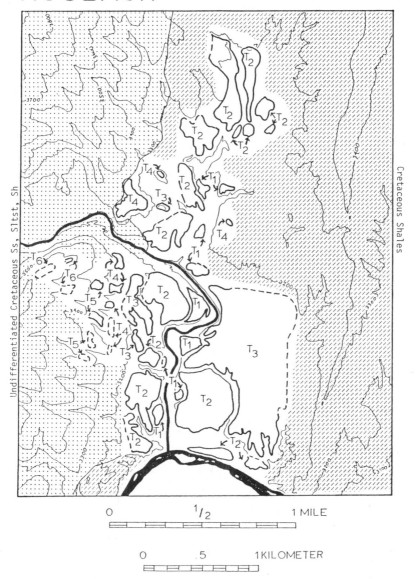

Figure 34. Map of terrace distribution, generalized bedrock geology, and topography—Hog Back segment (Figure 32). Terrace levels indicated by symbols T_1-T_6. Terrace boundaries dashed where inferred.

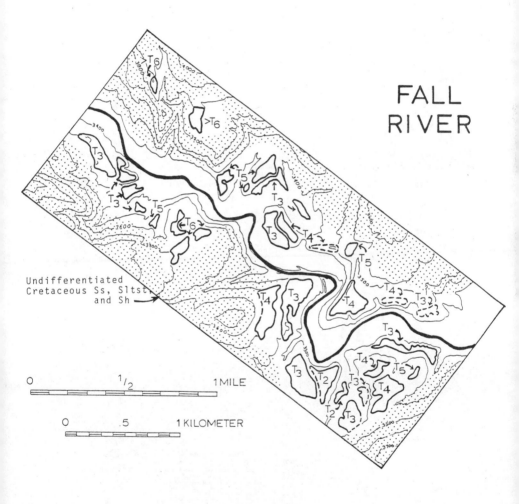

FALL
RIVER

Undifferentiated
Cretaceous Ss, Sltst
and Sh

0   1/2   1 MILE

0   .5   1 KILOMETER

Figure 35. Map of terrace distribution, generalized bedrock geology, and
topography—Fall River segment (Figure 32). Terrace levels indicated by
symbols T_2-T_6. Terrace boundaries dashed where inferred.

81

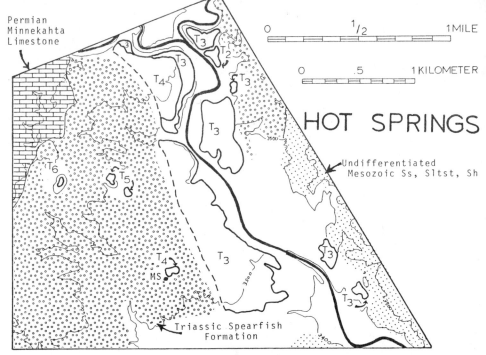

Figure 36. Map of terrace distribution, generalized bedrock geology, and topography—Hot Springs segment (Figure 32). Terrace levels indicated by symbols T_2-T_6. Terrace boundaries dashed where inferred. MS is location of Mammoth Site.

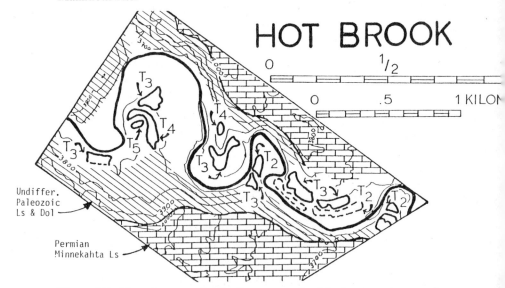

Figure 37. Map of terrace distribution, generalized bedrock geology, and topography—Hot Brook segment (Figure 32). Terrace levels indicated by symbols T_2-T_6. Terrace boundaries dashed where inferred.

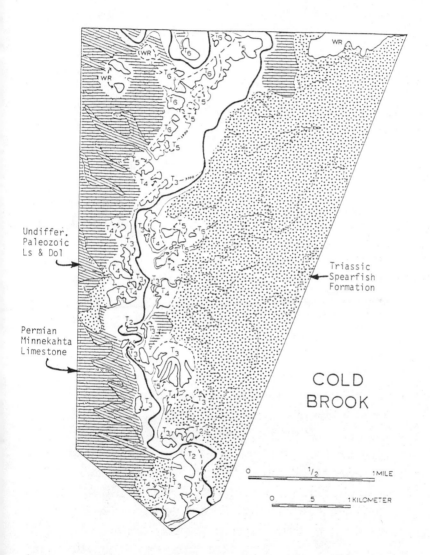

Figure 38. Map of terrace distribution, generalized bedrock geology, and topography—Cold Brook segment (Figure 32). Terrace levels indicated by symbols T_2-T_6. Terrace boundaries dashed where inferred. WR is the White River Formation, the highest gravel-covered surface.

sion-resistant shales would have permitted greater downcutting, resulting in thicker backfill deposits since more deposition would be required to maintain equilibrium.

A more unusual variation is exhibited by terrace T_3 located within the town of Hot Springs. This terrace is not only paired across the stream valley, but also has an alluvial deposit substantially thicker (greater than 30 m) than that of any other terrace. This deposit is also unusual in that it is bounded by a markedly irregular base, although a planar upper surface is maintained. The details of this terrace deposit and the significance of its formation will be discussed more fully later. All Fall River terraces tend to converge upstream with the present floodplain. T_1 does not extend beyond the knickpoint which exists in the stream profile at the outermost hogback ridge. T_2 is traceable along the length of the Fall River and for a short distance along each of the main tributaries, but it is only well developed where the terraces have formed on the shale units occurring east of the Fall River Formation. As has been mentioned, terraces T_1 and T_2 formed in this area are atypical in that their deposits are thicker than those found on other terraces and both upper and lower surfaces are essentially planar.

T_3 and T_4 are the best developed, the most consistently traceable and have the greatest areal extent along the stream length. Terraces older than T_4 have generally lost most of their planar character due to erosion and are located principally by the occurrence of relict gravel lag deposits. Unlike the terraces of Fillman (1929) and Plumley (1948) which have roughly constant heights above the present stream levels, the distance between terraces of the Fall River and the present floodplain decreases upstream as shown in Table 6. The data in Table 6 indicate that downcutting at the mouth of the Fall River has been nearly twice as great as that in the head region; the overall result is an increase in gradient from oldest to youngest terraces.

Although, in general, the heights of terraces above the stream are not consistent with those of Plumley (1948), terraces T_1 to T_4 may still be correlative with the sequence he defined. Since his study basically concentrated on the terraces formed on the soft Cretaceous

84

shale units which were delineated by aerial photographs, the constancy of the heights above the present stream level may be in part due to the restricted portion of the drainage he considered and the homogeneity of the bedrock. If comparison of heights above the present stream levels is restricted to those terraces formed on similar bedrock, it appears that the Fall River T_3 and T_4 are roughly correlative with the Sturgis and Rapid terraces defined by Plumley. T_3 and T_4 are also similar to the Sturgis and Rapid surfaces in that these terraces are generally the best developed and most easily traceable in their respective drainages. On the basis of their relative positions, Fall River terraces T_1 and T_2 may be related to Plumley's two lowest terraces, the Farmingdale and Bear Butte. However, the stimulus for terrace formation may be different for different streams; that is, uplift or a change in base level may not produce the same effect in separate drainages (Bull 1979), particularly for terraces of degradational origin. Therefore, there is little reason to believe that exact correlations can be achieved between distinct drainages. This may in fact explain the problems encountered by Fillman (1929) in extrapolating the Mountain Meadow, Rapid and Sturgis surfaces from drainages in the north to those of the eastern flank. The differences in topography, stream histories, bedrock type and rate of uplift occurring in different portions of the Black Hills almost surely produced a great spectrum of conditions for stream entrenchment and/ or aggradation. Thus, the timing and sequence of terrace development in separate drainages need not be strictly correlative; similarities in relative position above the present stream valleys are not necessarily an indication of time equivalent formation.

TERRACE GRADIENTS

An accurate assessment of paleo-stream gradients and profiles for the Fall River is complicated by several commonly encountered characteristics of the terraces:
1. a general upaired, discontinuous nature;
2. incomplete or total lack of exposure making location of basal

and upper surfaces difficult;
3. irregular basal surface for terrace deposits associated with collapse structures;
4. destruction of the planar nature of upper surfaces and the continuity of the terraces due to erosion and dissection;
5. differential erosion such that time equivalent terraces no longer possess similar elevations; and,
6. lack of information on actual paleo-stream lengths.

The errors resulting from nearly all these factors with respect to the gradients and profiles determined are not known. However, assuming that the first five can be adequately constrained by detailed observations, it is possible to construct profiles and determine reasonable estimates of the paleo-stream gradients.

Since all terraces tend to be elongated parallel to the present stream valley, gradients and profiles were calculated using the present-day length of the Fall River as a standard for estimating paleo-stream length. Knowing that the terrace surfaces are not strictly horizontal (sloping both toward the stream valley and in a downstream direction), a mean elevation, calculated as the average of the lowest and highest elevations on the surface, was used as the vertical datum.

The calculated profiles and gradients are presented graphically in Figure 39. Notice that unlike the more common concave upward profile expected of most streams, profiles of Fall River terraces tend to slightly convex upward, particularly in the older terraces T_4 to T_6. The patterns became flatter in the younger terraces, and the profile of the present stream valley is straight to very slightly concave upward. Such convex-upward patterns could have been the result of erosional or depositional perturbations (Ritter 1986: 246), but they have also been associated with ephemeral streams in arid and semi-arid environments where discharge decreases downstream due to infiltration or evaporation (Leopold *et al.* 1964; Schumm 1971; Morisawa 1968). In the southern Black Hills streams have experienced both situations, but it is infiltration into the subjacent karst system that may be most important.

The tendency for terraces to converge upstream is evident in these diagrams. The indication is one of a gradual increase in gradient from oldest to youngest terraces in response to a change in base level. The current Fall River has apparently not yet equilibrated to this base level change, as a knickpoint occurs in the stream profile (Figure 39). The knickpoint appears at the intersection of the Fall River with the soft shales of the plains. The cascade that results at this point is an indication of the more rapid downcutting possible in the Skull Creek, Mowry and Belle Fourche Shales (Cretaceous) than in the older, more resistant sandstone units.

GRAVEL ANALYSIS

Time-equivalent surfaces could not be traced longitudinally for significant distances because the terraces of the Fall River are unpaired and noncontinuous. Correlation of terraces using fossils is not possible since datable material has not yet been discovered in the terrace deposits. However, a date of $26,075 \pm 975/-790$ yr B.P. (GX-5895-A) has been obtained for the Hot Springs Mammoth Site (Laury 1980). Although this date must be considered a minimum due to the poor preservation of bone collagen in the Site, it still places constraints on terrace ages if stratigraphic relations between the terraces and the Site can be established. Unfortunately, partial removal by construction activities of both the upper Site sediments and portions of the terrace next to it, T_4, and the physical nature of the contact between the two made determination of their stratigraphic relationships uncertain. In order to better establish the chronologic order of events between development of the collapse feature and terrace formation, and to substantiate field correlations of the remaining terraces, an analysis of gravel characteristics was undertaken.

Gravel samples were analyzed for size, shape, roundness and lithology. Size was measured as the dimension of the intermediate axis of the clast. Shape was visually estimated using Zingg's classification (1935). Roundness was also visually estimated using the roundness scale of Powers (1953). The data are summarized in Figures 40 through 42. The data were statistically evaluated by com-

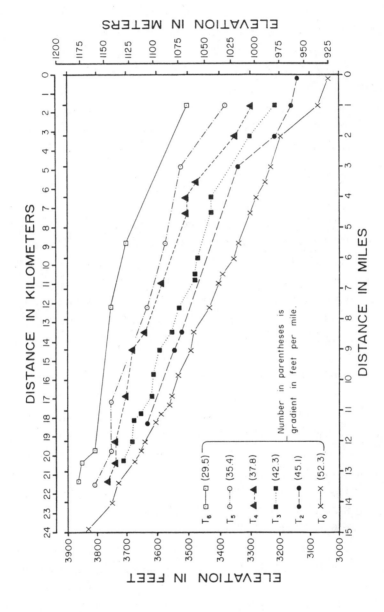

Figure 39. Fall River profiles and gradients for the present stream bed, T_o and terraces T_{2-6}.

88

puter using the Statistical Package for Social Sciences (Nie *et al.* 1975). Tabulated data and statistics occur in Kempton (1980). Lithology ultimately proved to be the most informative characteristic. It will, therefore, be considered separately from the morphological features (size, shape and roundness).

Size, Shape and Roundness

Mean clast size for nearly all terraces falls between 2.5-3.5 cm (coarse to very coarse pebble) (Figure 40). It must be pointed out, however, that due to the nature of the deposits involved, only pebbles larger than 1 cm could be sampled with confidence as representative of a terrace. the mean size value is, thus, biased toward larger grain sizes. Although statistically it cannot be stated that the mean size of the gravel fraction is constant for all terraces, the variation does not appear great enough to be useful in discriminating among the terraces. The variations in size reflect neither a systematic change relative to the age of the terraces nor to their position along their respective stream grades. Mean grain size also appears to bear no significant dependence on lithologic type. For the major constituent lithologies (in order of decreasing mean size), sandstone equals 3.75 cm, chert = 3.63 cm, limestone = 3.53 cm, Minnekahta Limestone = 3.19 cm, and quartz = 3.18 cm. These means cannot be discriminated statistically.

Mean roundness of clasts for each terrace sampled is consistently subangular to subrounded; the total population mean, 0.369, is approximately on the boundary between these two divisions (roundness scale of Powers (1953) — visual estimate chart). There appear to be minima in mean roundness during the times of T_4 and T_6 (Figure 41), but the scatter in the data is extremely large. No one segment reproduces the trend exactly nor does any one terrace level demonstrate systematic variation along the length of the stream.

Fall River terrace gravels do indicate that roundness is a function of lithology (Figure 42). Although most of the dominant lithologies composing the various terraces have similar roundness distributions and means (regardless of relative hardness), chert possesses a lower

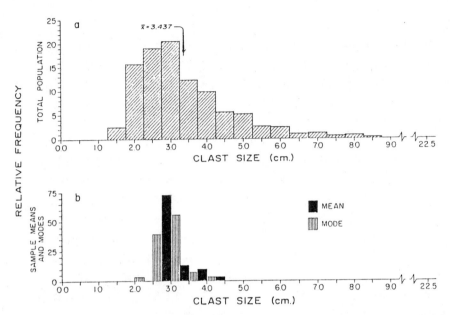

Figure 40. Size distribution for Fall River terrace gravels. Figure 40a. Total population. Figure 40b. Individual terrace means and modes.

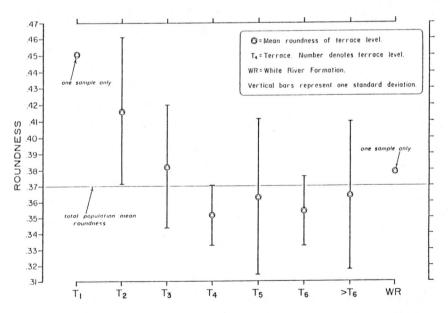

Figure 41. Variation of roundness with terrace level. Roundness scale after Powers (1953).

mean roundness. Similar effects appear to be represented in the gravels from the Colorado River of Texas. Sneed and Folk (1958) found that limestone reaches a limiting roundness within the first few miles of transport due to its softness; quartz rounds more slowly while chert tends to spall and rounds only slightly downstream. By comparison with their results it should be noted that quartz, although probably the most resistant composition and slowest to round, has the highest mean roundness. This implies that the quartz has in general undergone more abrasion than most of the other lithologies. The difference in relative map distances traveled by materials derived from the Precambrian core as opposed to the overlying sedimentary units is not great enough to account for the observed differences in roundness. Therefore, additional abrasion suffered by the quartz must result from multicyclic reworking rather than longer distance of initial transport.

It has been observed that the shapes of particles depend to a large extent on the inherent abrasional properties of the different rock types and that pebbles tend to approach either bladed or equant forms as traced away from their source (Sneed and Folk 1958; Selley 1982). However, shapes of Fall River terrace gravels are not strongly a function of composition; disks constitute the modal shape for all of the dominant lithologies. Quartz clasts exhibit a slightly higher percentage of more spherical shapes, such as rollers or spheres, and bladed forms are more abundant among the sedimentary clasts, particularly the Minnekahta Limestone (Figure 43); however, the mode in each case remains disk. For this reason terraces commonly possess a predominance of disk-shaped clasts except where Minnekahta pebbles constitute an unusually large percentage of the deposit. Such a shift in modal shape from disk to blade occurs in terraces located in the Hot Springs segment where Minnekahta Limestone forms as much as 60 percent of the deposit.

Although the parameters of size, shape and roundness for Fall River terrace gravels can be considered statistically different for different terraces on the basis of the F test statistic (Kempton 1980), the variation is not systematic and is generally not distinguishable by

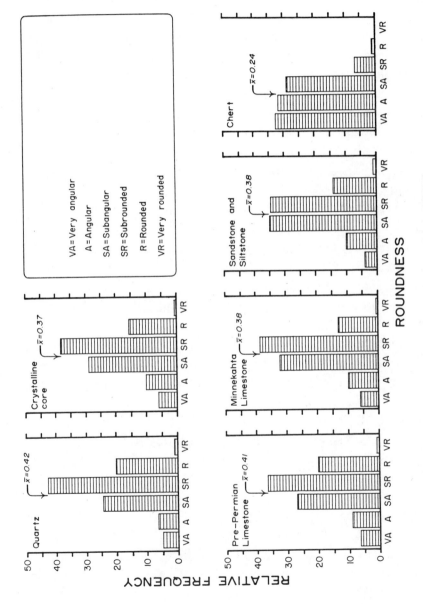

Figure 42. Distribution of roundness for the major clast lithologies in Fall River terraces.

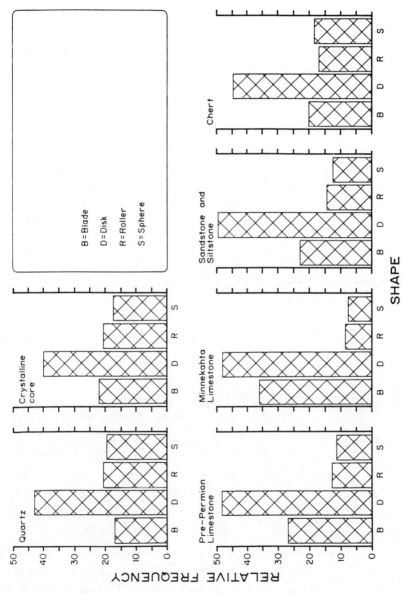

B = Blade
D = Disk
R = Roller
S = Sphere

Figure 43. Distribution of shapes for the major lithological types. Shape classification after Zingg (1935).

multiple comparison tests among the means. Thus, for terraces of degradational origin formed essentially on the source rocks, variations in size, shape and roundness are of limited utility in distinguishing terraces of similar age. Lithology, as will be discussed in the next section, is also a poor discriminator of time equivalent terraces. Correlations must, therefore, rely on field leveling techniques, relative position of the terrace in the sequence of terraces, gradients and heights above the present stream grade.

Gravel Composition

The gravel composition of Fall River terraces is in all cases strongly locally controlled; thus, the composition of a given terrace level is not homogeneous along the entire length of the stream. Gravel composition, then, does not prove to be a useful criterion in correlation of terraces where clast supply from local bedrock sources dominates. On the other hand, systematic changes through time, from oldest to youngest terraces, can be observed if the variability due to the local bedrock contribution is reduced by dividing the stream into segments.

The Fall River has been divided into five segments for this analysis (Figure 32): one corresponding to each main tributary (Cold Brook, Hot Brook), one including the area of the town of Hot Springs (Hot Springs), one extending along the Fall River southeast of the town (Fall River), and one reaching from the outermost cuesta to its junction with the Cheyenne River (Hogback).

Fortunately, many of the source rocks for the gravels are distinctive and readily recognized in hand specimen. In addition, the stratigraphy of the Black Hills is such that it is easily divided into three groups of lithologies which can approximate portions of the stratigraphic column. The rocks of the Precambrian core are essentially nonsedimentary crystalline rocks producing clasts of pegmatite, schist, amphibolite, gneiss, quartz, feldspar, etc. The Paleozoic rocks are predominantly limestones and dolomites; chert is also common in some of the early Paleozoic units. The Mesozoic lithologies are almost entirely sandstones, siltstone and shales. Ternary plots constructed for each segment represent the three divisions (Figure 44). The apices are: Q - quartz, chert, Precambrian igneous and metamorphic rocks; P - Paleozoic limestone and dolomites (excluding Minnekahta); M - Mesozoic sandstones, siltstones and shales (plus Minnekahta). The Minnekahta Limestone marks the boundary between the Paleozoic and Mesozoic rocks and has been included with the Mesozoic units in order to enhance the contribution made by the younger material. The sandstone, siltstone and shale clasts from the Mesozoic formations are commonly poorly cemented; they rapidly break down into sand, silt and clay components which are not considered in the analysis. This decreases the percentage of Mesozoic material represented in the gravel compositions to the point that their overall contribution is overshadowed by the more resistant limestones. Since the Minnekahta is late Permian in age, it was elected to include it with the clastic compositions as an indication of the variation in the amount of younger rock types through time.

For each segment the trend is the same; the composition of the oldest terrace for a segment has the composition richest in quartz, chert and Precambrian crystalline material. Compositional analyses for the deposits mapped by Wolcott (1967) as the White River Formation in Cold Brook Canyon plot on the Q apex, being essentially 100 percent quartz, chert and crystalline rocks (Figure 44). Successively younger terraces have decreasing amounts of this component while increasing amounts of all younger sedimentary material. The trend exhibits a very slight increase in Paleozoic limestones over Mesozoic material in the older terraces while the ultimate tendency is toward the younger material. This is primarily due to the inclusion of the Minnekahta with the M components. The Minnekahta is one of the dominant source rocks for the Fall River terrace gravels. If the Minnekahta has been included with the other Paleozoic clasts the trend would have been overwhelmingly toward the P apex with curvature toward the M apex occurring only in the very youngest terraces (T_1 and T_2). In either case, the conclusions derived from these plots would be the same.

Although the general trend is the same for each segment, the com-

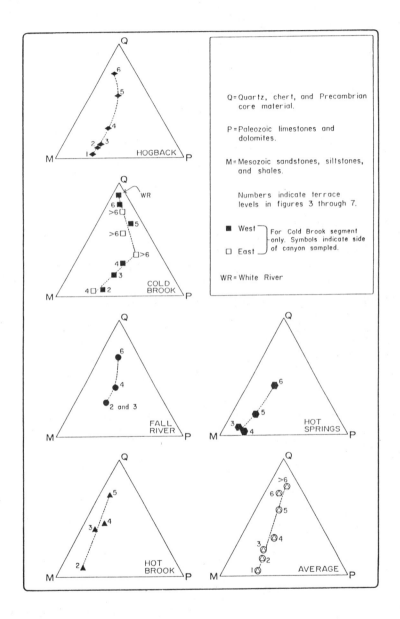

Figure 44. Terrace gravel compositions for Fall River segments. (see Figure 32 for location).

position of time equivalent terraces may differ significantly from one segment to another due to the contribution of local bedrock. The effect of the local bedrock geology on the composition of terrace alluvium is probably best demonstrated in the Cold Brook segment (see Figures 38 and 44). $T4$ was sampled from opposite sides of Cold Brook Canyon at the junction of two tributaries to the main channel. The two surfaces have the same elevations and are, thus, time equivalent. However, gravel analyses produced significantly different results. $T4$ sampled on the east side of the drainage (sample No. 24, Figure 38) has a composition of $Q28.4 \, P27.6 \, M68.4$ (shown as the open square in Figure 44). The discrepancy in the amount of Q relative to M for the two terraces in readily explained when differences in bedrock are observed. The terraces that developed on the west side of Cold Brook Canyon lie on Spearfish siltstone and gypsum. In addition, a deposit of gravels (mapped by Wolcott (1967) as White River Formation) consisting of essentially 100 percent quartz, chert and Precambrian core material is located at the head of the minor tributary on the east side of Cold Brook. This deposit apparently supplied the terraces formed below it on the east side with more Q component than was available for the terraces on the west, and the time was apparently insufficient to homogenize the sediments contributed by the two tributaries.

Hot Brook Canyon which does not extend into the Precambrian core (and there is no evidence that its course did so in the past), includes as much core material in its terrace fill as terraces in any other segment. This suggests that reworking of older Q-rich deposits formed prior to the present drainage has contributed significant material to the terraces. The existence of such deposits has been suggested by Harksen and Macdonald (1969), Harksen (1974), and Meyerhoff and Olmstead (1937). Remnants of the broad fan of sediment they have postulated can be found in Cold Brook Canyon. These deposits have been mapped by Wolcott as the Oligocene White River Formation, but this age is questionable and the deposits are more likely Pliocene in age (Plumley 1948; Meyerhoff and Olmstead 1937; Harksen 1974; Green and Gries 1963). Thus, the trend in gravel compositions demonstrates that the late Tertiary gravel deposits formed in the area of the Fall River are the major source for the multicycled crystalline material of younger terraces; the general compositional trend is one of dilution of this crystalline material by local bedrock contribution through time.

COLLAPSE FEATURES AND RELATED TERRACE FORMATION

Incision of the Fall River drainage effects a gradual lowering of the potentiometric ground-water surface (pressure surface) in its watershed. This event, in concert with dissolution and removal of soluble material in subsurface units prior to the downcutting, led to upward stoping and the development of breccia pipes and offtimes-associated sinks. That is, once the hydrostatic support of the solution-produced cavities was lessened or removed by sufficient lowering of the ground-water table, collapse structures began to form and the present subjacent karst terrain was initiated (Brink and Partridge 1965; Laury 1980). These breccia pipes and sinks have been documented by Bowles and Braddock (1963), who further demonstrated that the collapse must have resulted from the solution of anhydrite and gypsum by ground water in the Minnelusa Formation (Permian). Solution and removal of as much as 75 meters of calcium sulfate from this formation are reported, and breccia pipes may locally penetrate upward more than 300 meters into lower Cretaceous units.

Terrace T_3 within the town of Hot Springs formed in close association with these collapse events and possesses characteristics distinctive from all other alluvial deposits of the ancestral Fall River. As shown in Figure 36, T_3 exhibits a nearly continuous longitudinal dimension much greater than any other terrace, extending from above the junction of the two main tributaries to the southern edge of Hot Springs, a distance of approximately 3.2 km. The thickness of the T_3 alluvium is also substantially greater. Although the base is noticeably irregular and not everywhere exposed, total thickness must be in excess of 30 meters. Gravel thicknesses are greatest along an

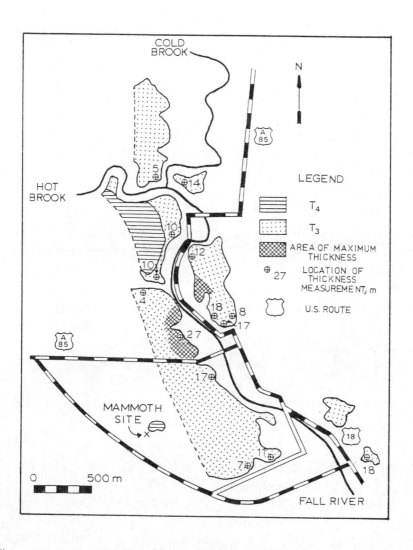

Figure 45. Generalized thickness distribution map for terrace T$_3$ in Hot Springs.

axis approximately described by the present Fall River channel; the maximum is observed at approximately the center of the terrace as mapped. Thickness diminishes rapidly both upstream and laterally as the base of the depression rises upward (Figure 45). Stratification ranges from horizontal to large-scale, downstream-accreting foreset beds. Horizontal bedding commonly occurs at the upstream terminus and toward the top of the deposit. Downstream from the horizontal bedding are low-angle foresets with an apparent downstream dip of 20 degrees and amplitudes essentially equivalent to the thickness of the deposits (greater than 15 meters; Figure 46). Crossbedding also occurs at the base of the deposit beneath the horizontal bedding; but set thicknesses are much less, ranging from 3 to 4 meters.

Figure 46. Terrace T3 in Hot Springs showing increase in dip angle of fluvial gravel accretionary sets toward the area of maximum deposit thickness (see Figure 45). View looking east.

Lithologically, the T3 deposit is a conglomerate composed of greater than 50 percent Minnekahta Limestone clasts. Particles range from sand and silt to boulder size. In the thickest portions the deposit is an orthoconglomerate; that is, it is clast- as opposed to matrix-supported. Since sand and silt are restricted to the interstices and are relatively minor in abundance, the deposit can be considered well sorted. In addition to the thinning described above, the T3 alluvium also becomes progressively finer-grained and more poorly sorted laterally and downstream. Gravels become matrix-supported as the abundance of sand and silt increases; at the lateral extremities of the main deposit, beds in excess of a meter occur which are devoid of gravel.

Terraces within the town of Hot Springs are also unique in that they are the only ones to display significant degrees of cementation. Cementation is produced by a rind of silty, micritic calcium carbonate which surrounds and binds the clasts. The association of these deposits, even today, with springs suggests that the cementation is due to precipitation of CaCO3 carried in solution by ground water. Many of the springs are warm or hot; this tends to further enhance the precipitation process. However, the cementation is not ubiquitous; gravels with lesser amounts of sand and silt matrix are consistently better cemented. The preference of cementation for matrix-poor areas is to be expected since ground water would migrate most readily through these more permeable regions.

The anomalous character of the terrace T3 in Hot Springs provides only indirect evidence for an origin related to collapse events. Direct evidence is derived from field observation of collapse structures in association with terrace deposits. In the outcrop shown in Figures 47a and 47b, contorted Spearfish and Sundance (Jurassic) sediments involved in the collapse are separated from adjacent Spearfish bedrock by a characteristically steep-walled contact. T3 gravels erosionally overlie the collapse fill, beveling both collapse sediments and Spearfish bedrock. Deposition of terrace fill obviously followed sinkhole development in this locality.

Gravel deposition apparently preceded the collapse event at the Hot Springs Mammoth Site. Although direct stratigraphic relationships cannot be observed, this conclusion is substantiated by the similarity between the gravels interstratified with the site fill with those in the terrace remnant, T4, adjacent to the site; Figure 48 shows that the gravel compositions are essentially identical.

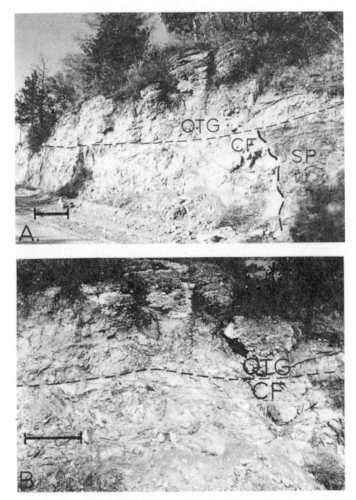

Figure 47a. Collapse structure in Spearfish bedrock overlain by undeformed T3 gravels. SP–Spearfish Formation, CF–collapse fill, QTG–Quaternary terrace gravels. Heavy dashed line indicates erosional contact between Spearfish bedrock and collapse fill; lighter dashed line denotes the base of undeformed terrace deposite. Bar equals one meter.

Figure 47b: Closer view of contact between collapse structure and terrace (T3) deposit for outcrop pictured in Fig. 46a. Location approximately 1 km north of Mammoth Site. Bar is approximately one meter.

102

Terrace T4 must have been abandoned by the ancestral Fall River prior to formation of the Mammoth Site. The sediments filling the Mammoth Site sinkhole are predominantly thinly-laminated, fine-grained sands, silts, and clays. Gravels occur along the margins of the pond and only locally extend into the deeper, central portions of the fill. If fluvial processes had still been operating sufficiently near the site locality subsequent to the collapse event, the delicate pond sediments would have been precluded; coarse gravels and cobbles transported by the Fall River in its bed load would have rapidly filled the depression.

An important consequence of establishing the nature of the relationship between the Hot Springs Mammoth Site and terrace T4 is that it places minimum age constraints on the formation of Fall River terraces in general. The youngest T4 could be is the age of the Mammoth Site itself (26,075 + 975/-790 yr B.P.). Assuming that the average rate of downcutting has not changed significantly with time, all terraces of the Fall River could have formed within a period of approximately 40,000-60,000 years.

The terraces in the town of Hot Springs indicate a genetic association with localized subsidence events (Figure 49). Collapse was found to occur both prior to and subsequent to terrace formation. In the former case, rapid filling of the depression or depressions was probably accomplished by migrating gravel bars carrying an unusually high percentage of Minnekahta Limestone, the bedrock exposed immediately upstream. Sands and silts were deposited laterally and downstream where energy levels were lower due to the greater distance from the main channel or to local ponding conditions. However, the predominantly coarse nature of the deposit may imply that few fines were being carried or deposited in this stream reach. Where collapse followed terrace formation, filling of the depression began by colluvial slope wash of material from the proximal abandoned terrace and other upland surfaces.

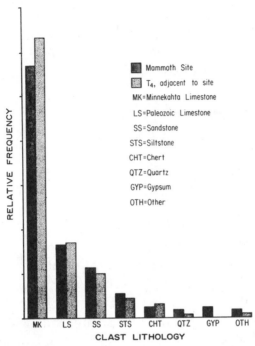

Figure 48. Comparison of gravel compositions for terrace T4 and the Hot Springs Mammoth Site.

GEOLOGIC HISTORY

Near the end of the Cretaceous, Laramide tectonics initiated a general uplift in the areas that were to become the Black Hills and the Rocky Mountains (Eardley 1962). At this time the streams radiated outward from the dome-like structure of the Black Hills, flowing eastward on the east flank across the surface which today is the divide between the South Fork of the Cheyenne River and the White River (Figure 50a). Deposition began in the Oligocene with the White river Group and continued through Miocene and Pliocene with various fluvial, eolian, and volcanic ash deposits (Harksen 1969; Swinehart *et al.* 1985). By late Pliocene most of western South Dakota as well as the states of Texas, Oklahoma, Kansas, Nebraska, Wyoming, Colorado, and New Mexico were nearly buried under an almost flat-lying blanket of Tertiary sediments (Frye and Leonard

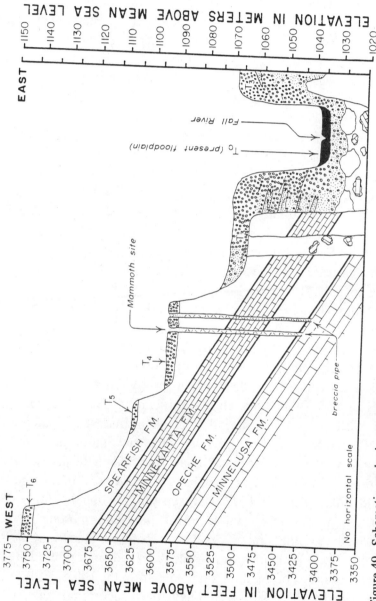

Figure 49. Schematic geologic cross-section of Fall River terraces showing their relationship to collapse structures in Hot Springs. Bedrock geology after Wolcott (1967); diagram modified after Laury (1980).

105

1957; Harksen and Macdonald 1969; Harksen 1974; Osterkamp *et al.* 1987: 166). This surface was designated by Darton (1901) as the "Ogallala surface" and has subsequently been investigated by Frye and Leonard (1957) and Harksen and Macdonald (1969). The Ogallala depositional surface, which has occasionally been referred to as the High Plains, exhibited a low gradient believed by Harksen (1969) to be a maximum of 9.75 ft/mi in the region east of the Black Hills. In western South Dakota the only terrain not buried under these sediments was that part of the Black Hills currently above 4400 ft (1350 m) above sea level (Harksen 1974).

Causes of entrenchment and the timing of entrenchment of the Ogallala surface are not well known. The last uplift associated with the Rocky Mountains and the Black Hills is believed by Harksen (1969: 22) to be approximately 4.5 my B.P. (middle to late Pliocene) and may have initiated rejuvenation. However, for the Fall River and similar drainages on the southeastern slopes of the Black Hills, this uplift by itself does not adequately account for the nature of the entrenchment or for the apparent capture of the eastern drainages by the Cheyenne River.

Although the Pleistocene glacial advances did not extend into the region of the Black Hills, the fluctuating climatic and drainage conditions which resulted during this time almost certainly enhanced the entrenchment initiated by tectonic uplift. Early Pleistocene glaciation in eastern South Dakota apparently did not affect the drainage patterns of the Black Hills significantly. For example, gravels derived from the Hills during Nebraskan time (the Medicine Root gravel) and Kansan time (gravels on the east end of the Cuny Table covered by Kansan Pearlette Ash) are reported on the divide between the present South Fork of the Cheyenne River and the White River (Todd 1902); Wanless 1923; Harksen and Macdonald 1969). However, the Wisconsin glacial advances imposed important modifications on the existing drainage patterns. By forcing the Missouri River approximately 200 miles westward, glacial advance altered the local base level and shortened the drainages from the Black Hills (Figure 50a). Headward erosion would have been accordingly enhanced in many of the eastern stream systems of the Black Hills.

The South Fork of the Cheyenne has long been attributed to just such an event of headward erosion (Todd 1902; Wanless 1923). By increasing its length southwestward, it sequentially captured all of the drainages along the southeastern section of the Black Hills (Figure 50b). The date of this capture, however, is still in question. The fact that the divide between the Cheyenne River and the White River is higher than any of the Fall River terraces at its junction with the Cheyenne indicates that all of these terraces were formed after the capture by the South Fork. A Pleistocene age for the capture was proposed by Todd (1902) and Wanless (1923). A few terraces older than T_6, as well as the deposits of White River/Ogallala gravels, are located well above the elevation of the divide and could easily have formed from drainages prior to the present one. Unfortunately, the origins of the "terraces" older than T_6 are not at all clear as their deposits have all but been eroded away. Capture, then, must have occurred between the deposition of the White River/Ogallala sediments and the creation of terraces T_6 and younger. Knowing T_4 to have a minimum age of 26,000 yr B.P. (based on its relationship to the Hot Springs Mammoth Site), and assuming a constant rate of terrace formation, capture may have occurred between 40,000-70,000 years ago. Although the assumption of a constant rate of downcutting may be questioned, Fall River terraces exhibit characteristics indicative of a degradational origin where lateral planation as well as vertical entrenchment was important. Entrenchment in this manner could occur continuously; terrace formation would not necessarily indicate static periods of alluviation alternating with times of entrenchment. Furthermore, even if entrenchment is noncontinuous, the time average of periods of entrenchment plus periods of terrace formation may still be closely approximated by such an assumption. Therefore, the assumption of a constant rate of downcutting may be more realistic than it first appears; and reasonable, order of magnitude estimates of the timing of entrenchment and capture of the Fall River watershed by the Cheyenne can at least be offered.

By comparison, studies elsewhere in the Great Plains have shown

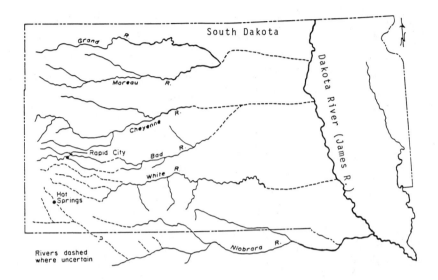

Figure 50a. Generalized configuration of major drainages during late Tertiary (after Todd 1902; Wanless 1923).

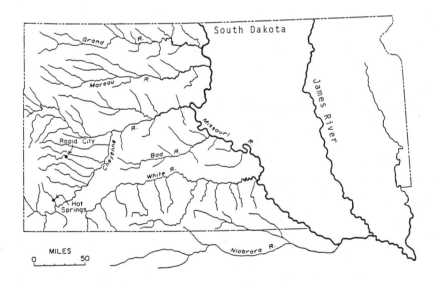

Figure 50b. Generalized mid-Pleistocene drainage patterns. Missouri River approximates Wisconsin glacial advance.

in the Colorado Piedmont between the Front Range and the South Platte River a succession of pediments and stream terraces. Five major "erosion-deposition- stability cycles" or "EDS cycles" are believed responsible for development of these surfaces (Osterkamp *et al.* 1987). The "megacycles" commenced about 1.8 Ma (latest Pliocene) and were induced principally by climatic changes; the effect of tectonism is believed trivial and very local (Osterkamp *et al.* 1987: 174). Timing of the EDS cycles recorded in the Great Plains of Colorado may also be applicable to the Black Hills region of the Great Plains. If so, all of the terraces of the Fall River (T_6 and younger) have formed during the youngest megacycle (V) which commenced between 80 and 60 ka (Osterkamp *et al.* 1987: 175)— dates corresponding very closely to those we suggest.

SYNTHESIS

Terraces of the Fall River are being studied in order to determine their sequence of development during the evolution of the Fall River drainage basin, to relate this sequence to the development of the Hot Springs Mammoth Site, and to integrate the history of the Fall River drainage basin with developments of the late Cenozoic of the greater Black Hills region. These problems are considered on the basis of field mapping, drainage basin analysis and variations in the size, shape, roundness, and lithologic compositions of gravel deposits from selected terraces.

The existence of streams that established courses transverse to the strike of beds and structures indicates that the Fall River drainage system has been superimposed on the present structural grain of the Black Hills by erosion through a preexisting surface. The elongate nature and radial orientation of the Cold Brook drainage basin of the Fall River suggests that it was established as a direct consequence of the dome-like structure of the eastern Black Hills; Hot Brook Creek, having a more circular drainage basin shape and an orientation defined by the relative resistance of the underlying bedrock, may have been subsequently added to the main Fall River drainage to compensate for the additional area incurred radially outward from the center of the Hills.

At least six and possibly as many as eight terraces occur along the Fall River; their geomorphic character demonstrates that they are, in general, rapidly formed, erosional surfaces. These characteristics include: (1) planar surfaces which bevel inclined strata and which slope toward the present stream valley and in a downstream direction; (2) an areal distribution essentially parallel to the present stream channel; (3) a general unpaired nature; (4) alluvial deposits commonly consisting of thin gravel veneers; and (5) gradients which increase from oldest to youngest producing upstream convergence of the terraces.

Gravel analyses show that the textural properties of size, shape and roundness of clasts from Fall River terraces do not possess systematic variations with distance along the stream or through time and as such cannot be used for the purpose of terrace correlation. However, comparisons of the shape and roundness of the different lithologic types reveal a tendency for quartz clasts to be slightly rounder and more spherical than clasts of most other lithologies. Considering that quartz and other Precambrian core material are probably the most abrasion resistant gravel types, their greater roundness and sphericity implies that they have undergone more than one cycle of transport and deposition.

Comparison of gravel compositions also proves to be a limited utility in correlation of terraces. Owing to the sizable influence of local bedrock, the compositions of time equivalent deposits need not be the same. However, gravel compositions do show a consistent trend through time ranging from crystalline-rich deposits for the older (higher) terraces to dominantly sedimentary material in the younger (lower) levels. The principal source of crystalline material for the Fall River is not directly the Precambrian core, but is, rather, from the reworking of the higher and older, Precambrian-clast-rich White River/Ogallala alluvium which blanketed most of the Hills during the Tertiary.

Thus, sedimentological/geomorphological observations in the Fall

River watershed support the existence of an extensive alluvial surface during the Tertiary. Entrenchment of this surface was apparently rapid and was probably induced by the advance of glacial ice in eastern South Dakota during the late Pleistocene. Although the timing of the entrenchment of the Tertiary sediment surface and the capture of the Fall River by the Cheyenne River are not precisely known, terrace development and its association with unusual collapse features within the Fall River watershed has placed minimum time constraints on these events.

Terraces T_6 and younger have elevations lower than the divide between the Cheyenne and White Rivers at the junction of the Fall River with the Cheyenne River, and could only have formed once capture had been completed. In addition, a minimum age of 26,000 yr B.P. can be attached to terrace T_4 based on its association with the Hot Springs Mammoth Site. Assuming a constant rate of terrace formation, the timing of capture and entrehcnment (which must have occurred between deposition of the Ogallala sediments and formation of T_6) is probably between 40,000-70,000 yr B.P.

Dissolution and removal of soluble material within the Minnelusa Formation prior to entrenchment resulted in the formation of collapse features once downcutting was initiated; the Hot Springs Mammoth Site is one such collapse structure. Terrace T_3 located within the town of Hot Springs exhibits unique characteristics due to its formation in association with these collapse events. Greater than average thickness, irregular basal surface, greater areal extent and more extensive cementation number among the attributes that characterize the singularity of this sink-filling terrace deposit. Stratigraphic relationships observed in outcrop suggest that the sequence of events began with collapse. Fluvial processes contributed to rapid filling of the depression as the gravels, cobbles and boulders carried as bedload by the river migrated into the area. Finer-grained deposits developed laterally and downstream where energy levels were lower. As filling neared completion, the nature of the contact between terrace alluvium and collapse structures and/or bedrock again became erosional (see Figure 47). In contrast, the presence and na-

111

ture of T4 gravels in the Hot Springs Mammoth Site justifies the reverse sequence of events—terrace formation, abandonment of the terrace and finally collapse. Thus, field relationships demonstrate that collapse events have occurred both prior to and subsequent to terrace formation. In fact, the earliest collapse events probably followed soon after the inception of downcutting and must have persisted throughout most of the Quaternary as entrenchment and terrace formation continued.

Further study will be necessary before more complete evaluation of the late Cenozoic history of the southeastern Black Hills can be ventured. Additional investigations of the Quaternary terraces in other drainages as well as detailed examination of the relationships between the Cheyenne River terraces and the terraces of its tributaries could potentially assess the timing of capture of successive drainages as the Cheyenne cut headward. Further studies may also define such characteristics as age, areal extent, and homogeneity of the high-level White River/Ogallala surface which acted as the clast source for younger terraces. Investigation of the character and distribution of sinkhole development in the southern Black Hills may also provide greater understanding of drainage patterns and their evolution in this area.

PART II:

PALEOECOLOGY AND PALEONTOLOGY

Part II: Paleoecology and Fossil Faunas

FORWARD

This portion of the volume deals with the fossils: flora and fauna recovered from the excavation of the site. It is from these data sets that we attempt to reconstruct the paleoenvironment during the time of entrapment. Based on the fossils, we look at the local ecology of ± 26,000 years ago.

The majority of the fossil evidence is represented by vertebrate remains—both mammalian and non-mammalian (Table 7), however, the invertebrates and the plant remains (mostly as pollen) tell their share of the story, as well.

Table 7. Non-mammalian and mammalian vertebrate fauna from the Hot Springs Mammoth Site. This is a composite list based on information from a number of chapters within this volume.

Class Osteichthyes (bony fish)

    Order Cypriniformes

        Genus et species indeterminate

Class Amphibia (Amphibians)

    Order Anura (frog/toad)

        Bufo cognatus (Great Plains toad)

        Bufo cf. woodhousei (woodhouse toad)

Class Aves (birds)

    Order indeterminate

Class Mammalia (mammals)

  Order Insectivora (insectivores)

    Family Talpidae (moles)

      Scalopus aquaticus (eastern mole)

  Order Lagomorpha (pikas, rabbits, hares)

    Family Leporidae (hares and rabbits)

      Sylvilagus sp. (cottontail rabbit)

      Lepus cf. *townsendii* (white-tailed jackrabbit)

  Order Rodentia (rodents)

    Family Sciuridae (squirrels)

      Spermophilus cf. *elegans/richardsonii*

      (Wyoming/Richardson's ground squirrel)

      Spermophilus cf. *tridecemlineatus* (13 lined ground

        squirrel)

      Cynomys (*Leucocrossuromys*) sp. (white-tailed prairie

        dog)

    Family Geomyidae (gopher)

      Thomomys talpoides (northern pocket gopher)

    Family Cricetidae (hamsters and voles)

      Peromyscus cf. *maniculatus* (deer mouse)

      Neotoma cf. *cinerea* (bushy-tailed woodrat)

      Phenacomys cf. *intermedius* (heather vole)

Microtus sp. (vole)

Order Carnivora (carnivores)

    Family Mustelidae (weasels)

        Mustela cf. *vison* or *nigripes* (mink or black-footed ferret)

        Taxidea taxus (badger)

    Family Canidae (dogs)

        Canis lupus (gray wolf)

        Canis latrans (coyote)

    Family Ursidae (bears)

        Arctodus simus (giant short-faced bear)

Order Artiodactyla

    Family Camelidae (camels)

        Camelops sp. (camel)

    Family Antilocapridae (pronghorns)

        Antilocapra americana (pronghorn)

    Family Bovidae

        cf. *Euceratherium collinum* (shrub ox)

Order Proboscidea

    Family Elephantidae

        Mammuthus columbi (Columbian mammoth)

        Mammuthus primigenius (woolly mammoth)

Chapter 5

LATE PLEISTOCENE INVERTEBRATE
AND PLANT REMAINS,
MAMMOTH SITE, BLACK HILLS, SOUTH DAKOTA

Jim I. Mead, Richard H. Hevly, and Larry D. Agenbroad

INTRODUCTION

Plant, invertebrate, and vertebrate remains indicate that grass-dominated communities (but with trees present) have occurred in the Great Plains of North America for millions of years providing sustenance for a variety of herbivores (Baker and Waln 1985). Through time this area has undergone significant climate change, with consequent adjustments in the distribution and composition of the local biota, particularly during the Late Pleistocene (Baker and Waln 1985). Plant and animal remains partially document the nature and magnitude of environmental change from middle Pleistocene time on in the southern plains and from early Wisconsin in the eastern plains. However, previously published ^{14}C dated biotic remains from the northern and western plains are rarely much older than late glacial to early Holocene (12,500 to 10,270 yr B.P.) either within or outside the areas formerly covered by the Laurentide ice sheet (Baker and Waln 1985; Graham 1981; Gilbert and Martin 1984; Kurten and Anderson 1980). Hence, the nature of late Wisconsin biotic communities within the northern plains have been reconstructed primarily from geographically and temporally remote data.

The Farmdalian (26,075 ± 975 yr B.P.) biotic remains (pollen and mollusks) reported here, which have been recovered from Hot Springs Mammoth Site (HSMS), Black Hills, South Dakota, now provide a rare glimpse of middle Wisconsin environmental conditions in the northern Great Plains/Black Hills southwest of the Laurentide ice sheet.

MAMMOTH SITE

The Hot Springs Mammoth site (discovered in 1974 during construction of a housing development) is an example of reverse topographic expression. The sedimentary fill of a former sinkhole became the top of a small hill by differential erosion. Excavations recovered more than 43 individual mammoths (from testing ± 20 percent of the site) that had been trapped and preserved in the sedimentary fill of this sinkhole (Agenbroad 1984b, this volume; Agenbroad and Laury 1984; Laury this volume). The sinkhole, 45 m wide on its major axis, was apparently formed by solution collapse of an underlying limestone formation. The breccia pipe formed by this collapse extended upward to a surficial exposure of the Permo-Triassic Spearfish Shale, which became the wall rock of the sinkhole.

The maximum depth of this sinkhole may not be possible to reconstruct, but on the basis of remnant sediments exposed by drilling, it was at least 22 m deep. The breccia pipe became a conduit for artesian hot water, temperatures of which have been estimated to have ranged as high as 35°C on the basis of biological and sedimentary evidence (Agenbroad and Laury 1984; Laury 1980). Water filled the bottom of the sinkhole with a pond to which animals were attracted and where, on occasion, they were trapped by the steep walls (slope > 60°). Depth of the water probably varied during the history of the pond, but mammal tracks (Agenbroad and Laury 1984) and the presence of both terrestrial and aquatic plant fossils (this report) indicate shallow depth, at least marginally.

PRESENT ENVIRONMENTS IN THE BLACK HILLS

"A forested mountain island in a grassland sea" is a phrase commonly used to describe the present Black Hills of South Dakota (Froiland 1978). The Black Hills are an isolated mountain complex that rises to an elevation of 2228 m above the surrounding northern Great Plains (925 to 1075 m elevation). Four major physiographic regions (Hogback Ridge, Red Valley, Limestone Plateau, and the Central Area) comprise a very diversified mountain mass of approximately 15,540 sq km.

There is no evidence that the Black Hills were ever glaciated (Lemke *et al.* 1965). The Bighorn Mountains in Wyoming 250 km west, and the area north of the Missouri River, South Dakota 250 km east were the nearest glaciated regions during the late Wisconsin (Woodfordian) glacial maximum (Figure 51). Climatically the Black Hills can be divided, today, into two zones: the northern and the southern hills. The northern hills are typically higher in elevation and therefore cooler and wetter. The southern hills receive approximately 475 mm precipitation per year and average several degrees warmer than the northern hills, which receive an average of 725 mm precipitation per year.

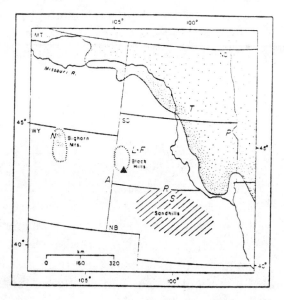

Figure 51. Map of the northern Great Plains centering on the Black Hills. Stippling represents Wisconsin glacier extent both in the Bighorn Mountains and on the plains. A, Agate Basin; L-F, Lange-Ferguson Clovis kill site; N, Natural Trap cave; P, Pickerel Lake; R, Rosebud; S, Sandhills; and T, Tappen.

119

Four distinct vegetation complexes are present in the Black Hills today: Rocky Mountain Coniferous Forest, Northern Coniferous Forest, Grassland Complex of the northern Great Plains, and Deciduous Forest (Froiland 1978). Thirty percent of the present vegetation belongs to the Rocky Mountain Coniferous Forest Complex, with ponderosa pine (*Pinus ponderosa*) the single most common element. Other important conifers include white spruce (*Picea glauca*), limber pine (*P. flexilis*), lodgepole pine (*P. contorta*), and juniper (*Juniperus communis, J. horizontalis*, and *J. scopulorum*). To our knowledge the modern pollen rain of the Black Hills region has not been studied in depth.

Although the present mammalian and avian faunas are fairly well known for the Black Hills (Froiland 1978; Pettingill and Whitney 1965; and Turner 1974) the mollusks are only cursorily understood. Roscoe (1954) has examined eight localities in the Black Hills for terrestrial gastropods. A variety of collecting stations in South Dakota, including some in the Black Hills and adjacent ponds, were examined for gastropods and pelecypods by Henderson (1927) and Over (1915). Hubricht (1985) included South Dakota in his study of the mollusks of the United States.

MATERIALS AND METHODS

Excavation of the HSMS followed standard archaeological and paleontological procedures (Agenbroad 1978a, 1984b). The fill of the sinkhole is characterized by a series of laminar increments with alternating size gradations ranging from clay to sand-sized particles containing occasional pebbles (Laury 1980). Vertebrate remains and tracks occur in all phases of the sedimentary fill, and it is from this continuum of mammoth tracks that Laury (1980) suggested that the water depth probably did not exceed 5 m during any phase of the history of the pond.

Spring conduits occurred in the north and east portions of the pond and the sediments found there (Figure 52) are more sand-rich due to winnowing of fine materials by hydraulic action. Sediments

120

collected from this area and extracted for pollen and other plant remains in 1974-1979, by different analysts and different laboratories, were unproductive. It is likely that the pollen remains had been destroyed by oxidation and leaching by the thermal waters or even may have been transported by water movement to less turbulent areas of the pond. The western portion of the deposit contained more clay and silt. The 1983-1989 field seasons concentrated on this western area of the sinkhole deposits, which had never been more than cursorily tested in the 1974-1979 seasons, as a comparative test of abundance of faunal and floral remains.

Pollen

Pollen samples were collected from clay-rich units directly associated with mammal remains (Figure 52). Approximately 200 ml of sediment was suspended in an equal volume of water, to which HCl was added for the solution of carbonates. After cessation of carbonate solution the suspension was stirred and allowed to stand for 1-1/2 min., allowing the heavier sediments to settle out of the mixture. The supernatant, in which the pollen still remains suspended, was then subjected to standard HF-acetolysis procedures of pollen extraction. Several samples of the 1983-1986 excavation units were found to contain pollen, which was identified using references suitable for the geographic area and the recovered pollen types (Geisler 1945; Jones and Newell 1948; MacAndrews *et al.* 1973).

Mollusks

During the course of excavations, sediment samples were washed through sieves of 1 mm mesh; such screening has been implemented in all areas of excavation. Only in the area in and adjacent to the major spring feeder conduit and in the far western region (Figure 52) were remains of ostracods and mollusks recovered. Gastropods and pelecypods were identified using the criteria provided by Herrington (1962), LaRocque (1967), and Pilsbry (1948), and with the modern comparative collections at the University of Arizona, Tucson, and Northern Arizona University, Flagstaff.

121

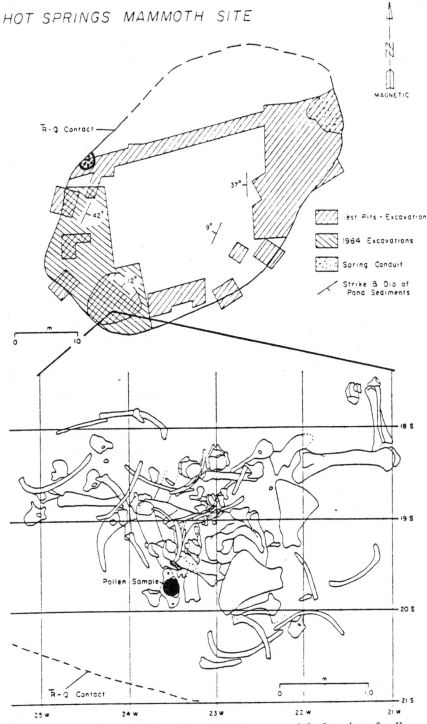

Figure 52. Map of the site showing spring conduits, and the location of pollen samples.

RESULTS

Pollen

A total of 657 pollen grains were recovered from three sediment samples, of which 304 (46% of total) were derived from grasses (Poaceae) (Table 8). Several different morphologies were represented among the grasses.

The second most abundant pollen type recovered was that of Cyperaceae (sedge; 15% of total; Table 8). Additional aquatic pollen types included *Potamogeton* (pond weed), *Polygonum* (water smartweed, *P. persicaria*-type), *Myriophyllum* (parrotweed), and *Acorus* (sweet flag). Other aquatic palynomorphs included dinoflagellates, colonial green algae, and diatoms. Other terrestrial pollen types found are listed in Table 8.

In addition to the 304 grains of grass pollen, other pollen types included the non-arboreal taxa: Asteraceae (*Ambrosia* or short-spine spine types); Cheno-Am (Chenopodiaceae/*Amaranthus*), Brassicaceae (mustards), Apiaceae (parsley), Ranunculaceae (crowfoot), Saxifragaceae (saxifage), Rosaceae (roses), and Polygonaceae (*Rumex*-type). Arboreal pollen types included *Pinus* (pine), *Picea* (spruce), *Larix* (larch), *Abies* (fir), *Juniperus* (juniper), *Betula* (birch), *Celtis* (hackberry), *Fraxinus* (ash), *Juglans* (walnut), *Populus* (poplar), *Quercus* (oak), *Ulmus* (elm), and *Salix* (willow). Other more rare terrestrial palynomorphs observed included spores of bryophytes, ferns and other free-sporing vascular plants such as *Lycopodium*, *Selaginella* and *Isoetes*.

Mollusks

Molluscan species were recovered from numerous localities within the sinkhole, although they were never numerous. Most of the specimens represent aquatic species (Table 9). Aquatic snails include *Gyraulus* cf. *parvus*, *Fossaria* sp. and *F.* cf. *dallii*. The shells of the later species have the distinct shoulder and an innerlip reflected, but not as much as with *F. parva*. The apex of the HSMS *Fossaria* shells are not as pointed as with *F. obrussa*.

Table 8. Pollen identified from three sediment samples from Hot Springs Mammoth Site, South Dakota.

Pollen Types	Locus 1	Locus 2	Locus 3	Total	Percent Terrest.
Terrestrial Arboreal Pollen:					
Pinus (Total/1/3's)	4	10	14	28	5.1
Abies	1	1		2	+
Picea	2	1	1	4	+
Larix	3	1		4	+
Thuja?/Juniperus		1	1	2	+
Alnus		1	1	2	+
Betula	1	1	1	3	+
Celtis	3	6	2	11	2.0
Fraxinus		1		1	+
Juglans			1	1	+
Populus		1	1	2	+
Quercus		1	2	3	+
Salix	1	2	1	4	+
Ulmus			1	1	+
Total Arboreal	15	27	26	68	
Terrestrial Nonarboreal Pollen					
Poaceae (thinwalled)	142	66	96	304	56.0
Asteraceae-Artemisia	1	10	6	17	3.1
Ambrosia type	7	16	28	51	9.4
Tubiflorae-undif.	3	12	9	24	4.4
Liguliflorae	1		1	2	+
Chenopod +Amaranthus	2	20	37	59	10.8
Ranuncul. - Thallictrum		3	2	5	1.0
Ranuncul. - Ranunculus	1	1	1	3	+
Rosaceae	1			1	+
Saxifragaceae	1			1	+
Lamiaceae		1		1	+
Fabaceae			1	1	+
Apiaceae	1			1	+
Brassicaceae	1			1	+
Polygonaceae -Rumex	1	1	1	3	+
Total Nonarboreal	162	130	182	474	
Total Terrestrial Pollen	177	157	208	542	
Potamogeton	5	1	1	7	
Polygonum - (P. persicaria)	3	22	12	37	
Myriophyllum	3	4	1	8	
Acorus?	2			2	
Cyperaceae	25	40	36	101	
Total Aquatic Pollen	38	67	49	115	
Total of all Pollen	215	224	257	657	

124

The aquatic snail, *Physa*, was by far the most abundant species recovered from the site. Although no species are designated for the recovered shells, three forms are noted. *Physa* "A" is a shell of medium size, thin, and somewhat translucent with 4 1/2 to 5 whorls. The surface is shiny; the sculpture is thin but with distinct growth lines. The last whorl is large, with the aperature taking about 65 to 70% of the length. The outer lip is flattened with a minute shoulder. The callus is large and perforate. At least 50 entire shells and over 200 fragments are of the "A" form.

Physa "B" is small in size; the spire is long with 4 1/2 to 5 whorls total. The callus is thin and not perforate. The whorls are rounded and slightly shouldered. The aperature comprises about 65% of the length. Less than 10 adult species fit this "B" form.

Physa "C" is a shell that is slightly perforate, with a long spire and about 4 whorls. The callus is wide and curled. The aperature comprises about 55 to 60% of the length. Only one shell is ascribed to this form.

Three species of fingernail clam (*Pisidium*) were identified: *P. walkeri, P. compressum*, and *P. obtusale*. Only a single angular fragment was assignable to *P. compressum*.

The identified terrestrial gastropods include the slug, *Deroceras laeve*, and the snails *Columella simplex edentula, Pupilla muscorum*, and *Valloni gracilicosta*. The single *Deroceras* shell is overall thin except for a thickened maximal end. Only one shell was identified as *Columella*; the shell is toothless, five-whorled, and tapers toward the apex. Ten shells are assignable to *Pulpilla muscorum*. All contain 5 1/2 to 5 3/4 whorls, are toothless, and have a collus within the aperature, unlike that of *P. hebes*. Eight shells are assignable to *Vallonia gracilicosta*, as described in LaRocque (1970).

DISCUSSION

The high proportions of grass and sedge pollen (61.1% of total) in the sediment samples suggest that these plants grew locally in some abundance. Analysis of macroscopic materials recovered from

Table 9: Late Pleistocene and Recent mollusks identified from the Black Hills, South Dakota and vicinity. Recent distributions from Henderson (1927), Hubricht (1985), Over (1915), and Roscoe (1954). HSMS, Hot Springs Mammoth Site; BH, Black Hills; SD, South Dakota; AB, Agate Basin site, Wyoming.

	HSMS	BH	SD	AB
GASTROPODA (snails)				
Pulmonata (freshwater snails)				
Lymnaeidae				
Lymnea caperata		X	X	
Fossaria parva			X	X
Fossaria obrussa		X	X	
Fossaria cf. *dallii*	X		?	
Fossaria sp.	X	X	X	
Stagnicola palustiis				X
Planorbidae				
Gyraulus parvus	X		X	
Physidae				
Aplexa hypnorum				X
Physa sayii			X	
Physa sp.	X	X	X	
Pulmonata (terrestrial snails)				
Limacidae				
Deroceras laeve	X	?		
Zonitidae				
Euconulus fluvus		X	X	X
Nesovitrea electrina		X	X	
Zonitoides arboreus		X	X	X
Vitrinidae				
Vitrina pellucida alaskana		X	X	
Endondontidae				
Discus cronkhitei		X	X	X
D. shimekii cockerelli		X	X	
Succineidae				
Succinea avara		X	X	
Succinea sp.			X	X
Catinella sp.				X
Oxyloma sp.				X
Pupillidae				
Gastrocopta holzingeri		X	X	
G. procera			X	
Pupilla blandii		X	X	
P. muscorum	X		X	
Valloniidae				
Vallonia gracilicosta		X	X	X
V. cyclophorella		X	X	X
Cionellidae				
Cionella lubrica		X	X	X
Oreohelicidae				
Oreohelix strigosa cooperi		X	X	
Pelecypoda (bivalves)				
Sphaeriidae				
Pisidium cf. *walkeri*	X		X	
P. obtusale	X		X	
P. compressum	X			

126

mammoth dung preserved in the arid Southwest of North America indicate that grass and sedge were a preferred dietary item (Hansen 1980; Agenbroad *et al.* 1984; Davis *et al.* 1985; Mead *et al.* 1986). It is possible that the high proportions of grass and sedge pollen in the analyzed sediment samples were derived from the stomach contents of mammoths trapped in the sinkhole. However, sediment samples not so directly associated with mammoth remains also contain high proportions of these pollens. In either case, it is likely that the local environment was truly one in which arboreal taxa played only a very minor role in the valley community of the southern Black Hills during the Farmdalian. *Salix*, which is insect pollinated, apparently also occurred in the local community, but it need not have been a tree since several species occurring in tundra and steppe communities are small shrubs.

Three clam species, three aquatic lung-breathing snails, one slug, and three terrestrial snails were identified. The aquatic snail *Physa* was overwhelmingly dominant. The aquatic forms undoubtedly represent species living in or nearby the pond. The few terrestrial forms were either living along the shore area or, adjacent to the rim of the sinkhole. *Pisidium*, *Physa*, and *Gyraulus* are commonly found in permanent springs, lakes, and streams all with slow to moderate current flow. *Gyraulus* is often found with aquatic vegetation. *Fossaria dallii* is generally found out of water in the wet marshy area adjacent to permanent water (LaRocque 1967).

The slug, *Deroceras*, is found living in leaf litter, grass roots in open terrain, meadows, marshes, and woodlands. *Pupilla muscorum* is a calciphil, requiring, generally, limestone rocky regions and grassy meadows — in Arizona it occurs only above timberline. *Columella simplex edentula* and *Vallonia gracilicosta* are found in leaf litter in talus slopes or ravines, in addition to meadows and woodlands. In the west, *V. gracilicosta* is found in meadows well above the timberline.

No single species of mollusk is indicative of a particular restricted environment other than a freshwater habitat. The sinkhole pond/lake certainly contained nearshore vegetation of aquatic species. It would appear that this shore-side plant biome was not extensive or dense because of the rare finds of the snails living in such a community. Had the sinkhole been rimmed by a diverse "woodland" of deciduous trees such as *Celtis, Fraxinus, Salix, Ulmus*, etc., there again would have been a much more abundant representation of gastropod species and number of shells.

Many of the identified mollusks are known to live in South Dakota today, but not all in the Black Hills (Table 9). *Deroceras laeve* and *Columella simplex edentula* are not reported living today in South Dakota. The terrestrial snails of the Black Hills are somewhat understood, at least for the higher regions and the northern and eastern sectors, but the Limestone Plateau and the arid southern areas are in need of study (Over 1915; Roscoe 1954). Little is understood about aquatic mollusks living in the Black Hills because so few permanent free-standing bodies of water exist.

Water Temperature

Laury (1980) stated that the sinkhole pond was continuously warm during its existence in the Farmdalian, with an ambient water temperature of at least 35°C inferred from ostracod and chemical data. Aquatic plant pollen and mollusk remains reported herein and the recovery of fish would not discount this conclusion. Vascular plants generally have maximum temperature limits of about 45°C, with mosses approximately 50°C (Brock 1978). Submerged aquatics such as *Myriophyllum* and *Potamogeton* have a wide latitudinal and elevational range in North America today, but they do not thrive or reproduce in waters with ambient temperatures in excess of 35°C (Blinn 1976).

The 1983 and 1988 excavations at HSMS turned up the skeletons of minnow-sized fish. Although these specimens have yet to be identified, cyprinid minnows (*Notropis lutipinnis, N. cummingsae,* and *Semotilus atromaculatus*) are known to die (even when acclimated) in water temperatures of about 40°C (McFarlane *et al.* 1976).

Brues (1932) found in his study of 150 hot springs in the western United States that the snail *Stagnicola (Lymnaea) palustris* did inhabit springs with temperatures of up to 40.8°C and having a pH of 8.5 (Cortez, Nevada). *Physa* spp. were found to be most plentiful in hot springs when water temperatures ranged from 30.8°C to 39.5°C, including a pH of 7.4 to 9.5 (Brues 1932). The recovered molluscan and plant (pollen) data would seem to indicate that HSMS did not have an overall ambient water temperature in excess of about 40°C, even adjacent to the spring conduit where some of the mollusks apparently lived, and in the western, cooler (?) portions of the pond, temperatures were probably approximately 35°C.

The molluscan faunal assemblage is seemingly poor in number of species, and is dominated by aquatic taxa. At first this would seem to be a most unfortunate fossil assemblage. But in view of what is understood about "hot" springs, such warm bodies of water tend to have a less diverse molluscan community. Cool ("normal") temperature ponds generally contain numerous examples of many species (e.g. Pickerel Lake, South Dakota; Watts and Bright 1968). The implication from the molluscan assemblage, and possibly the plants and minnow-sized fish, is that the HSMS was indeed a warm water pond. How warm the water was cannot be unequivocally stated, but temperatures ranging from 30°C to a maximum of 35°C seem very probable.

Paleoenvironments

The Wisconsin glacial episode can be loosely divided into stades and interstades. The first stade, or early Wisconsin glacial, Altonian, occurred from approximately 84,000 to 28,000 yr B.P. (Delcourt and Delcourt 1981; Watts 1983). Ice is absent in Illinois and Iowa from approximately 28,000 to 22,000 yr B.P., and is referred to the "warm" Farmdalian interstade. This was followed by another glacial maximum, Woodfordian, roughly dated between 22,000 and 12,500 yr B.P. (Delcourt and Delcourt 1981; Watts 1983).

It is not fully agreed upon whether or not the Farmdalian is a continential-wide phenomenon or if it should be restricted to just those areas affected by the Lake Michigan ice lobe (which does not include the Black Hills of South Dakota) (Watts 1983). There is evidence outside the lobe area of a climatic amelioration during this time (Delcourt *et al.* 1983). The Craigmile local fauna (dating ± 23,000 yr B.P., late Farmdalian) in western Iowa records a predominantly grassland habitat with few conifer and deciduous tree species present (Rhodes 1984).

Enough pollen diagrams have been completed for the northern Great Plains to permit a reconstruction of the Wisconsin history of the present prairie region (Baker and Waln 1985; Wright 1970; Watts 1983), although few dating to the Farmdalian. During the Wisconsin, Woodfordian, maximum glaciation (approximately 22,000 to 18,000 yr B.P.), the Laurentide ice sheet occurred west to the Missouri River (James River lobe), about 250 km east of the Black Hills (Lemke *et al.* 1965; Figure 51). Spruce forest covered most of central and eastern United States as far west as northeastern Kansas; west of there it may have been interrupted by a vast area of sand dunes (Baker and Woln 1985; Delcourt and Delcourt 1981; Wright 1970). The best available Woodfordian (all terminal late glacial) age pollen and molluscan data for this region are from sites well east of the Black Hills: Tappen, North Dakota, Pickerel, South Dakota; and Rosebud-Sandhills, Nebraska (Figure 51). Taylor (1960, 1965) states that based on some molluscan data, the central Great Plains were a "cold-steppe" environment. Leonard and Frye (1954) determined from the molluscan assemblage recorded in the loess region that the central Great Plains must have been wooded.

A fossil vertebrate locality (Smith Falls) along the northern edge of the Nebraska Sandhills (Figure 51) dates from the late Wisconsin (Voorhies and Corner 1985). Sixty-five percent of the species (90% of the minimum number of individuals) are of boreal affinities, including *Ochotona* (pika) and *Dicrostonyx* (collared lemming). Approximately 21% of the species were of a steppe environment (Voorhies and Corner 1985). The implication from this site is that at least along the Niobrara River bordering the northern edge of the Sandhills there was some sort of forest gallery, but steppe environments were very nearby, and possibly in mosaic.

The Lange-Ferguson Clovis kill site is located in the badlands just east of the northern Black Hills (Figure 51). The 10,670 ± 300 yr B.P. radiocarbon age is associated with mammoths and other animals indicating that the immediate area was a marsh and pond habitat (Hannus 1982, 1990; Martin 1982, 1984, 1987). Two-thirds of the molluscan species indicate the site was surrounded by a brush, wooded, or grassy slope during the late glacial (Leonard 1982). The area appears to be a mosaic of grassland and pond community.

West of the Black Hills the paleoenvironmental data tend toward the vegetational reconstruction based on the mammalian assemblages. In the Bighorn Mountains of north-central Wyoming (Figure 51), the Natural Trap locality (with 100,000 years of stratigraphy) has turned up evidence that at least portions of that region must have had a tundra to steppe-tundra community (Gilbert et al. 1978; Martin et al. 1979; Chomko 1982). Walker (1982), working on the fauna from the Agate Basin Paleoindian site (Figure 51), states that an arctic steppe-savanna occurred just west of the Black Hills during the Wisconsin late-glacial.

Although a variety of plant communities probably existed immediately around the Black Hills during the Woodfordian, only inferences actually can be made from the data recovered from sites located away from the area. Those sites available indicate that spruce forest was an important habitat in the region, but it is questionable whether such a forest was actually around the Black Hills, especially the southern region. Delcourt et al. (1983, Figure 51) imply that spruce and jack pine (*Pinus banksiana*) covered the northern Great Plains and the Black Hills at 18,000 yr B.P. During the end of the late glacial, it appears that what spruce forests were in existence were "moving" north out of the Sandhills country and were rapidly being replaced by grasslands.

The molluscan data from the HSMS (at best a local record) does little for reconstructing the Farmdalian age environments of the entire southern Black Hills. The record indicates that the immediate environment was one of a warm pond habitat surrounded by some (sparse) aquatic and shore vegetation. Leaf litter occurred but was apparently rare and probably only on the western fringe.

The pollen record at the HSMS reveals more about the local environmental setting, although only three sediment samples provide this information. Studies of the proportions of arboreal pollen in samples of sediments obtained from modern plant communities with, and without, the various other arboreal pollen types observed in the fossil sample would suggest that scattered individuals of spruce, fir, larch, birch, and hackberry may have been present in at least the southern Black Hills during the Farmdalian, just prior to the Wisconsin glacial maximum. Pine was probably not present, or if present, it was sufficiently depauperate to preclude abundant pollen production.

Members of the plant families Poaceae, Cyperaceae, and Araceae extend northward beyond the arctic circle, but *Acorus* and most other arums rarely occur north of 50° north latitude, suggesting that the immediate area of the HSMS pond was not a true tundra. No members of the Araceae presently occur in the Dakotas, but *Acorus* does occur in grassland marshes to the south and wooded areas to the east and north, where it grows on the margins of shallow ponds, streams and spring-fed marshes.

It is tempting to interpret the Farmdalian environment of the southern Black Hills of 26,000 yr B.P. as some type of tundra. However, modern tundra environments are not typically dominated by grasses; instead, sedges are more characteristic. Steppe environments typically contain grass-dominated communities and often include various woody or partially woody taxa. It seems reasonable to suggest that some form of cold steppe-grassland (with scattered trees) was the immediate environment around the warm pond waters of the HSMS during the Farmdalian.

The HSMS deposit does not contain remains dating to the Woodfordian glacial. Based on little evidence adjacent to, but not in, the Black Hills, it would appear the mountains were not forest-covered with *Pinus* or *Picea* during the Woodfordian. However, this still remains to be solved.

Black Hills Environment - Origin

For a number of years researchers have been trying to determine the glacial-age vegetation of the Black Hills. Unfortunately when a pollen locality was recovered, it was neither in the Black Hills nor did it contain sediments dating older than the late glacial (Wright 1970; Watts 1983). Watts and Wright (1966) hypothesize that during the waning phases of the late glacial, there was a further decrease in periglacial wind action and the stabilization of the sand dunes in the Nebraska Sandhills (Figure 51). The spruce forest covering the central Great Plains during the glacial maximum were then able to rapidly spread westward across the Sandhills and perhaps into the Black Hills (during the full glacial or late glacial?), where they occur as relics surrounded by prairie.

It is important to note that most of the present plant and vertebrate species in the Black Hills are western representatives (Froiland 1978). The dominant forest species in the Black Hills is the ponderosa pine, today reaching its eastern-most extent along the modern prairie border. At present 30% of the plant species in the hills are of a Rocky Mountain origin, whereas only 9% are eastern deciduous forms (Hayward 1928; Dorn 1977). The great majority of the birds in the hills are western species, but there is a geographic mixture (Pettingill and Whitney 1965). Many of the mammal species have their origin either to the west or southwest (Hoffman and Jones 1970). Additional plant and animal remains recovered from dated Wisconsin locations east, west, and south of the Black Hills are needed before the origins and timing of today's biotic communities can be fully understood.

CONCLUSIONS

Pollen and molluscan assemblages presented here are the first late Pleistocene (Farmdalian) paleoecological data reported from the Black Hills of South Dakota, and are some of the oldest from the northern Great Plains region.

The implication from the pollen data is that the local environment around the Hot Springs Mammoth site was a cold steppe-grass-land habitat. The recovery of *Cynomys* and *Spermophilus* cf. *tridecemlineatus* implies that the immediate area was not a tundra. The molluscan record, and to a lesser degree the pollen data, imply that the freshwater pond was of a warm temperature, probably hot enough to drastically limit the diversity of the plant-molluscan communities. The temperature of the pond cannot be estimated solely on the basis of the presented pollen and molluscan record, but it seems reasonable to assume from the data that temperatures were between 30° and 35°C. The environmental record as reconstructed would seem most suitable for supporting mammoths. Having the local water table high enough to force artesian springs, and those warm enough not to freeze over, obviously was most appealing to some of the mammoths, as they became part of the fossil record. Because the artesian water was warm, it is possible that the HSMS is recording an atypical microhabitat, a "warm oasis," surrounded by more adverse environments.

Although far from complete, this fossil assemblage provides the basis to understanding the southern Black Hills during the last glacial age. It must be remembered that the Hot Springs Mammoth site is located in the far southern sector of the hills, environmentally drastically different than the central and northern regions. It appears that the lacustrine record of pollen will be hard to find in the Black Hills (Eric Grimm, personal communication 1983); possibly the route to understanding the late Pleistocene paleoenvironments of the Black Hills will be through analyzing the fluvial sediments, caves, and packrat midden records of the arid southern and western sectors.

ACKNOWLEDGMENTS

Many individuals have contributed to the excavation of the Hot Springs Mammoth site. We greatly appreciate the continued help of the members and staff of the Mammoth Site, Incorporated, who over the years have aided in all aspects of the project. Emilee M. Mead provided drafting for this report (Figure 51) and field help. Funding has been provided by the National Geographic Society, Earthwatch, High Plains Center, Geological Society of America, and Organized Research, Northern Arizona University. Louelle Holter and Evelyn Wong, Bilby Research Center, typed the manuscript. We thank Phil Bjork and others from the South Dakota School of Mines and Technology and Nich Czaplewski (University of Oklahoma) for their active role in microfaunal analysis and screen washing. Appreciation is extended to Eric Grimm and Herbert E. Wright, University of Minnesota, for their continued support and discussions concerning the paleoecology of the Black Hills. Cathy and Tony Barnosky (Carnegie Museum of Natural History, Pennsylvania) provided comments on a much earlier draft of this paper—their help is greatly appreciated.

Chapter 6

LATE PLEISTOCENE SMALL MAMMALS FROM HOT SPRINGS MAMMOTH SITE, SOUTH DAKOTA

Nicholas J. Czaplewski and Jim I. Mead

INTRODUCTION

The Mammoth Site at Hot Springs, South Dakota, is a sediment-filled sinkhole that held a spring-fed pond during the late Pleistocene. Previous work at the site has revealed details of its geologic setting and taphonomy (Agenbroad 1984b; Agenbroad and Laury 1984; Agenbroad and Mead 1986; Laury 1980). As of this writing, the available radiometric dates (Agenbroad this volume) suggest the site dates to the Wisconsin glacial. Pollen samples from the spring sediments were processed that indicated a cold steppe-grassland environment (Mead *et al.* this volume). The pond and sinkhole acted as a natural trap accumulating the remains of large animals, particularly mammoths (*Mammuthus columbi* and *M. primigenius*), but also other animals. Wet sieving of the spring deposits has allowed recovery of the remains of small vertebrates that were previously poorly known at the site and in the late Pleistocene of South Dakota generally. Screenwashing for microvertebrates at the Mammoth Site of Hot Springs, South Dakota, has been carried on since 1976, most intensively during the last three years. Although the remains of small vertebrates are not abundant in the spring deposits, a representative faunule is beginning to accumulate. In the earliest preliminary report on the microvertebrates at Hot Springs Mammoth Site (HSMS), Bjork (1978) listed four taxa of small mammals. Large mammals were reported by Agenbroad and Mead (1986) to include short-faced bear (*Arctodus simus*), wolf *(Canis lupus),* coyote (*C. latrans*), Columbian mammoth (*Mammuthus columbi*), and camel (*Camelops* sp.) (see also this volume). The present paper details the small mammal remains (78 specimens) which currently comprise twelve taxa:

136

one insectivoran, two lagomorphs, eight rodents, and one carnivoran (Table 10). In addition, remains of two types of cypriniform fish and one amphibian (Anura; frog), and a terminal phalanx from a medium-sized hawk have been recovered but will not be dealt with here. Although they still comprise a relatively small faunule, the small mammals that are the focus of this report include some extralimital varieties.

SPECIES ACCOUNTS
Order Insectivora
Family Talpidae (moles)
Scalopus aquaticus (eastern mole)
  Referred material: right humerus.

The specimen is virtually complete, lacking only the tips of the entepicondylar, ectepicondylar, and deltoid processes. Measurements of the bone are: length 14.65 mm; proximal width, 11.39 mm; distal width, 9.42 mm.

Table 10. Relative abundance of fossil remains (indicated as number of identified skeletal parts, NISP) of small mammals at Hot Springs Mammoth Site, South Dakota.

taxon	NISP
Cynomys (Leucocrossuromys)	32
Microtus sp.	17
Thomomys talpoides	7
Spermophilus cf. *tridecemlineatus*	6
Spermophilus cf. *elegans/richardsonii*	5
Peromyscus cf. *maniculatus*	3
Lepus cf. *townsendii*	2
Sylvilagus sp.	2
Scalopus aquaticus	1
Neotoma cf. *cinerea*	1
Phenacomys cf. *intermedius*	1
Mustela cf. *vison* or *nigripes*	1

Preservation of this bone is unusual (it is much darker than other fossils from the site) and it was likely found in the uppermost sediments of the HSMS. It is possible the mole is not contemporaneous with the late Pleistocene faunule but is an intrusive element that burrowed into the HSMS site at a later time. Most Pleistocene records of the eastern mole are within the present geographic range of the species. This occurrence is extralimital, representing a small northwestern extension of its range in the late Pleistocene.

Sylvilagus sp. indet. (cottontail rabbit)
Referred material: fused palatal branches of maxillaries; left calcaneus.

Three species of cottontails, *S. audubonii, S. floridanus*, and *S. nuttallii,* occur today near the Hot Springs area. The HSMS specimens do not allow a species identification.

Lepus cf. *townsendii* (white-tailed jackrabbit)
Referred material: unfused proximal epiphysis of right tibia, distal end of a metatarsal, upper cheek tooth.

Lepus californicus and *L. townsendii* both occur near the Hot Springs area in modern times. The tibial epiphysis is much larger than that of specimens of *L. californicus* and *L. americanus* with which it was compared; its size matches that of comparative specimens of *L. townsendii* closely.

Spermophilus cf. *elegans/richardsonii* (Wyoming/Richardson's ground squirrel)
Referred material: right P3; abraded right $M^{1 \text{ or } 2}$; posterior fragment of left M3; right P4; right distal tibia.

The teeth are clearly hypsodont for a ground squirrel. The P^3 is large, with a distinct anterior cingulum, posterior cingulum, and functional obliquely oriented loph that is wider anterolingually than posterolabially. The $M^{1 \text{ or } 2}$ is relatively high-crowned; its anterior cingulum joins the protocone with an abrupt change of direction. In P^4 the anterior cingulum (protolophid) extends lingually from the protoconid but does not contact the metaconid, and the protoconid and metaconid are relatively widely separated.

No relatively large *Spermophilus* species occur today in the vicinity of Hot Springs, but *S. (Spermophilus) elegans* occurs 240 km to the southwest and *Spermophilus richardsonii* occurs 370 km to the north and northeast. *Spermophilus (Poliocitellus) franklinii* occurs 210 km to the east and southeast; *S. (Callospermophilus)lateralis* occurs 160 km to the southwest in the Laramie Mountains. Of these, *S. lateralis* is smaller than the fossils and is brachydont. *Spermophilus franklinii* is said by Hall (1981) to possess mesostyles on P^4 and M^{1-2} and to have higher-crowned cheek teeth than the subgenus *Otospermophilus* (the lowest-crowned subgenus) but lower crowned than in the subgenus *Spermophilus* (the highest-crowned subgenus).

The species represented by the fossils is as large as *S. elegans* and *S. richardsonii* and agrees in details of tooth morphology. Although these two sibling species are exceedingly similar, they differ in skeletal morphology (Neuner 1975; Robinson and Hoffmann 1975; Fagerstone 1982) and many other characteristics (Zegers 1984; Michener and Koeppl 1985). They apparently represent the results of the vicariant splitting of an ancestral population with divergence of the isolated populations during the Quaternary (Nadler *et al.* 1971; Neuner 1975). In fact, both living species may be distinct from their supposed ancestral population (Neuner and Schultz 1979). In any case, more complete skeletal material is required for a precise identification of the species than is available in the sample from HSMS.

Spermophilus cf. *tridecemlineatus* (thirteen-lined ground squirrel)
Referred material: left M3 fragment; broken left P4; right dP4; right M3; right distal tibia; right calcancus fragment.

The deciduous P4 is relatively hypsodont and lacks an anteroconid (anterior cingulum). The permanent P4 is relatively hypsodont with a prominent, narrow anteroconid. The M^3 fragment is judged to be relatively hypsodont; its metaloph is mostly broken away but appears to have been indistinct, and the posterior cingulum is mostly broken away but appears to bend abruptly posteriorly from the protocone.

Spermophilus tridecemlineatus is the only small species of ground squirrel present today at Hot Springs, but *S. spilosoma* occurs about 80 km to the southeast. Both these species are hypsodont members of the subgenus *Ictidomys*, and are of the same general size. *Spermophilus spilosoma* has a slightly weaker anteroconid of P4 Mammoth Site specimens are referred tentatively to *S.* cf. *tridecemlineatus* based on size and on the presence of only that species in the Hot Springs area today.

Cynomys (Leucocrossuromys) sp. (white-tailed prairie dog)

Referred material: left dentary with M1-2; right dentary without teeth; I_1 fragment; left I_1 tip; right dP4; left M_1; two right M_1; right M 1 or 2; two lower cheek teeth; right M3 crown fragment; left M3 in small fragment of dentary; left M3 crown; labial portion of right M3 in small fragment of dentary; talonid of right M3; I^1 fragment; two left P^3, two left M_1 or 2; left upper cheek tooth; left M^3, right M^3, numerous cheek tooth fragments of maxilla or dentary with alveoli; right humerus; right ulna; left distal tibia fragment; left calcaneus; two right cancanei.

Although the black-tailed prairie dog, *Cynomys ludovicianus*, has been common in short grass plains of the Black Hills area of South Dakota throughout historic times (Turner 1974), it is not known in the late Pleistocene fauna at HSMS. Instead, the late Pleistocene prairie dog of this portion of South Dakota appears to have been a kind of white-tailed prairie dog of the subgenus *Leucocrossuromys*.

Species of *Cynomys* are placed in different subgenera, *C. (Cynomys)* and *C. (Leucocrossuromys)*. The latter includes *C. (L.) gunnisoni, C. (L.) parvidens* and *C. (L.) leucurus*, as well as a recently described extinct species, *C. (L.) churcheri* (Burns and McGillivray 1989). The subgenera usually can be differentiated on the basis of crown morphology of the lower third molar. Semken

140

(1966) found he could separate ninety percent of a recent sample into their respective subgenera based on the presence (in *Leucocrossuromys*) or absence (in *Cynomys*) of a stylid on the talonid basin joining the ectolophid and thus separating the talonid basin into two parts (Eshelman 1975; Dalquest 1988). Four M3s are available from the Mammoth Site; one is a fragment including the labial half of the tooth, one is a fragment including the posterolingual three-fourths of the crown, one is a complete, unerupted crown cap, and the last is a slightly worn adult tooth (Figure 53). In the latter three specimens the stylid characteristic of *Leucocrossuromys* clearly is manifest (the same may be true of the first fragmentary specimen as well, but the tooth is greatly worn and the stylid separation might appear somewhat exaggerated as a result). The specimens possibly pertain to *C. leucurus* or *C. churcheri* rather than *C. gunnisoni* or *C. parvidens* based on their relatively large size. However, a larger sample, providing quantitative data will be necessary for a species identification.

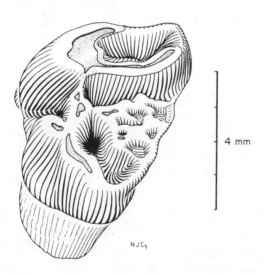

4 mm

Figure 53. *Cynomys* (*Leucocrossuromys*) sp. left lower third molar from Hot Springs Mammoth Site, South Dakota. View is occlusal and slightly posterior.

141

Thomomys talpoides (northern pocket gopher)

Referred material: right P4; two left P4; right I_1 tip; right $M^{1 \text{ or } 2}$; right M^3; right M_3.

Size is smaller than *Geomys bursarius lutescens*. Lower premolars lack cementum in their reentrant angles and have an anterolophid that is narrow and obliquely elongated with a wide anterolabial dentine tract and narrow lingual dentine tracts. The anterolingual enamel plate of the anterolophid is flat or indented lingually. One small P4 is from a subadult, at a stage of wear in which the dentine tracts are not yet exposed at the occlusal surface, but the tracts would form breaks in the enamel given another 1 mm of wear. The $M^{1 \text{ or } 2}$ has an enamel plate on its anterior face as well as its posterior face; its occlusal outline is constricted labially. The I_1 has a flattened (squarish) enamel face. The M^3 has a narrow posterior labial dentine tract and a wide lingual tract; its anterior enamel plate in occlusal view is angled with the anterior portion slightly convex and the lingual portion slightly concave.

The species is a member of the modern fauna of western South Dakota, including the Hot Springs area. It is also common as a fossil in late Pleistocene and Holocene faunas of the northern Great Plains (Semken and Falk 1987). A "lower molar" listed as that of cf. *Dipodomys* by Bjork (1978) and Pinsof (1985) is a right M_3 of *Thomomys*. The tooth is hypselodont and bears dentine tracts that span the complete height of the tooth.

Peromyscus cf. *maniculatus* (deer mouse)

Referred material: left M1; left dentary fragment with M_{1-2}; right M_1.

An ectostylid is present on the right M1 but is absent on the left one. No other accessory cusps(-ids) or lophs(-ids) are present on the lower teeth. The anteroconid is undivided. The M^1 has a strong paralophule and mesoloph. All three specimens compare in size and details of crown and cusp morphology to smaller species of *Peromyscus*, especially *P. maniculatus*. The masseteric scar on the dentary fragment is rather weakly developed and situated relatively far posterially, as in *P. maniculatus*. Measurements are: M^1 anteroposterior length, 1.69 mm, transverse width, 1.08 mm; right M$_1$ length 1.48 mm, width, 0.97 mm; left M$_1$ length, 1.54 mm, width, 0.92 mm; left M$_2$ length, 1.23 mm, width, 0.98 mm.

Peromyscus leucopus and *P. maniculatus* occur in the Hot Springs vicinity today. Although the two species are exceedingly similar in tooth morphology, *P. leucopus* is typically a mouse of woodland habitats, whereas *P. maniculatus* frequents grassland areas on the Great Plains. Because of the predominance of steppe and grassland forms in the remainder of the fossil fauna, these specimens likely represent *P. maniculatus*. The lower molar preliminarily assigned to *Reithrodontomys* by Bjork (1978) and Pinsof (1985) is referred herein to *Peromyscus*.

Neotoma cf. *cinerea* (bushy-tailed woodrat)
     Referred material: right M1.
     The specimen is a little-worn tooth of a young adult with considerable height of crown. Much of the original enamel has been removed or eroded away. Development of incipient dentine tracts occurs at the bases of the external angles of all lophs, although this feature is probably exaggerated due to the missing enamel. The anterior loph is divided by a deep anterointernal reentrant angle that remains deep all the way to the base of the crown. Measurements are: anteroposterior length of the crown, 4.1 mm; transverse width of crown at occlusal surface, 2.2 mm, at base, 2.5 mm.

     The bushy-tailed woodrat, N*eotoma cinerea*, is the only species of woodrat that currently inhabits the Black Hills and surrounding areas, where it is common (Turner 1974). A subspecies of the eastern woodrat, *Neotoma floridana baileyi*, presently has a relict distribution in the northern Great Plains (Hoffmann and Jones 1970) that includes a single recorded occurrence in South Dakota east of the Black Hills area along Spring Creek, 18 miles southeast of Rapid City (Jones 1964: 218). Both species have an upper first molar with an anterointernal reentrant angle, but according to Hall (1981), the reentrant angle of *N. floridana* is moderately developed whereas that of *N. cinerea* is deep, as in the fossil. The HSMS specimen is tentatively referred to *N. cinerea* until a larger sample can be recovered.

Phenacomys cf. *intermedius* (heather vole)
   Referred material: molar fragment.
   Although only a fragment of a molar of unknown position in the toothrow is available, it is clearly that of a microtine rodent with strongly rooted cheek teeth. The root (unfortunately) is the best-preserved portion of this fragment and is rather angular in cross-section. Of the crown portion remaining, parts of only an anterior or posterior loop and one alternating triangle are preserved. No cementum is present in the reentrant folds. Transverse width is *ca.* 0.98 mm.
   According to Repenning (in press; Repenning *et al.* 1987; Repenning and Grady 1988), polarization of the dental characteristics that separate fossils of the subgenera of *Phenacomys (Arborimus* and *Phenacomys)* occurred in Beringia less than 400,000 years ago. The HSMS specimen probably represents a heather vole, *Phenacomys (Phenacomys) intermedius,* whose modern range approaches nearest the Black Hills region in the Laramie Mountains in eastern Wyoming, approximately 200 km southwest of HSMS, and whose late Pleistocene distribution extended much farther south to Kansas, Arkansas, Tennessee, and Virginia (Guilday and Parmalee 1972; Parmalee and Klippel 1981).

Microtus sp. (vole)
   Referred material: right dentary fragment with M_{1-2}; left dentary fragment with M_1; left M^1; right M^3; two left M^3; left M_1; two left M_1 fragments; two left M_3; two right M_3; left M^2; two right M^2; palate fragment from cranium.
   These teeth are hypselodont (rootless) and haved cementum in the reentrant folds. Available specimens of M1 have five closed triangles; a specimen of M_2 has four closed triangles; specimens of M_3 have three transverse loops; one specimen of M^3 has three closed triangles and one has three closed and one open triangle. These char-

acteristics generally fit those of *Microtus pennsylvanicus* and *M. longicaudus* molars. They differ from the dental details of *M. (Pedomys) ochrogaster.* Because of the intraspecific variability and interspecific overlap in the morphology of the prismatic teeth of these microtine rodents (Carleton 1985), isolated teeth of *Microtus* can be difficult or impossible to identify. The specimens presently available from the Mammoth Site are insufficient to establish the species identity.

Microtus spp. are grazing rodents typical of grassland and steppe environments across Holarctica. *Microtus pennsylvanicus* and *M. longicaudus* both occur in the Black Hills area today where *M. longicaudus* tends to be found more commonly at higher elevations, in the boreal forests and riparian areas bordering cold streams (Turner 1974). Turner (1974) observed that a distinct ecological separation between these two species is not discernible in the Black Hills proper, but only *M. pennsylvanicus* presently occurs out onto the foothills and surrounding semi-arid plains in suitable riparian habitats.

Mustela cf. *vison* or *nigripes* (mink or black-footed ferret)

Referred material: radius.

Postcranial skeletal variation is poorly known in wild mustelids and the sole specimen currently at hand does not allow a precise species identification. The nearness to riparian habitat of the Fall River and the presence of fish fossils in HSMS deposits (pharyngeal arches and teeth of two types of Cyprinidae, a cycloid scale, and several vertebrae) indicate fish populations that could have attracted a mink to the spring. Alternatively, the abundance of prairie dogs and ground squirrels might have attracted a black-footed ferret to the area. Other small vertebrates would have provided prey for either of these mustelids, and either could be represented by the radius.

DISCUSSION

Remains of small mammals are relatively rare in the spring deposits of the Mammoth Site. No small mammal bones have been found in articulation. Unfortunately, specimens recovered up to now are often incomplete and do not allow accurate species identification in some cases. Nevertheless, some interesting conclusions can be drawn. Since current radiometric dates are a minimum age for HSMS, we do not know the span of time during which the faunule accumulated. It is possible that the small mammals are not all contemporaneous with each other and with the mammoths and other large species in the deposits. Four forms, *Scalopus aquaticus, Spermophilus elegans/richardsonii, Cynomys (Leucocrossuromys),* and *Phenacomys intermedius* are extralimital at the HSMS. They occurred at Hot Springs in the late Pleistocene but do not at the present time. The eastern mole, *Scalopus aquaticus,* is widely distributed in the eastern United States and central and southern Great Plains, but its present northwestern geographic limits are along the White River drainage in northwestern Nebraska (Jones 1964; Jones *et al.* 1983). In light of the possibility that the mole is non-contemporaneous with the HSMS late Pleistocene faunule, the species is not considered in the discussion below and is not included in the sympatry map (Figure 54).

The nearest populations of S*permophilus elegans* in historic times are south of the North Platte River in western Nebraska and adjacent southeastern Wyoming (Jones 1964; Long 1965; Hall 1981), about 210 km away. The nearest populations of *S. richardsonii* are in central South Dakota, also about 210 km away (Michener and Koeppl 1985). Both *S. elegans* and *S. richardsonii* are (or were before recent extirpations) often found living within black-tailed prairie dog towns (Jones *et al.* 1983). Fossils of ground squirrels of the *S. richardsonii*-complex are known from the late Pleistocene of Alberta, Idaho, Wyoming, South Dakota, Nebraska, Colorado, Kansas, New Mexico, Oklahoma, and Texas (Storer 1976; Kurtén and Anderson 1980; Zegers 1984; Michener and Koeppl 1985; Graham *et al.* 1987a;

146

several of these occurrences are extralimital, like the one at Hot Springs.

Cynomys leucurus and *C. ludovicianus* are approximately parapatric in their geographic ranges across Wyoming. Goodwin (1989) noted that the two subgenera of prairie dogs currently exhibit limited overlap in North America, but in contrast, in the late Pleistocene they apparently were broadly sympatric in the central Great Plains (in Kansas and Nebraska). White-tailed prairie dogs (*Leucocrossuromys*) occurred west, north, and east of their current range, as far southeast as Kansas, whereas the subgenus *Cynomys* occurred less far north (no farther north than Nebraska) but farther eastward than today. The nearest populations of *C. leucurus* to Hot Springs today are about 240 km to the southwest. *Cynomys leucurus* is known from late Pleistocene sites in Wyoming at Horned Owl Cave (Guilday *et al.*, 1967) and Little Box Elder Cave (Indeck 1987) that are within its modern range. Other extralimital records of this species include Rainbow Beach, Idaho (McDonald and Anderson 1975) and Hand Hills, Alberta (Graham *et al.* 1987a). The ranges of all living species of *Leucocrossuromys* were used in the construction of the sympatry map (Figure 54).

The radiation of heather voles, mentioned in the taxonomic account above, is postulated to have been related to the dynamics of the continental ice fields and probably was accompanied by distinct changes in the habitats occupied by *Phenacomys* and *Arborimus* (Repenning in press). Repenning further believes that the late Pleistocene habitats occupied by *Phenacomys* (*sensu lato*) spp. may be distinctly different from the habitats currently selected by them.

Excluding the eastern mole, eight kinds of small mammals from HSMS are referable to species (in one case, only to subgenus) and enable us to draws a map of their area of sympatry. This technique, commonly used in Pleistocene mammalian biogeography, discloses a geographic region where most of the species of a fossil fauna co-occur at the present time (Graham and Semken 1987). The area of sympatry, then is considered to partly define or parallel the paleoenvironmental conditions at the fossil site. In the case of the

HSMS faunule, the area of sympatry is moderate in size and does not include what is now Hot Springs, South Dakota, therefore indicating environmental change, but probably not a great change. The area occurs in southern Wyoming and portions of northwestern Colorado (Figure 54). The area of sympatry is primarily delimited by the overlap of the ranges of *S. tridecemlineatus, S. elegans, P. intermedius*, and *C. (Leucocrossuromys)*. Presumably, ecological conditions in this area are partly analogous to the conditions at Hot Springs in the late Pleistocene. Today, the area is shortgrass prairie, characterized by Küchler (1964) as potentially grama-buffalo grass (*Bouteloua-Buchloe*). All eight identifiable species are sympatric there today, so the late Pleistocene small mammal fauna has a modern analog.

Figure 54. Zone of sympatry of eight species of small mammals (shaded area) known as fossils from the late Pleistocene of Hot Springs Mammoth Site, South Dakota. Dot indicates location of Hot Springs Mammoth Site.

Three members of the late Pleistocene small mammal fauna are indicators of grassland conditions. These are the sciurids, *S. elegans/ richardsonii* and *S. tridecemlineatus*, and the microtine *Microtus*. The prairie dog *Cynomys leucurus* typically inhabits xeric sites with mixed stands of shrubs and grasses in the Wyoming Basin and in Colorado (Armstrong 1972). The woodrat *Neotoma cinerea* is a species that strongly prefers rocky terrain, where it dens in vertical crevices and caves in rocky outcrops. It is usually associated with forested or woodland habitats, although it often occurs above timberline (Harris 1985). However, it does occur in desert grasslands with scattered junipers and rocky outcrops in the extreme southern parts of its modern range (in the Colorado Plateau) (Dial 1984; Hoffmeister 1986). Other taxa of small mammals have broader habitat tolerances but usually select open environments. They do not refute the inferred presence of grassland or cold steppe-grassland at Hot Springs in the late Pleistocene. Although the number of species of small mammals yet known from HSMS is still low, these mammals form a relatively diverse assemblage. Their variety suggests that the paleohabitat was not pure grassland, but was some more diverse or heterogeneous mixture of vegetation such as that referred to by Guthrie (1984) as "mammoth steppe." Thus, the cold steppe-grassland environment indicated by pollen (Agenbroad and Mead 1986; Mead *et al.* this volume) and by the abundance of mammoths within the sinkhole sediments is concordant with the grassy environment indicated by the small mammals that lived adjacent to the spring. Several spring deposits similar to that at HSMS occur in the Hot Springs and Black Hills area. When more of these are excavated for their contained vertebrate remains—as at HSMS—a more complete picture of the late Pleistocene setting of this portion of the northern plains will materialize.

Chapter 7

LATE PLEISTOCENE FISH AND AMPHIBIANS FROM HOT SPRINGS MAMMOTH SITE, SOUTH DAKOTA

Jim I. Mead

The Mammoth Site at Hot Springs, South Dakota is a sediment-filled sinkhole that held a spring-fed pond during the late Pleistocene (radiocarbon dating approximately 26,000 yr B.P.; Agenbroad this volume). Pollen samples from the west end of the sinkhole indicate that the reconstructed environment was a cold steppe-grassland (Mead *et al.* this volume). Some evidence recovered is consistent with a reconstruction of a warm water-filled sinkhole (Mead *et al.* this volume). The west end of the pond appears to be the shallower end of the pond, based on the recovery of aquatic plant impressions, mollusks, fish, carnivore skeletons, and carnivore scats.

During the course of excavation for mammoths (*Mammuthus*) and other large mammals, excavators were also looking for evidence of post-deposition burrows (none found) and *in situ* small animal remains. Sediments were taken at random from throughout the site since 1978 for screen washing for microvertebrates. One of the fish remains reported here was found in such washings. A fish skeleton was recovered in the course of careful excavations in the sediments at the west end of the sinkhole. Of the two anuran (frog-toad) remains recovered, the smaller one (woodhouse toad) was found in such a manner that we are not completely sure if it was from an intrusive burrow or if it was *in situ*, although all indications are that it was in primary position. Examination of the sediments from 5 cm away from the skeleton would imply that the specimen was contemporaneous with the mammoth and fish.

The second anuran skeleton was found in the bottom of a burrow, excavated in profile view. Although described in detail elsewhere (Laury this volume), the sedimentation infilling of the sink-hole includes a phase (II) where the warm pond water was deep enough that mammoths were not able to climb out and died either of starvation or by drowning. During this segment of deposition within the site, anurans would probably have existed only at the west end of the locality, where all the fish remains are also found. This region would have had somewhat shallower water, some aquatic vegetation, calmer water, probably cooler water, and afforded access into and out of the pond for most animals except for the less agile (e.g., mammoths), sick, or hurt.

The terminal segment of deposition (Phase III) included shallower water, as evidenced by the rare occurrence of mammoth skeletons and their foot prints. The end of this sedimentation phase might be envisioned as a shallow sinkhole filled with a wet, muddy "meadow" (although there are no plant remains from this period). Mammoths could have walked across the wet sinkhole without getting trapped. It is during this phase that a toad apparently burrowed down into the slighly older sediments to escape the surface environment, but then died and became a portion of the deposit. How much younger this toad and the mammoth footprints are than the older "drowned" mammoths is not precisely known, although it is assumed that the entire life-span of the sinkhole is much less than 3,000 years (and possibly as short as 300 years), dating approximately 26,000 yr B.P.

FOSSIL ACCOUNT

Class Osteichthys (bony fish)
Family Cypriniformes (minnows)
Genus et species indeterminate

Referred material: isolate vertebrae and approximately 50% of two complete skeletons. The fish remains have yet to be examined by a specialist. They are the size of the small minnows that live today in the various streams and artesian springs in the southern Black Hills.

Class Amphibia (amphibians)
Order Anura (frogs and toads)
Family Bufonidae (true toads)

Bufo cognatus Say 1823 (Great Plains toad)
Referred material: one near-complete skeleton.
Bufo cognatus and *B. woodhousei* (woodhouse toad) are the only two species living today in the Black Hills and surrounding region. The next closest toad to live near the Black Hills is *B. hemiophrys*, which occurs no nearer than northeastern South Dakota (Stebbins 1985). All three of these species belong to the *americanus* group. One skeletal character of this group is "the very high ilial [dorsal] prominence, though not completely universal within the group, is unique to it" (Tihen 1962:179). *Bufo* ilia from the Mammoth Site have high dorsal prominence on the ilium.

The ilia from the *in situ* skeleton has a robust dorsal prominence; its height about equal to the width of its base. Both the anterior and posterior slopes of the dorsal prominence are steep. The dorsal prominence is raised in *B. woodhousei*, however it is not as well developed as it is in *B. cognatus*, *B. speciousus* (Texas toad), and the specimen from the Mammoth Site. Holman (1969) felt that the ilia of these two species could not be differentiated from one another, although it is highly unlikely that the smaller *B. speciousus* ever lived as far north as South Dakota. Today *B. speciosus* lives no farther north than southern-most Kansas and pan-handle Oklahoma (Stebbins 1985).

Bufo cf. *B. woodhousei* Girard 1854 (woodhouse toad)
Referred material: one near-complete skeleton.
The ilium is small (from posterior basal edge of dorsal prominence to tip of shaft is 1.4 mm), but appears to be from a young individual of a large species vs. from a small species). The dorsal prominence is raised, but is not robust as it is in B. *cognatus*. The anterior slope to the prominence is slanted, at a low angle, again

different than that on *B. cognatus*; the posterior slope is more vertical. These characters and lack of certain characters imply that the skeleton is of *B. woodhousei*, however, the juvenile age makes the identification tentative.

DISCUSSION AND CONCLUSIONS

The semi-arid Black Hills today are not very well suited to a highly developed herpetological fauna. The climate, in conjunction with a relatively high altitude, the geographic position within the middle of the continent, and the surrounding environments are not conducive to a large herpetofauna. This is the same reason why we do not expect to recover a varied, or large, Pleistocene herpetofauna. Pleistocene age faunas containing fish and amphibians are not common in the region of the Black Hills. Martin (1987) identified cyprinid fish and *Rana* cf. *pipiens* (leopard frog) from the Lange-Ferguson local fauna (dating 10,670 yr B.P.), north and east of the Mammoth Site in the Badlands, South Dakota. The middle Pleistocene locality of Java, north-central South Dakota, has produced *Bufo woodhousei* (Holman 1977). The Mammoth Site is significant in that it contains fish and amphibian remains, albeit rare. The reason for the fauna being depauperate could be that we are working with a warm water environment, although one would still expect some turtles even during an interstadial warming at this latitude. More likely the reason for the scant remains is a bias in collecting and sampling. We expect to recover a more diverse herpetofauna as excavation continues, especially in the western portion of the site.

Chapter 8

LATE PLEISTOCENE ARTIODACTYLS FROM HOT SPRINGS MAMMOTH SITE, SOUTH DAKOTA

Jim I. Mead and Larry D. Agenbroad

INTRODUCTION

The Mammoth Site at Hot Springs, South Dakota is a sediment-filled sinkhole that held a spring-fed pond during the late Pleistocene (radiocarbon dating approximately 26,000 yr B.P.), which is described in more detail elsewhere in this book (Agenbroad this volume). Pollen samples from the west end of the sinkhole indicate that the reconstructed environment was a cold steppe-grassland (Mead *et al.* this volume). Some evidence recovered (described elsewhere) is consistent with a reconstruction of a warm water-filled sinkhole. The west end of the pond appears to be the shallower end to the pond, based on the recovery of aquatic plant impressions, mollusks, fish, carnivore skeletons, and carnivore scats.

The predominant faunal remains recovered from the sinkhole are the mammoth (*Mammuthus*). Carnivores are diverse and are described by Baryshnikov *et al.* (this volume) and the other small mammals being presented in Czaplewski and Mead (this volume). Here we present the rare remains of the artiodactyls.

FOSSIL ACCOUNT

Class Mammalia (mammals)
Order Artiodactyla (artiodactyls)
Family Antilocapridae (pronghorns)

Antilocapra americana (Ord 1815) (pronghorn)

Referred material: third phalanx, patella, and unciform.

The three bones are identical in shape, form, and size to those elements in modern *Antilocapra americana*. Skinner (1942) indicates that the carpals and phalanges in *Stockoceros onusrosagris* (Quentin's pronghorn, extinct) show slight differences, mainly in size and proportion to those of *A. americana*. This is the same for essentially all the bones of *Stockoceros*, in that they are smaller than those of *Antilocapra*. For this reason we feel that the antilocaprid bones recovered from the Mammoth Site are best assigned to *Antilocapra* and not *Stockoceros*. There are two species within the genus *Antilocapra*, the living form and the extinct Pliocene, *A. garciae*, which is known only from Florida (Webb1973).

Chorn *et al.* (1988) have reviewed the late Pleistocene (Wisconsin glacial) distribution of *Antilocapra*. The specimens from the Mammoth Site are apparently the first late Pleistocene remains of *Antilocapra* from South Dakota and the Black Hills. The species was recovered from the late Wisconsin deposits at Agate Basin (Wyoming), and it is known from the Black Hills and surrounding region throughout the Holocene. Late Pleistocene remains of *Antilocapra* are not uncommon from the deposits west of the Black Hills in Wyoming (Walker 1987).

Harris (1985) records the various species of *Stockoceros* as having lived in New Mexico and Arizona, south into Texas and Mexico. *Stockoceros* is not known from late Rancholabrean faunas in the Great Plains and prairies (see various chapters in Graham *et al.* 1987a).

Today the pronghorn is both a grazer and a browser, eating grasses, forbs, and shrubs depending on the season and locality (O'Gara 1978). Although its habitat is typically thought of as short-grass prairie, it will also live in open shrublands, mountain parks, and open sagebrush-pinyon-juniper woodlands.

Family Camelidae (camels and llamas)

Camelops sp. Leidy 1854 (camel)

Referred material: $I_{2,3}$, P_4, M_2, and distal epiphysis (unfused) of metapodial.

The unfused epiphysis and the unworn nature of the cheek teeth indicate that the camel is sub-adult in age. The remains, although small, are larger than those same elements observed in adult *Hemiauchenia* (extinct llama) and are therefore referred to *Camelops*. Both genera are found in late Rancholabrean age localities of the Great Plains surrounding the Black Hills (Graham *et al.* 1987a; Kurten and Anderson 1980; Walker 1987). *Camelops* has not been reported previously from the Black Hills (Martin 1987).

Family Bovidae (cattle, sheep, musk-oxen)

cf. *Euceratherium collinum* Furlong and Sinclair 1904 (shrub-ox)
    Referred material: fragment of M^1.

The fragmented molar appears to be an upper first molar in full occlusion wear. The open selens and lack of mesostyle indicate that the tooth belongs to the tribe Ovibovinae (musk-oxen), and not to the tribe Bovinae (bison and cattle). The tooth appears less robust as with the euceratherines and not robust as with *Ovibos*, *Bootherium*, and *Symbos.*; this is our only criterion for the identification. *Euceratherium* is not typically associated with Pleistocene environments reconstructed for the Great Plains; however it is known from Wyoming. *Bootherium/Symbos* are the typical ovibovines from the region surrounding the Black Hills (Kurten and Anderson 1980; Lundelius *et al.* 1983; McDonald *et al.* 1987; McDonald and Ray 1989). The known distributions of *Euceratherium* and *Bootherium/Symbos* would tend to imply that a specimen from the Black Hills would be the latter species, with the former species being restricted more to the west. However, the Black Hills may have been an "ecotone" of western and eastern species, forming a mosaic community that occurs in no other region, as it does today.

DISCUSSION AND CONCLUSION

The Lange/Ferguson Clovis site (10,670 yr B.P.) immediately

north and east of the Black Hills has produced a variety of mammalian species, including *Bison* sp. (bison) and cf. *Odocoileus* sp. (deer) (Martin 1987). The Mammoth Site is producing the the only known Pleistocene remains of *Camelops, Antilocapra,* and *Euceratherium* from the Black Hills region. Walker (1987) does record the former two species from Wyoming localites, west of the Black Hills.

Based on previous studies in Wyoming and the northern Great Plains, one would expect *Bootherium/Symbos* to be recovered from the Mammoth Site (Walker 1987). If the identification of *Euceratherium* from the Mammoth Site is correct, it is unique that this species is found at this high latitude in the central portion of the continent (see various articles in Graham *et al.* 1987a). Additional material is needed for a better understanding if the shrub-ox lived in the Black Hills during the Pleistocene. Harris (1985) determined that *Euceratherium* lived in middle-elevation savannas and sagebrush steppe-woodlands with relatively low mountainous terrains in western North America. The reconstruction of the Mammoth Site environment of 26,000 yr B.P. as being a cold steppe-grassland fits into Harris' environmental setting for the shrub-ox.

As additional late Pleistocene faunal localities with different taphonomic settings are excavated in the Black Hills, we assume that more variety of species will be discovered. Given the taphonomic setting of the Mammoth Site as a steep-walled (but climbable) sinkhole, it is surprising that we recovered the artiodactlys listed above. All would be expected to climb fairly steep inclines. Other localites should produce specimens of *Equus* (horse), more ovibovines, *Bison*, other antilocaprines, additional camels, deer, and possibly representatives of the peccaries (*Mylohyus* and *Platygonus*).

Chapter 9

TAXONOMY OF NORTH AMERICAN *MAMMUTHUS* AND BIOMETRICS OF THE HOT SPRINGS MAMMOTHS

Larry D. Agenbroad

There is a sizable body of literature on the taxonomy of North American mammoths. Some of the major publications in this regard include Osborn (1942), Maglio (1973), Kurtén and Anderson (1980), Madden (1981), and Graham (1986). I briefly expressed my viewpoint on the confusion in mammoth taxonomy in an earlier publication (Agenbroad 1984a). My purpose, now, is not to reiterate these data, but to attempt to express my view of this taxonomic problem, based on my own research and experience.

Osborn's (1942) summary of North American mammoths provides us with fifteen (16 according to Maglio 1973) species of mammoths. If one uses Osborn's subspecific classifications, we have at least eight additional subspecies. Maglio (1973) condensed Osborn's classification system to four species of New World mammoths, and provided his arguments and reasoning for combinations of Osborn's work. Kurtén and Anderson (1980) kept four species, but changed the nomenclature of the two intermediate forms, using Maglio's more progressive species terminology of *M. columbi* to represent Maglio's *M. imperator. M. imperator* was deleted as a species, and *M. jeffersoni* was substituted for the *M. columbi* proposed by Maglio (1973). Madden (1981) went even further. He denied the presence of *Mammuthus meridionalis* in the New World, and presented *Mammuthus hayi* as the oldest form of mammoth in the New World; speculating it is most closely related to the late Pliocene *Mammuthus gromovi* of Asia. He also proposes that *M. hayi* is late Pliocene in age, in the New World. Madden also denies the presence of woolly mammoth, south of Canada. Graham (1986) reviews the state of mammoth taxonomy, reflecting the contribution of Maglio (1973) and using those discussions to counter revised nomenclature used by Kurtén and Anderson (1980) and Madden (1981). He concludes that *M. columbi* and *M. primigenius* are the Wisconsinan mammoths of North America, as proposed in the taxonomic sequences published by Maglio (1973) and Agenbroad (1984a). The only difference between the sequences proposed by Maglio (1973), Graham (1986) and my own (1984a, this volume) is the inclusion of *M. exilis* in the Wisconsinan (late Pleistocene) occurrences.

In 1984, I argued that the Kurtén and Anderson (1980) sequence interchanged the nomenclature, i.e., *M. columbi* for *M. imperator*, and *M. jeffersoni* for *M. columbi* confusing the nomenclature since the latter species (in each case) was that which had been used by most authors, since Osborn's (1942) classification. Madden (1981) made taxonomic nomenclature even more confusing, by denying the presence of *M. meridionalis*, proposing *M. hayi* as the ancestral form—from the late Pliocene! More progressive forms were given new (and different) nomenclature, plus he states that *M. primigenius* [*M. mammonteus* (Madden 1981)] does not occur south of the Canadian border. The result of these two recent revisions means that one must either accept, or reject them. If accepted, one is faced with the monumental task of reassigning the existing species designations provided in the literature and museum collections, to one or the other of the proposed systems. In my opinion, this would entail personal examination of all the specimens, to allow assignment in the proposed systems. I stated (1984) that Maglio's (1973) taxonomy was defended by persuasive reasoning, and in the literature by the common usage of *Mammuthus* specific names since approximately 1942. Graham (1986) is in agreement with Maglio's system, and my own statements (Agenbroad 1984a). I have found no reason to revise the basic sequence proposed by Maglio, with the minor exception of giving *M. exilis* a formal position in the late Pleistocene mammoths of North America. Table 11 provides a comparison of the taxonomic systems proposed since 1942, for New World mammoths.

Table 11. Taxonomy of North American mammoths (*Mammuthus*) (Agenbroad and Barton 1991)

Osborn	Maglio (1973)	Kurten & Anderson (1980)	Madden (1980)	Graham (1986)	Agenbroad 1984;1991
Late Pleistocene					
Mammonteus primigenius	*M. primigenius*	*M. primigenius*	*M. mommonteus*	*M. primigenius*	*M. primigenius*
Paraelephas progressus		*M. (Paraelephas) jacksonii*			
Paraelephas jeffersoni		*M. jeffersoni*			
Paraelephas roosevelti					
Paraelephas jacksoni	*M. columbi*		*M. (Paraelephas) exilis*	*M. columbi*	**M. exilis*
Paraelephas floridanus			*M. (Paraelephas) columbi*		*M. columbi*
Paraelephas columbi					
Paraelephas washingtonii					
Paraelephas eellsi					
Middle Pleistocene					
Archidiskodon imperator (maibeni)	*M. imperator*	*M. columbi*	*M. (Paraelephas) imperator*	*M. imperator*	*M. imperator*
Early Pleistocene					
Archidiskodon meridionalis	*M. meridionalis*	*M. meridionalis*	*M.(Archaeomammuthus) hayi*	*M. meridionalis*	*M. meriodionalis*
Archidiskodon exilis					
Archidiskodon haroldcooki					
Archidiskodon hayi					
Archidiskodon imperator					
Archidiskodon sonorensis					

*M. exilis included as *M. imperator* in Maglio (1973)

160

Order Proboscidea (Elephants, mastodonts and relatives)
Family Elephantidae (Elephants)
Genus *Mammuthus* (Mammoths)
Mammuthus columbi (Columbian mammoths)

Initially, bones were exposed in two concentrations, A and B (Figure 55). Subsequent testing proved mammoth bone to be present in every area of the site, especially at the periphery of the deposit, usually within six meters (laterally) of the contact with the Spearfish Formation.

The northeastern portion of the deposit contained a dense concentration of disarticulated bone in a sandy matrix, suggesting a high energy environment, such as a spring conduit. The southwestern portion of the deposit contained articulated and semiarticulated remains in laminated silts and silty clay, suggesting a low energy, pond environment.

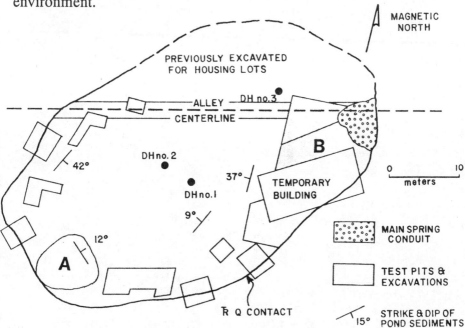

Figure 55: Areas of excavation (HSMS).

As a portion of the deposit (northern edge) had been removed during leveling of house lots, the northern edge of the remaining material was to be removed for the construction of an alley. The 1974-79 field work was concentrated in the northern edge of the deposit to clear the proposed alley right-of-way. The 1983 field season provided a test of the southwestern portion of the site. It was concluded that mammoth remains occur in rather uniform abundance throughout the site.

A limited sample of mammoth mandibles revealed an age range of 13-43 AEY (African elephant years), with a mean age of 25 AEY (Dutrow 1980). Calves are missing from the population. The age-structure analysis of 43 (MNI) animals is presented later.

Each field season produced additional individuals (Table 12). In 1976 we estimated at least 100 individuals would be discovered. Based on the count at the end of the 1990 field season, that number seems conservative.

Table 12. Mammoth Inventory at the end of each field season.

Year	No. of mammoths (cumulative)
1974	4-6
1975	9-12
1976	15
1977	22
1978	25
1979	30
*	
1983	34
*	
1986	37
1987	41
1988	42
1989	43
1990	44

*1980-82 and 1984-85 were non-excavation seasons due to fund raising and construction of the building houseing the site.

Since the sinkhole-trap contained a large number of late Pleistocene mammoths, taken from the local populations, in the local environment, the material seemed ideal, for metric analyses of skeletal elements. The deposit was of special significance due to the fact that the population was locally derived, as contrasted to an alluvial deposit which might represent animals from diverse regions within the drainage system, or accumulated remains from several temporal intervals, due to erosional exposure, incorporation, and redeposition.

No large, local population metrics were available for *Mammuthus columbi*; Hot Springs promised to fill this void. Initially, the population was considered to be composed entirely of *M. columbi*. We now recognize at least three *M. primigenius* individuals in the population, and as excavations continue, there may be others. There is one bias inherent with the Hot Springs population—as will be noted in the discussion of dentition, and the resultant age-structure analysis, the majority of the individuals from the Hot Springs Mammoth Site are immature and young-adult mammoths.

Initially, we naively assumed there would likely be sexual dimorphism exhibited for any skeletal element under consideration. As the research progressed, it appeared the trap was selective for young males—which fits behavioral patterns which still exist in modern *Loxodonta africana* (Moss 1988).

A problem in our early analyses was the fact that we could not assign individual age to specimens that were disarticulated. It was not until the 1979 field season that we began to find articulated specimens, so age correlations, with metrics of a given element, could be made (Figure 56). This was also compounded by finding completely articulated specimens—minus crania, and therefore dentition, preventing individual age assignments (Figure 57).

With the decision to leave as many of the specimens *in situ*, as possible, it provided additional difficulties for metric analyses, in that some specimens were covered, or partially covered, by overlying specimens, preventing the acquisition of some measurements.

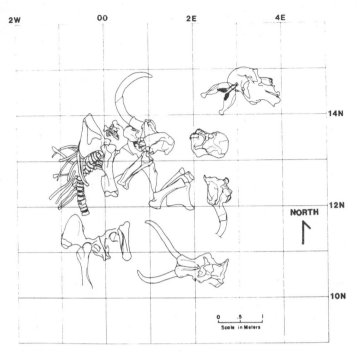

Figure 56. The position of an articulated skeleton (Napoleon) in the north east portion of the sinkhole, at the deepest level of excavation to date.

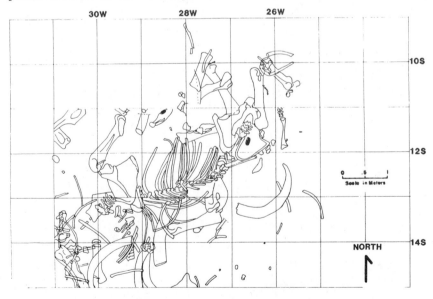

Figure 57. A fully articulated mammoth skeleton (Murray), minus the skull, from the western portion of the sinkhole.

BIOMETRIC ANALYSES OF SELECTED ELEMENTS FROM THE HOT SPRINGS MAMMOTHS

In the tables and discussions that follow, methods derived from several sources (von den Driesch 1976; Maglio 1973; Beden 1979; and others) have been selected from, amalgamated, or rejected. In an attempt to make the measurements clear to other investigators, diagrams, with the location of the measurements taken, have been provided.

The reader must be cautioned that the metric data presented here predominantly represents the ±10 to ±35 year old, male individuals, with a few +35 year olds, and no animals less than 10 years old. It is apparent then, that this metric information does not represent the entire age spectrum for the species.

Crania

Incomplete cranial measurements (Table 13) were obtained for twenty-three individuals. Dependent on their *in situ* position, the complexity of the local bone bed, and the degree of excavation of the specimen, the data base is somewhat fragmented. Of the twenty-three measured crania, fourteen can be assigned an individual age in African elephant years (AEY). The majority (71.4%) is in the 20-29 AEY age grouping, with 14.3% in the 10-19 AEY age group and 14.3% in the greater than 35 AEY age group. This distribution is similar to the age-structure analysis, based on dentition. Based on pelvic rations (discussed later) the cranial population is considered to represent an all-male population.

A plot (Figure 58) of cranial length versus dental age (AEY) compared to a similar plot for *Loxodonta africana* from Kenya and Uganda (Beden 1979), indicates a longer skull for *Mammuthus columbi*, for corresponding individual ages.

Hyoids

The proboscidean hyoid is a tripartite skeletal support at the base of the tongue. In elephants and mammoth, the hyoid is divided into

Table 13. Selected Cranial Measurements (cm).

Specimen	1	2	3	4	5	6	7	8	9	10	11	12
83-216	117.6	52.5		58.8		95.4			51.1		62.6	
HS-140	118.7	35.7	44.5			74.8	82.3	73.8		35.9	51.3	21.5
HS-146						59.5	74.1				62.2	
HS-147	102.6	38.7				39.2	65.2				64.6	17.0
HS-220	128.2	53.3	44.6	51.6		64.7	76.1	78.1	10.0	34.0		17.6
HS-203		55.8		57.5								24.4
HS-204		34.4									66.9	
HS-205	141.0	47.6	52.1	58.6		74.2	67.8	83.4	49.8	30.9		20.8
HS-293						70.3						
HS-336	139.5	54.0	47.7			69.4	87.0	94.0	46.0	37.3		(16.4)
HS-515			52.0			66.0	78.3		45.0	41.8		
HS-364		44.2		52.8					40.4			16.4
HS-369											59.2	
HS-074	137.4	45.7	55.0			54.3	93.5	77.0	40.2	30.2		
HS-408		44.1	41.5	48.9				76.9	33.8			19.0
HS-406	116.3	43.9	56.0			88.9	77.0	72.0	43.8	37.1		
HS-070	122.9	43.4									50.7	22.6
HS-017											62.7	
89-033											63.0	
89-062												
T-3-S	141.2	53.9	52.0	58.5		70.7	91.3		54.3	31.4	72.5	
76-226	75.1	29.3		41.0								
75-103	143.2	62.3	49.4	61.7		69.8	87.5			31.6		

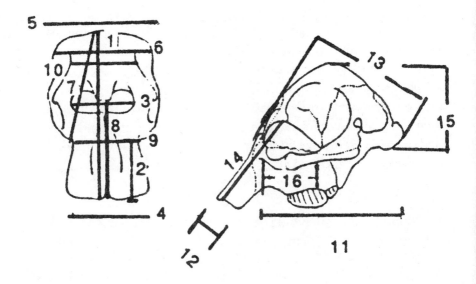

Table 13 (continued)

Specimen	13	14	15	16	17	18	19	20	21	Age	Field #
83-216	84.0		33.5	9.4		14.6	54.8	30.4	58.4		83-216
HS-140	75.8	63.9	35.1		79.4	10.9	64.0	24.1	46.2	28	79-504
HS-146		60.6	39.1	4.4		11.1		23.8	56.0	24	79-265
HS-147	52.0	53.7	32.2	7.2		10.5	62.6	23.2	48.6	27	79-203
HS-220	82.3										79-217
HS-203				7.6	75.3	11.2	72.2	26.5	55.0	27	86-036
HS-204		46.4	29.4	7.3		8.1	(52.1)	23.7	57.9	27	77-148
HS-205	70.9										77-147
HS-293		(57.0)		7.6		13.1		23.8	60.1	28	76-390
HS-336	81.0			6.6		11.1	59.8			54	76-380
HS-515											87-072
HS-364			32.6	7.9		17.0	63.0			38	76-372
HS-369		55.5						20.8	47.2	17	87-005
HS-074	81.4				(74.7)						79-223
HS-408	83.8			4.1	65.4	11.3	61.1			27	86-082
HS-406	75.5				81.3					28	87-016
HS-070	66.5	71.7	34.5	8.2		12.8	57.8	22.2	42.7	27	83-166
HS-017		52.4	52.2	8.5		12.7		23.4	55.3		83-181
89-033		56.9			81.8	26.8	70.5	20.5	60.5		89-033
89-062		54.3		7.7	(82.4)	17.1		27.8	49.2	28	89-062
T-3-S	53.3	70.2	59.8								T-3-S
76-226										12	76-226
75-103		78.9									75-103

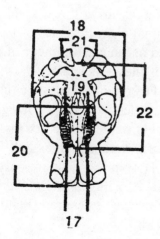

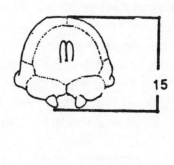

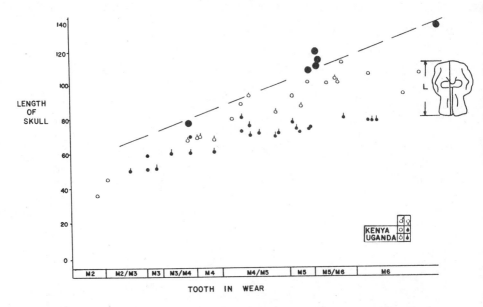

Figure 58. Length of the cranium (cm) as a function of dental age (after Beden 1979). This plot contrasts *M. columbi* (large dots) with Beden's *Loxodonta africana* populations (small dots and circles).

three components (Figure 59) as described in Inuzuka *et al.* (1975); the stylohyoid, the thyrohyoid, and the basihyoid.

The first description of *M. columbi* hyoids was done on the Colby mammoths, by Graham (1986). The Colby mammoth site (Frison and Todd 1986) provided a sample representing three stylohyoids for the species. The unique depositional characteristics of the Hot Springs Mammoth Site has preserved an unusual number of these delicate bones. The fragile nature of these skeletal elements and their non-osteological connection to the cranium predestine them to early loss and destruction in skeletal disarticulation in fluvial regimes. For example, a typical stylohyoid would remain intact for less than 100 m in typical bed load transport of a stream such as Fall River. The sinkhole spring and pond of the Hot Springs site not only preserved these bones, but the slow, quiet depositional mode of the fine grain sediments actually preserved them in life position (Figure 60) in the cranium of "Napoleon" (MSL-140).

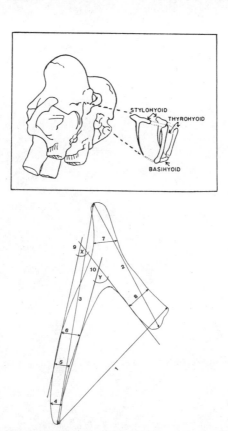

Figure 59. Diagram of the position of the hyoid bones and their position in the skull (after Graham 1986; Inuzuka *et al.* 1975). A stylohyoid bone from *M. columbi* illustrating measurements taken.

Stylohyoids

A total of eight measurable stylohyoid bones and three fragments of the ventral extremity (Graham 1986) have been removed from the site (Table 14). One stylohyoid (79-251) is *in situ*, in "Napoleon's" skull. Nine thyrohyoid bones, (six nearly complete and three partials) have been recovered (Table 14; Figure 61). In addition three basihyoids (Figure 61) have been recovered. This provides a greater inventory of hyoid bones from the Hot Springs Mammoth Site (with 20-25% of the site excavated) than is known from the total reported *M. columbi* localities in North America.

Hyoid bones from a collection made in Hwange National Park, Zimbabwe, of *Loxodonta africana* were made available for comparison, by Gary Haynes. This collection is comprised of thirteen speci-

Figure 60. A stylohyoid *in situ* in the skull of 'Napoleon' (MSL 140).

mens ranging in age (of individual) from less than one year old through greater than 40 AEY. The latter specimen is comprised of a set of thyrohyoids fused to the basihyoids. The collection also includes a stylohyoid from *Mammuthus* cf. *columbi* from Largo, Maryland. The mammoth was dated at ± 20,000 yr B.P., and the individual was 12-15 years of age (AEY) at death (Haynes, personal communication).

As would be expected, the shape of the stylohyoids of *Mammuthus columbi, Loxodonta africana,* and *Elephas maximus* are similar in size and shape, with differences allowed for individual variation as well as species difference. The angle of divergence of the inferior ramus with the posterior ramus is considerably more acute for *Loxodonta*, as compared to *Mammuthus*. In general, the Hot Springs specimens compare favorably with the younger elephant specimens. The Maryland mammoth specimen is nearly identical in size and shape with the Hot Springs specimen 88-026 (other than apparent pathology of the anterior posterior rami of the latter). This specimen approximates that (in size and shape) of the 12-15 year old individual from Maryland.

Three of the Hot Springs stylohyoids are aberrant. Specimen 88-026, noted above, and specimen 83-002 (Figure 61) display pathogenic abnormalities. In the case of 88-026 the entire superior-posterior ramus is disfigured, presenting a fan shaped bone instead of the flat curve of a more normal articular angle. In specimen 83-002, the entire superior ramus is a dense, bulbous bone mass, distinctly different in shape and thickness from normal superior rami. The ventral portion of the muscular angle is not an acute angle on 83-001, creating an obtuse angle instead. In addition to the above, the ventral extremity of 83-108 is flatter than the other specimens, though other characteristics are "normal" for this population.

Thyrohyoids

Nine thyrohyoids (Figure 61) have been recovered (6 left, 3 right). This relatively flat bone has spatulate anterior and posterior portions (Table 14) with epiphyses at the fusion with the basihyoid (anterior) and the muscular angle (posterior ramus) of the stylohyoid (poste-

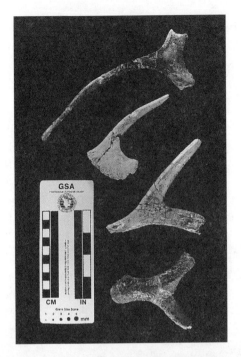

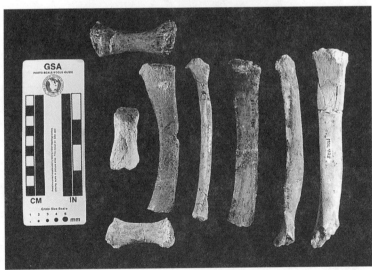

Figure 61. Stylohyoids (top) 83-001, 88-026, 83-108, 83-002 as discussed in the text; Thyrohyoids (bottom) right five specimens; Basihyoids (bottom) left three specimens.

Table 14. Measurements (mm) of hyoids of *M. columbi* from Hot Springs and *L. africana* from Zimbabwe (*Loxodonta* specimens courtesy of G. Haynes)

STYLOHYOIDS

Mammuthus columbi: Hot Springs Mammoth Site

	83-001	88-026		83-108	83-002	76-180	75-039	79-251
1	(160)	(131.0)	(139.0)	(108.0)				141
2	67.1	61.3	(89.2)	117.0	106.3	110.9	83.4	162
3	(172.0)	(133.3)	(169)	(149.1)				223.5
4	6.7 x 12.5		7.1 x 7.7					
5	8.7 x 14.5	8.3 x 12.7	8.6 x 13.1	11.0 x 7.0				
6	10.4 x 11.1	11.9 x 12.1	14.2 x 11.8	18.3 x 6.8	19.3 x 12.2			
7	23.5 x 11.7	21.0 x 8.7	27.9 x 14.3	20.5 x 9.0	24.5 x 18.0	21.8 x 9.5	16.3 x 13.1	
8	25.9 x 10.3	32.1 x 9.9	19.3 x 11.2	20.8 x 9.2	18.5 z 12.1	13.6 x 11.0	18.8 x 10.2	25.5 x -
9 (< x)	113°	52°	51°	60°				
10 (< y)	115°	55°	61°	65°				
side	left	right	right	right	right	right	left	left

Loxodonta africana: Hwange N.P. Zimbabwe

	Misc (1)	Misc (2)	Misc (3)	Misc (4)	±20 AEY	- 4 AEY	- 1 AEY
1	148	93.5	106	125	112.0	101	76.6
2	112.6	93.5	112.1	124	153	88.1	52.6
3	196	159	169	204	195	151	103.2
4	4.6 x 2.5	4.3 x 2.4	3.1 x 2.0	4.0 x 2.8	2.4 x 2.4	5.5 x 2.7	2.0 x 1.9
5	7.2 x 0.1	5.8 x 6.4	7.6 x 5.8	6.3 x 6.0	7.0 x 6.1	8.0 x 5.4	4.0 x 3.3
6	8.2 x 10.4	3.8 x 6.3	7.4 x 4.4	5.7 x 9.3	7.8 x 7.8	4.8 x 4.8	4.5 x 2.7
7	19.3 x 12.5	12.4 x 5.3	15.3 x 7.4	18.1 x 8.5	19.0 x 11.5	15.1 x 5	
8	17.0 x 8.4	9.2 x 5.6	10.0 x 6.5	12.8 x 8.1	14.5 x 10.7	10 x 6.5	
9 (< x)	55°	28°	40°	40°	35°	48°	47°
10 (< y)	65°	33°	46°	42°	43°	55°	54°
side	left	left	right	right	right		

Table 14. Continued

THYROHYOIDS

Mammuthus columbi: Hot Springs Mammoth Site

Specimen	Length	Anterior		Center		Posterior		Side
		Width	Thickness	Width	Thickness	Width	Thickness	
83-031	[147.0]	44.5	18.0	20.8	11.8	[25.3]	15.2	left
83-009	184.0	42.9	20.4	20.8	11.8	26.1	19.8	left
MSL-428	195.0	39.6	23.3	22.7	12.4			left
83-014	(164)	39.9	17.4	24.1	12.8			left
no number				19.8	9.5			left
MSL-001	159	37.7	22.7	17.6	11.0	29.4	16.0	right
79-108				19.8	9.5			right
MSL-002		34.9	22.6	20.5	10.5			left
MSL-003						(20.8)	10.5	right

Loxodonta africana: Hwange N.P., Zimbabwe

Specimen	Length	Anterior		Center		Posterior		Side
		Width	Thickness	Width	Thickness	Width	Thickness	
(+ 40 AEY)	171	38.7	16.7	20.7	9.2	38.8	12.4	left & right
(± AEY)	175	54.9	17.4	20.7	13.8	44.8	14.2	left
(- 4 AEY)	11.6	26.5	10.3	16.4	5.2	26.2	7.2	left & right
- 1 AEY	66.0	15.5	8.1	8.4	3.5	15.8	4.9	left & right

BASIHYOIDS

Mammuthus columbi: Hot Springs Mammoth Site (measurements as for Thyrohyoids)

Specimen	Length	Anterior		Center		Posterior		Side
		Width	Thickness	Width	Thickness	Width	Thickness	
83-034	87.8	35.2	21.8	21.7	12.6	36.5	20.1	
no number	67.8	29.5	19.1	19.1	10.3	31.4	18.8	

Loxodonta africana: Hwange N.P., Zimbabwe

Specimen	Length	Anterior		Center		Posterior		Side
		Width	Thickness	Width	Thickness	Width	Thickness	
+ 40 AEY	70.3	35.9	13.2	24.6	12.2	37.4	16.9	
± 20 AEY	77.9	42.8	20.0	28.8	13.1	44.5	19.2	

rior). The thyrohyoid has nearly a 90° twist between the in-curving posterior and the out-curving anterior ends. The superior margin of the bone has a sharp (knife-edge) ridge running from anterior to posterior; the interior side tends to be flattened. A complete thyrohyoid will "sit" on the interior margin when positioned on a flat surface.

Basihyoids

Basihyoids are a "bow-tie" shaped bone which connects the anterior portions of the left and right thyrohyoids. Only three basihyoids have yet been recognized in the Hot Springs mammoth bone inventory (Figure 61). As noted in Table 14, there is a little measurable difference between *Loxodonta* and *Mammuthus* in this element.

Mandibles

A total of twelve complete and partial mandibles have been recovered from the site, to date (Figure 62).

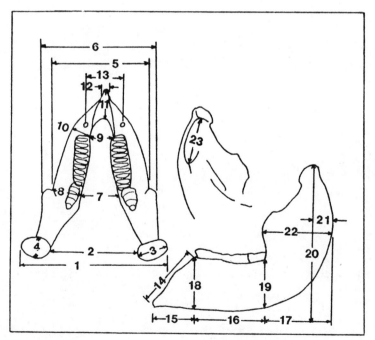

Figure 62. Diagram of a mandible illustrating the measurements used.

175

Table 15 presents the metric analyses of eleven complete, and partial, mandibles from the Hot Springs Mammoth Site. Eleven of the specimens have been given individual age assignments in African Elephant Years (AEY) using the Laws (1966) method. Four of these individuals fall in the 10-19 AEY age group, five are in the 20-29 AEY age group and two are in the 40-49 AEY age group. The age-structure analysis of the Hot Springs population places the majority of the animals in the younger two of these age groups. In addition, pelvic measurements indicate the entire measured population is composed of male animals.

Figure 63 plots the available mandibular data for length of mandible (O) and length of tooth row (X) versus the age (AEY) for the Hot Springs specimens. As might be anticipated, both the length of the mandible and the length of the tooth row increase with age.

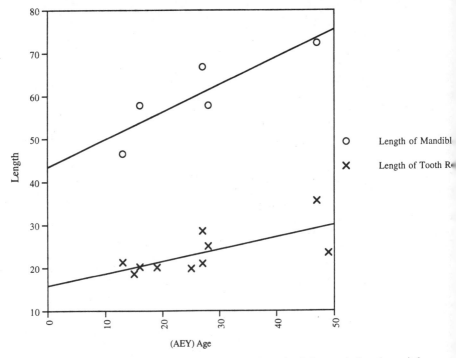

Figure 63. A plot of mandibular length and the length of the tooth (tooth row) for *M. columbi* from Hot Springs.

Table 15. Mandibular metric analysis

Field No.	Lab No.	1	2	3	4	5	6	7	8	9	10	11	12	13	14	15	16	17	18	19	20	21	22	23	(AEY) Age
NAU		67.0	48.5	9.9	7.3	51.5	50.6	10.5	19.3	9.1	10.6	15.9	4.2	7.5	29.2	11.5	21.3	13.7	20.4	13.5	47.3	9.0	30.9	21.0	13
75-108		—	—	—	—	(49.4)	(52.0)	22.7	17.3	8.75	15.3	(17.9)	(6.2)	9.8	(23.2)	(13.4)	19.8	—	19.8	19.4	—	—	(23.9)	—	25
79-089		62.3	40.6	11.3	9.1	47.3	51.2	21.3	17.6	6.2	11.8	19.8	4.8	6.2	29.1	11.3	35.5	25.5	24.5	—	—	12.8	31.8	26.6	47
Display		—	—	—	—	48.0	—	17.3	18.2	3.7	11.3	16.3	5.3	4.0	(26.1)	19.3	18.6	—	23.7	17.0	—	—	—	—	15
87-045	HS-514	—	—	—	—	(39.4)c	—	11.4c	19.0	—	15.9	—	—	—	—	—	28.5	23.8	21.5	18.5	—	—	—	—	27
	HS-275	—	—	—	—	—	—	—	—	—	—	18.0	5.5	6.6	—	—	—	—	19.6	18.2	—	12.5	28.6	—	—
	HS-141	51.3	33.6	11.6	10.4	38.5	—	19.1	16.8	6.0	10.7	—	—	—	—	—	23.4	29.7	21.3	19.5	44.7	10.5	—	—	49
89-067		51.5	29.6	11.2	7.8	48.2	45.7	10.5	15.7	5.8	15.2	—	—	—	—	—	20.1	—	—	—	—	—	—	—	19
83-110	HS-035	53.9	33.5	11.4	9.1	48.2	47.7	12.4	18.0	8.6	13.6	13.4	2.3	6.1	20.2	11.5	25.0	21.3	19.8	15.0	49.0	13.2	29.6	30.3	28
83-167	HS-071	—	—	—	9.0	43.2	(40.5)	9.8	16.8	8.2	11.3	17.0	4.5	6.4	27.5	18.3	21.0	27.5	18.7	12.0	44.5	8.4	23.8	—	27
83-215	HS-067	46.1	27.2	10.4	8.4	46.6	43.5	9.9	19.5	5.8	15.6	(13.1)	4.1	(8.3)	(29.0)	15.1	20.2	22.5	24.8	13.0	(42.5)	—	22.1	27.4	16
	HS-283	—	—	—	—	—	—	22.8	14.5	5.2	10.1	—	—	—	—	—	—	—	19.6	18.2	—	12.5	28.6	—	22

177

Teeth

Biometric data (Figure 64) on small samples of dentition of the Hot Springs mammoth fauna were presented by Dutrow (1977, 1980) with a ± 10% sample of the population as we now know it.

Dutrow's (1980) analysis of 46 teeth, assigned an age (AEY) to only eight of the specimens. Agenbroad and Mead (1987) did an age-structure analysis on the basis of 26 individuals. A more complete inventory of 83 teeth were analyzed in 1989, providing 59 ages including an age-assignment revisions of half the animals for which Dutrow (1980) determined age. The current analysis (Table 16) provides a revised age structure analysis of part of the population.

In addition, plotting the index of hypsodonty (100 ht/w) against the length/lamellae ratio places 70% of the plotted specimens within the *Mammuthus columbi* envelope as presented by Cooke (1960) and Whitmore *et al*. (1967). Of those outside that envelope 24% fall in the *Mammuthus floridanus* envelope, 1% falls in the *Mammuthus jeffersoni* envelope (1 specimen on the intersection of 3 envelopes!), and 5% (1 animal) in the *Mammuthus imperator* envelope. Maglio (1973) includes *Elephas floridanus* (*M. floridanus*) and *Mammuthus jeffersoni* as a synonym for *M. columbi*, which would mean that 95% of the plotted points (Figure 65) are within the *Mammuthus columbi* designation, substantiating our working hypothesis. *M. jeffersoni* and *M. primigenius* envelopes overlap; the recent substantiation of three *M. primigenius* specimens reduce *M. jeffersoni* further.

This sample places 82% of the study population within the juvenile and young adult age groups (Figure 66). Using modern African elephant behavioral patterns (Douglas-Hamilton 1975; Moss 1988; Haynes 1990) it appears the majority of individuals entrapped in the Hot Springs sinkhole are juvenile and young adults, which were probably representatives of the bachelor male grouping. A second group of animals appears to be old animals with most of their last tooth (M6) worn out, putting them in dietary stress. These animals could have been drawn into a dangerous situation—in spite of life experiences—by the relative abundance and quality of feed at the warm pond margins in a glacial winter. Therefore, a tentative conclusion is

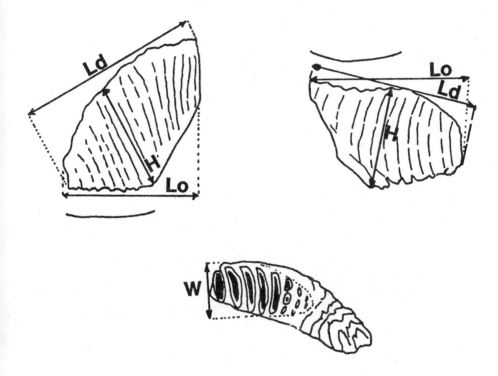

Figure 64. A profile view of a maxillary tooth (upper left diagram), a mandibular tooth (upper right diagram) and an occlusal (lower diagram) view of a mammoth tooth. Measurement positions are noted: Lo = maximum length in the occlusal plane; Ld = maximum length in a diagonal plane; H = maximum height of tooth parallel to plate orientation; W = maximum width (can be taken as Wc = with the cement thickness on both sides of the tooth, or We = maximum width of the largest enamel plate). The curved line below the maxillary tooth and above the mandibular tooth are indicative of the convex occlusal surface (maxillary) and the concave occlusal surface (mandible) of the teeth. The dotted line in the occlusal view indicates the occlusal surface, with those portions outside this line having not yet come into wear. The dark areas are exposed dentine. The front of the tooth is to the left in all views. (Modified from Saunders 1970).

Table 16. Dental metrics: Hot Springs Mammoth Site.

Field #	Lab #	Side	PL	A	Lg	Ht	W	En	C	Lf	R	IH	Max	Mand	AEY Age
	HS00141	L	12	12	208		89	3.2	7	7	17.33			6	49
76-380	HS00336				157		104	2.4		8					27
76-227		R	14	11	195		81.3	1.9		7.19	13.93			5	15
76-364		R	13	12	189		72.3	1.96	2.7	6.7	14.54			4	15
76-375		L	9	9	210		89	2		6.25	23.33			5	22
76-372		L	5	5	223		82	2.5	2.8	5.66	44.6		5		28
					202		84.8						6		49
	HS00140														
87-045	HS00514	L	12	12	255		106	4.4	13.1	5.5	21.25	158.5		5	27
75-108		R	15	8	201		83	2.5	3.6	8	13.4	160.6		5	25
77-148	HS00204	L & R	13	13	214		99	2.6	6.6	7.5	16.46	139.4	5		30
83-166	HS00070	R	14	14	195		86	3.1	3.7	7.5	13.93		5		27
83-167	HS00071	L	13	13	199		75	4.4	4.7	6.5	15.31			5	27
83-215	HS00067	R	12	12	185		80	3.8	6.2	7	15.42	150.0		4	16
83-110	HS00035	L & R	12	12	200		83	2.6	6.4	8	16.67			5	28
83-181	HS00017	R	11	11	200		89	2.4	7.9	6	18.18	206.7	5		28
		R	9	9	179		81	3.7	4.21	6	19.89			4	15
	HS00326	L	13	13	193		90	3.4	5.6	6.5	14.85			5	27
87-216	HS00406	R	13	13	204		76.1	2.9		8.5	15.65		5		28
87-038	HS00490	L.	11	11	186		81.1	4.2	4.2	5.5	16.91	164.0		4	15
	HS00293	L & R	11	11	185		84	3.5	3.9	7	16.82	159.5	5		28
	HS00283	L	10	10	210		87	2.6	8.8	6.5	21			5	22
79-203	HS00147	L	11	11	185		90	2.5	5.9	7.5	16.77	152.2	5		27
79-265	HS00154	L	9	9	182		82.8	2.3	9.6	9	20.17		5		24
	HS00479	R	13	13	169		105	3.6		10.5	13		6		49
79-089			17	14	294	37	100	4.2	2	5.5	17.29			6	47
76-380		R	12	12	165		104	1.7	1.3	9	13.75		6		54
	HS00364	L	16	6	223	177	97	3.9	7.6	7	13.94	182.5	6		38
89-002		L & R	12	12	176		98	3.9	9.6	7	14.67		5		28
85-005		L	9	10	181		81	3.9	4.9	6	20.11			4	15
83-190	HS00026		13	10	200		80	3.6	2.35	7	15.38			5	27
89-001			11	11	139		79	3.2	5.6	8	12.64			4	19
86-036	HS00203	L & R	12	12	203		112	3.2	7	8	16.92	111.6	5		30
76-364		R	12	12	189		78	2.8		7	15.75			4	18
85-004		R	12	12	212		92	2.5	6.5	7	17.67	208.7	5		28
		R	13	5	242		103	3	6.8	6	18.62	225.0	6		36
75-117		R	11	11	165		91	2.9	4.2	6.5	15.0			4	18
		R	13	4	229		88	1.9		7	17.62			6	33
89-062		L & R	10	10	149		78.5	1.9	6.1	7	14.9		5		28
89-167		L & R	12	12	207		68	3.0	2.9	7.5	17.25			5	27
77-144		L			205		92						5		27
85-002	MSL744	L	13	13	177.5	172	82	2.2		7	13.65	209.8		5	26
85-004		R	11	11	(132)	(122)	99	2.7		7.5	14.3	113.2		5	28

that adventurous juvenile and young adult males, and older animals in dietary stress were the most common victims of the Hot Springs Mammoth Site sinkhole.

With the African human population explosion and increasing demand for land for agricultural use, large free-roaming herbivores such as elephants became endangered. Many African countries established national parks or game preserves. To prevent over-crowding (over-populating) these resources, a program of culling (cropping) the elephant herds was initiated. This slaughter of wild elephants produced large study populations for interested researchers. Since Laws (1966) published his research on establishing the individual age of *Loxodonta africana* from the length, width, and stage of wear of mandibular teeth, that data has been used for estimating *Mammuthus* age. Although the African elephant is less like the mammoth than is the Asian elephant, they are being killed off in large numbers, for the reasons expressed above. Asian elephants (*Elephas*

180

maximus) was the domesticated "bulldozer" of Asian forests; it had a high (live) economic value, and was not experiencing the "crowding" by agricultural demands as was its African cousin. The result is that only recently (Roth and Shoshani 1988) has similar dental data become available for *E. maximus*.

Researchers working with *Mammuthus* have long realized the closer physiologic resemblance of these animals to *Elephas*, yet the dental comparison was most complete for *Loxodonta*. Hence we used Laws' (1966) method, almost exclusively, applying a numerical age for an individual in African elephant years (AEY). The Hot Springs population is no exception, although we used a second method proposed by Gary Haynes, as a cross-check (Agenbroad and Mead 1987).

The methodology of dental measurement and age assignment used for the Hot Springs Columbian mammoth population is similar to that used by Laws (1966) for African elephant studies. Figure 64 indicates the methodology for tooth measurement; tables (Table 17) of length-width tooth assignments for maxillary and mandibular dentition of the Hot Springs mammoth teeth are presented in Figure 67 (after Saunders 1970; Graham 1986). The use of Laws (1966) age assignment diagrams provides the age of the individual specimen in African elephant years (AEY), for *Mammuthus columbi*. A theoretical concept, based on a closer biologic relationship of *Mammuthus primigenius* and *Elephas maximus*, was that an age sequence based on dental comparisons with the Asian elephant should be a better model. Until 1988, such a data base for *E. maximus* was lacking (Roth and Shoshani 1988). Comparison of the Hot Springs *M. columbi* dental metrics with those of *E. maximus* indicates a greater divergence, as a model, than the use of *Loxodonta africana*.

Conversations and correspondence with Roth indicates there may be a difference in measurement techniques, such as illustrated in Figure 64. The major difference appears to be the orientation of the measurement for length of the tooth. In the method used by Roth and Shoshani (1988) and Saunders (1970) the length of a tooth is measured perpendicular to the long axis of an individual enamel plate

Table 17. Average Values of length and width of proboscidean teeth for M4 through M6 (values in mm).

*Elephas maximus (Roth & Shoshani 1988)	Mammuthus columbi (Saunders 1970)	Mammuthus columbi (Graham 1986)	Mammuthus columbi (Agenbroad 1990)	*Loxodonta africana (Laws 1966)
n=84	n=39	n=53	n=59	n=88
L = 241.3	213.5	210.0	195.0	194.7
W = 72.6	79.1	72.2	89.8	69.0

* = extrapolated data from published charts.

(also the height of the specimen). This length measurement is greater than, and at an angle to, a length measurement taken parallel to the occlusal surface. However, in the Hot Springs Mammoth Site population, the majority of the teeth are still *in situ* in the jaw preventing a length measurement as indicated in the method used by Saunders, Roth, and Shoshani. In specimens where portions of the maxilla, or mandible, have been removed, it is also possible to determine a greater tooth length than in teeth surrounded by undamaged bone.

Since the majority of the dental population at Hot Springs is *in situ* in the jaw, as well as *in situ* in the excavated portion of the bone bed, we have adapted the methodology of other investigators applied to our *in situ* population. Length of tooth measurements are determined parallel to the occlusal surface (Lo) for the Hot Springs population. Even with this recognized methodological difference, the length of *E. maximus* teeth is considerably greater than *M. columbi*. Similarly, the width of the tooth (with no difference in methodology of measurement) is considerably smaller in *E. maximus*. This is indicative of an evolutionary lengthening and narrowing of dentition in *E. maximus*, as contrasted to *M. columbi*. It is also indicative that *L. africana* serves as a better analog for comparison to *M. columbi* than does *E. maximus*. This conclusion, based on different criteria, has also been proposed by Haynes (1990). Perhaps an extensive dental metric analysis of *M. primigenius* as compared, or contrasted, to *E. maximus* and *M. columbi* would shed some light on this difference.

The methodological difference noted above is probably more pronounced in mandibular teeth due to the compressional forces producing more curved enamel plates, caused by lack of vertical space in the jaw, as contrasted to maxillary teeth.

With several recently published sets of data on length versus width plots and age assignments (AEY) available for mammoth (Dutrow [using Saunders unpublished data] 1980); (Graham [using Graham

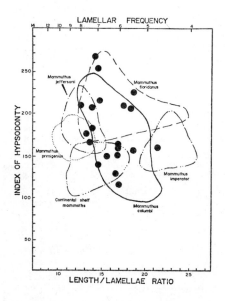

Figure 65. Variation in hypsodonty (ordinate) and lamellae compression (abscissae) of molars referred to *Mammuthus columbi* from Hot Springs (after Cooke 1960; and in Whitmore *et al.* 1967; Saunders 1970)

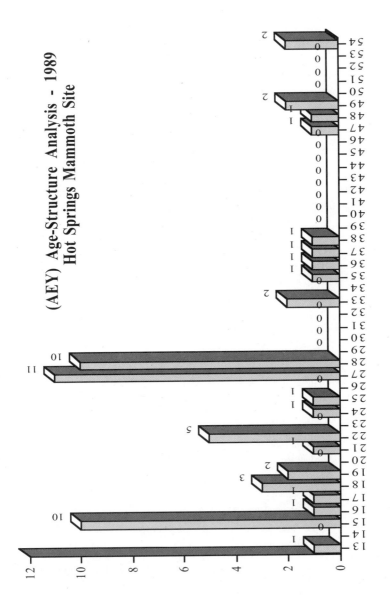

Figure 66. Age Structure analysis (AEY) in 1989.

184

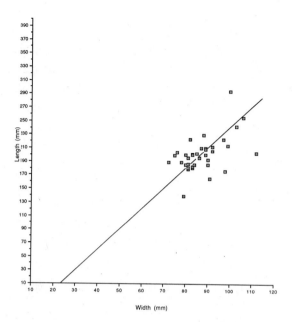

Figure 67. Mandibular & Maxillary Teeth length-width graph for *M. columbi* from Hot Springs.

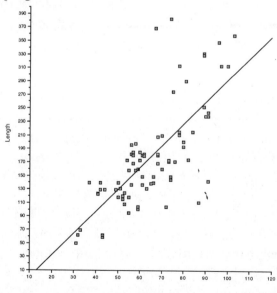

Figure 68. Length vs. width of *M. columbi* teeth: Graham and Saunders (*in* Graham 1986).

185

and Saunders field data] 1986) and the *Elephas maximus* data (Roth and Shoshani 1988) it was possible to examine the Hot Springs mammoth population, contrasting these methodologies. Roth and Shoshani (1988; 568) state, "...although for many fossil taxa (such as *Mammuthus*) the Asian elephant is a more appropriate living analogue....".

Extrapolation of the Graham and Saunders (Graham 1986), Roth and Shoshani (1988), and Laws (1966) graphs provided comparative data for large mammoth, Asian elephant and African elephant populations. Plotting these data (Figures 68-69-70) and the mammoth data from Hot Springs in a similar format, it became apparent that there was considerable spread, and overlap, in the data points. More significantly, the lines of best fit for each data plot were displaced (Figure 71). Whereas *Loxodonta africana* and *Mammuthus columbi* (Southwest and Great Plains) data sets are very similar both *Elephas maximus* and *Mammuthus columbi* (Hot Springs population) are divergent—in opposite directions. More simply stated, *Elephas maximus* dentition is longer and narrower than any of the other groups; *Mammuthus columbi* from Hot Springs have wider and shorter teeth than the other populations; and *Loxodonta africana* and *Mammuthus columbi* from the Southwest and Great Plains are the most similar in a length/width comparison of dentition.

The conclusion of this comparison is that *Loxodonta* is a better corollary for *Mammuthus columbi* than *Elephas*, at least for age determination by dentition. A plot of tooth-in-wear versus age (Figure 72) also indicates a closer correlation between *Mammuthus* and *Loxodonta*, contrary to the supposed better correlation with *Elephas*. In comparing mandibular teeth of *Loxodonta, Elephas, M. columbi* (Saunders 1970; unpublished data as it appears in Dutrow, 1980), and *M. columbi* from Hot Springs (Figure 73) striking dissimilarities are noted in length and width of *Elephas* teeth compared to length and width in the combined *M. columbi* populations. A similar plot of maxillary teeth from these populations provides analogous disparities. In some cases, *Elephas* mandibular teeth (M6) are as much as 50 mm longer and 20 mm narrower than the corresponding

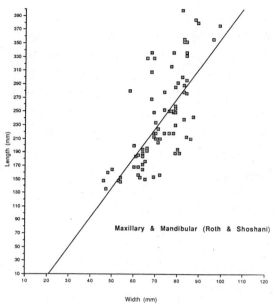

Figure 69. Length versus width of *Elephas maximus* teeth [extrapolated from Figure 3 Roth and Shoshani (1988)].

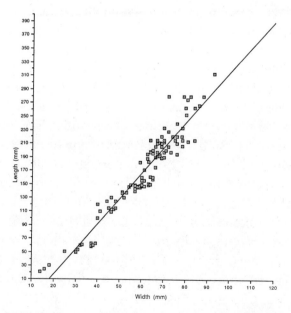

Figure 70. Length versus width of *Loxodonta africana* (Laws 1966).

187

Mammuthus molar. Similar ranges of difference are noted in maxillary teeth. Both the *Elephas* and *M. columbi* from the Southwest and Great Plains are derived from a large geographic distribution of all ages of animals. The Hot Springs data reflects a local population from a restricted geographic range. Furthermore, the Hot Springs material is selective for the 10-30 year age group. These comparisons begin to show that tooth-in-wear designations may vary as much as 30 mm in *Elephas/Mammuthus* comparisons. Part of the variability may be due to the *Mammuthus* data having been generated using Laws' criteria. This does not account for the length and width anomalies, however. Table 17 provides averages of length and width for the dentition of the sample populations, and is indicative of the same disparities noted graphically, above. On the basis of these data sets it appears that *A. loxodonta* dental metrics and age assignments more closely reflect *M. columbi* than do *E. maximus*.

AGE PROFILE

Haynes refers to 12 year intervals in mammoth and elephant populations (Haynes 1990). Using his 12 year groupings, he sees three age profiles in extinct populations: 1) Type A: subadults dominate; stable or expanding population; 2) Type B: subadults dominate but out number mature animals (mass death); 3) Type C: Prime adults predominate, subadults are rare; a fourth type: 4) Type D: is composed of small assemblages for which an age profile is not clear.

The Hot Springs deposit does not clearly fit any of the types described above, although Haynes (1990) has assigned Hot Springs to Type C. An age structure analysis of the Hot Springs population was conducted in 1987 (Agenbroad and Mead) and again in 1990 (Agenbroad). Using both the individual age plot (Figure 66) (Laws 1966), 10 year age groupings (Figure 74) and Haynes' 12 year age-grouping plots, it is clear that the Hot Springs assemblage is dominated by juvenile and young-adult animals; specifically, animals in the 10-19 and 20-29 age groupings.

188

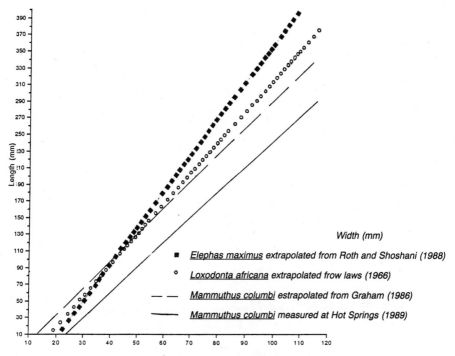

Figure 71. Average (Line of best fit). values of length versus width for large samples of proboscidean teeth.

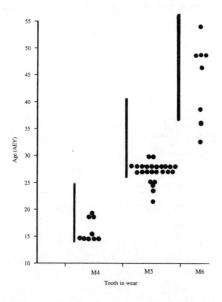

Figure 72. Age (AEY) versus tooth-in-wear at the Hot Springs Mammoth Site. Vertical bar = L. africana; ● = M. columbi from the Hot Springs Mammoth Site.

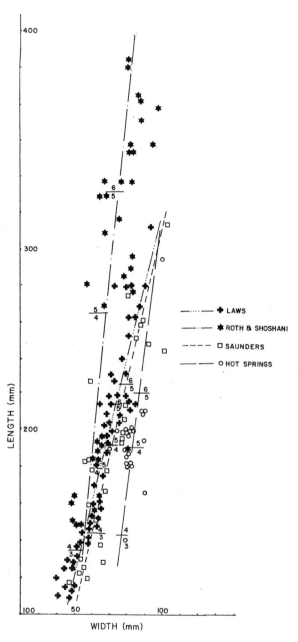

Figure 73. A comparison of *Elephas maximus* (Roth and Shoshani 1988), *Loxodonta africana* (Laws 1966), and *Mammuthus columbi* (Saunders, in Dutrow 1980; Hot Springs this report) mandibular dentition. Note that divisions between M4, M5, M6 are similar for *Loxodonta* and *Mammuthus*, but much elongated for *Elephas*.

190

Comparisons

New World Paleontological Sites: The mastodon (*Mammut americanum*) deposits of Trolinger Spring and Boney Spring, Missouri (Saunders 1977) total 9 and 31 animals, respectively. Although not a sinkhole trap, such as Hot Springs, the spring bog did trap mastodons, in a non-archaeological context. The age-distribution patterns of these paleontological assemblages were used as a comparison for the Hot Springs assemblage. Both of the mastodon localities show a predominance of mature animals (Figure 75). In contrast, the Hot Springs assemblage is represented by greater than 80% of the animals falling in the 10-19 and 20-29 year age categories, a selection for immature and young-adult animals.

Archaeological Assemblages: USSR. Using data provided by Soffer (1985) plots of age-structure for mammoth populations from four Upper Paleolithic archaeological sites were plotted for comparison to the Hot Springs assemblage (Figure 76). The paleolithic assemblages are skewed toward younger age groups in the population. Hot Springs is similar in the 10-19 and >30 year old age group, but notably different in the 20-29 year old age-set.

Soffer (1985) provides composite data for Old World archaeological sites, New World archaeological sites and modern African elephant data. Comparing these age-set groups, it is obvious, again, that the Hot Springs assemblage is anomalous with nearly twice the frequency of animals in the 20-29 year age group.

Tusks

Tusks were measured using three criteria: 1) total medial curvilinear length; 2) diameter of tusk base at the alveolar margin, or base of tusk, if free of the alveolus; 3) straight-line distance from the tip to the base, or alveolar margin (Table 18). Not all specimens are totally exposed, and not all are complete. Still others had been broken in life, exhibit near wear bevels in the process of formation, and do not represent true length of the tusk. Figure 77 depicts tusk frequency versus basal diameter; Figure78 is a similar graph of tusk length versus tusk frequency. Figure 79 is a plot of the straight-line base to tip

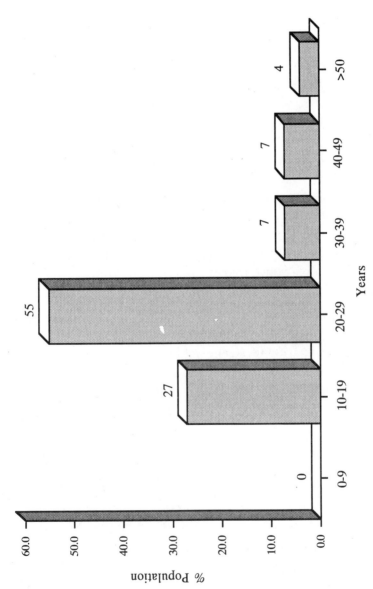

Figure 74. Age-Structure analysis: percent frequency versus 10 year age sets at the Hot Springs Mammoth Site.

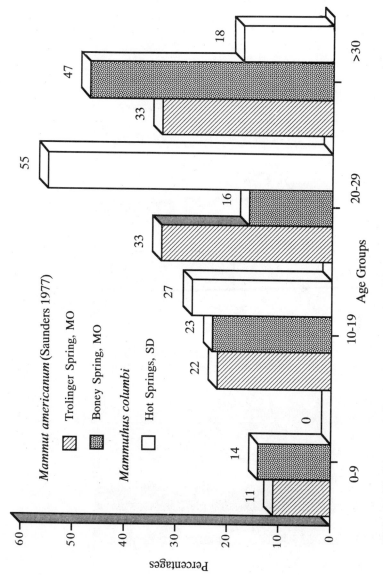

Figure 75. Age group distribution in North American paleontological proboscidean localities

193

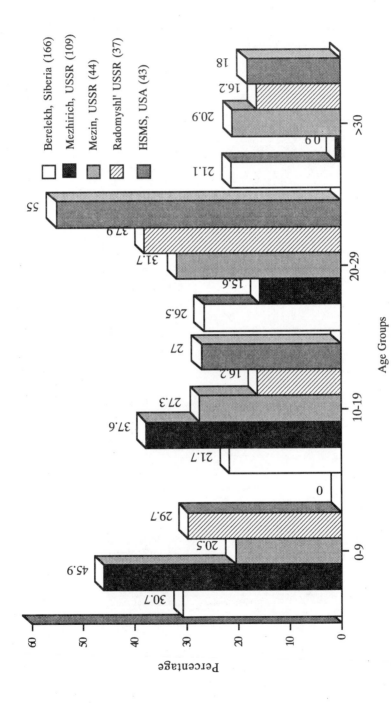

Figure 76. Comparison of Hot Springs Mammoth Population and Soviet archaeological localities (after Soffer 1985).

Table 18. Tusk Metrics, Hot Springs Mammoth Site

Specimen	Side	Curve measurement (cm)		Straight line measurement (cm)		base diameter (cm)	
		Alveolus-tip	base-tip	Alveolus-tip	base-tip	alveolus	base
90-061	R		170		135		
Open cast	R		200		140		14.8
Cast w/pipe	L				158		
Cast w/2x4	R		185		120		
Cast w/blue pipe	L		175		135		
140	L	170		110		18.9	
79-217	R	125		109		14.1	
79-217	L	120		110		13.8	
147	L	105		88		14.3	
79-173	R						20.6
77-147	R	135		120	158	17.7	
	L	145		118		16.8	
206	L	143		120		16.8	
168	R		148				18.7
281	L		148				20.7
284	R		187				17.7
297	R	150	193	120			16.1
301	R		200		177		18.5
308	R		277		173		22.7
306	L		190		143		20.6
89-005	R		170		130		16.6
361	L		205		165		19.1
79-153	L		191		155		19.2
017(82-181)	L	109		95		20.6	
018	R						19.3
042			186		150		22.5
070	L	130		92		19.4	
168							18.8
074	R	93		71		14.1	
324	L		275		165		22.2
319							12.5
Display			117	107			16.1
Anderson			180	131	143		
89-061			218		166		.224
NAU			97		95		10.4
TISK			197	161	153		16.7
T6SK			203				15.4

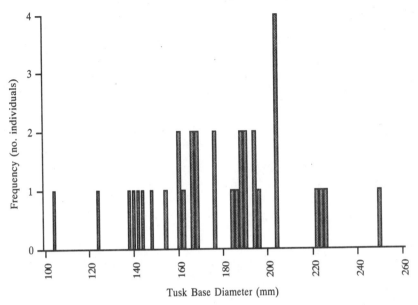

Figure 77. Tusk basal diameter versus frequency at Hot Springs.

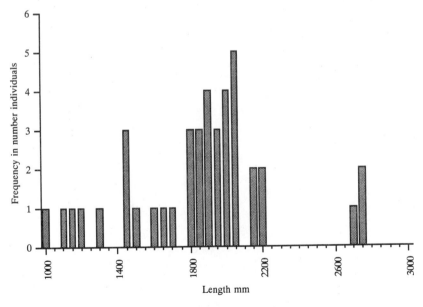

Figure 78. Tusk length frequency at Hot Springs.

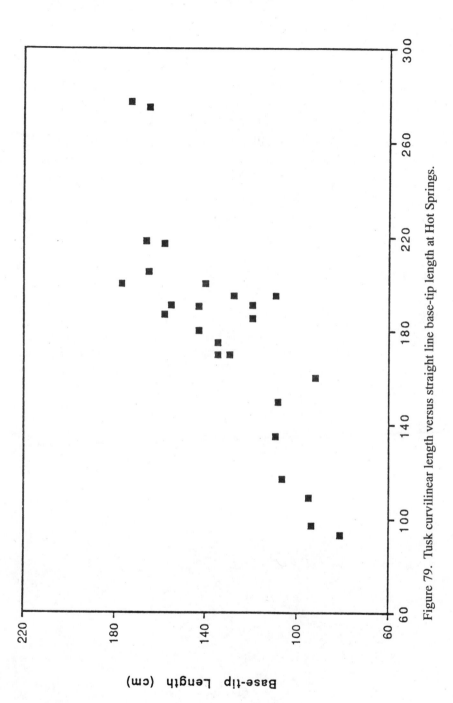

Figure 79. Tusk curvilinear length versus straight line base-tip length at Hot Springs.

length of a tusk plotted against the medial curvilinear length of the same tusk. It is tempting to infer sexual dimorphism from this plot, but considering the age-structure analysis, and not knowing the AEY age of isolate tusks, it would be impossible to determine juvenile males from adult females on these criteria alone. Also, the pelvic ratios support a large population of juvenile and young adult males (Lister and Agenbroad this volume). Two very large isolate tusks can be identified, on metric characteristics, alone, as belonging to the same animal.

Scapula

Table 19 and Figure 80 provide metric attributes of twenty-three nearly complete scapulae from the site. Only two specimens can be assigned individual age, preventing any meaningful size vs. age analyses at this point. Knowing the age-structure of the Hot Springs population, however, the specimens are derived from juvenile and young adult mammoths.

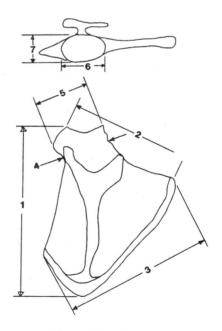

Figure 80. Metric attributes of the scapula.

Table 19. Scapula measurements of *Mammuthus columbi* from Hot Springs, South Dakota.

Field No.	HSMS#	1	2	3	4	5	6	7	Side	Age
86-042	HS-263	–	755	–	309	327	(242)	137	lft	
75-107(T5)		849	–	–	293	285	239	162	lft	
79-257	HS-131	992	831	1038	301	325	262	166	rt	47AEY
86-088	HS-249	–	635	–	266	303	239	147	lft	
83-187	HS-066	1047	823	1111	214	311	267	162	rt	
83-169	HS-091	980	698	833	273	283	234	142	rt	27 AEY
83-182	HS-001	803	660	763	234	299	223	142	rt	
	HS-347	798	720	–	247	275	236	120	rt	
87-098		949	734	815	285	343	251	–	lft	
Cast T_1		867.5	695	750	249	311	261	131.5	rt	
Cast T_2		918	722	900	287	265	240	131.5	rt	
Cast T_3		941	(730)	(643)	263	(276)	258	(156)	rt	
Cast T_4		879	680	870	301	316	283	174	lft	
Cast T_5		849	–	–	293	285	239	162	lft	
Cast T_6		900	621	(800)	257	245	217	170	rt	
Lab Cast		875	701	839	269	–	269	140	rt	
Cast		869	702	(797)	277	(263)	231	146	lft	
Cast		985	797	868	267	–	296	–	rt	
83-107		–	477	(718)	(254)	(269)	218	212	lft	
74-049		(875)	520	828	267	271	219	–	rt	
79-268		(995)	602	813	305	–	–	192	rt	
87-098		949	734	815	285	343	251	–	lft	
77-197		–	–	841	(260)	–	–	–	lft	

Humeri

Measurement of the exposed humeri (Table 20) of Hot Springs mammoth population that has been exposed to date reveal two significant pieces of information: 1) shoulder height of nine animals has been calculated using the method of Harington *et al.* (1974); 2) there are 45% less humeri than scapulas in the exposed portion of the bone bed.

Shoulder height calculations changed the "sex" of one animal from the western side of the pit. This headless animal was nicknamed "Marie Antoinette" by the field crew of 1983. The animal is laying on its left side, fully exposing the articulated right half of the skeleton, from the caudal vertebra to the atlas vertebrae. The specimen is lacking the skull, however, hence the name. Shoulder height calculations based on humerus length, plus a cross-check using the elements of the right foreleg for this animal yield a skeletal shoulder height of 3.76 m (12.39 ft), and an estimated live height of 3.94 m (12.92 ft). This is the largest animal in the measured population, which precludes it being female (Figure 81). Haynes (1990) states that adult African elephants stature may be 1/5 to 1/3 greater in males, than females, whereas the weight may be as great as double the female weight. Using this criteria, #132 (Napoleon) is nearly 1/5 larger than #485. Napoleon was ± 49 (AEY) whereas #485 was 27 AEY at the time of death. Figure 82 indicates the relative displacement of these two animals of known age on the shoulder height curve, however the base of tusk values (Figure 77) indicate #70 slightly larger, with a shorter, less curved tusk. Until additional criteria are available, it would be risky to assign sex characteristics based on shoulder height, alone.

Stature

On the basis of measured skeletal shoulder height for three of nine individuals, and the calculated shoulder height using Harington's method (1974) of all nine individuals (Table 21) the range of height for Hot Springs mammoth can be determined. Figure 83 depicts the minimum (294.1 cm; 9.75 ft), average (338.1 cm; 11.2 ft), and maxi-

Table 20. Measurements of humeri of *Mammuthus columbi* from Hot Springs, South Dakota.

Field/Lab No.	1	2	3	4	5	6	Fusion
83-171/076	1300	843	1260	159	159	367	F
83-234/077		793			327	348	N/F
83-187/069	1288	968	1276	168	290	269	F
83-248/047	1191	894	1108	115	336		F
79-238/485					260		F
87-092/525				158	312		F
76-52/		940		140	318	288	N/F
/132	1225	952	1207	167	333	288	F
/139				154			F
79-269						272	
74-141/						258	
77-51/		618		112			N
77-36/MSL 026						243	F

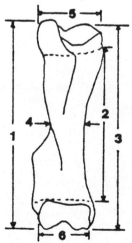

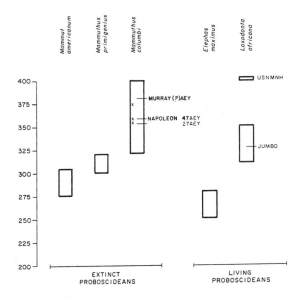

Figure 81. Graphic representation of proboscidean shoulder height (after Haynes 1990).

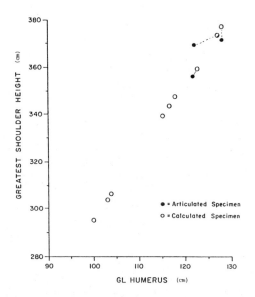

Figure 82. Shoulder height calculated from the greatest length of the humerus of Hot Springs mammoths (after Harington *et al.* 1974).

Table 21. Humerus length and calculated shoulder height for Hot Springs mammoths.

Specimen	GL humerus	Calculated shoulder (Skeletal) height		Estimated height with skin & tissue	
		(mm)	(ft)	(mm)	(ft)
067	1280	3765	12'5"	3929	12'11"
132	1222	3594	11'10"	3755	12'4"
485	1000	2941	9'8"	3124	10'4"
Display	1180	3471	11'5"	3633	11'11"
076	1270	3735	12'3"	3898	12'9"
077	1033	3038	10'0"	3197	10'6"
79-040	1040	3059	10'1"	3219	10'7"
221	1155	3397	11'2"	3560	11'8"

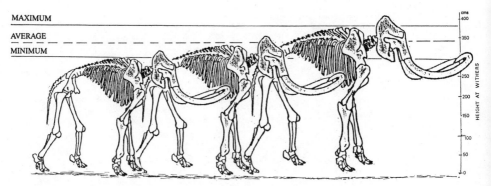

Figure 83. Maximum, median, and minimum stature of the Hot Springs mammoths.

203

mum (376.5 cm; 12.39 ft) skeletal shoulder heights for the nine individuals.

Radius/Ulna

Table 22 provides metric data for eleven radii. Table 23 provides similar data for five ulnae from the exposed portion of the Mammoth Site population. Approximately half of the epypheses are fused in each case, indicative of the juvenile and young adult composition of the population of the site.

Table 22. Measurements of Radii of *Mammuthus columbi* from Hot Springs, South Dakota (measurements in mm).

Field/Lab No.	1	2	3	4	Fusion
76-331/MSL 216		410/520		138	N/F
79-58		/670		116	F
77-029				105	F
74-5/		540/610		111	F
76-185		450/690		121	F
		330/520		110	N/F
78-043/		590/750		162	N/F
79-159			220		N
		520/710		145	N/F
/00143			168		F
/00129		/690			F

Table 23. Measurements of ulnae of *Mammuthus columbi* from Hot Springs, South Dakota (measurements in mm).

Field/Lab No.	1	2	3	4	5	6	7	Fusion
"Display"		740	223	200	273	115/138	270	F/N
/143	110		208	257	274	/50		F/N
78-161/223	976		221	330	386		2760	F
79-221/089	864		192	318	194	99/107		F
86-053/411		725	200					F/N

Pelvi

A total of 21 pelvi were utilized in a metric analysis of this post-cranial element in the Hot Springs Mammoth Site population. Using a model proposed by Lister (1989; Lister and Agenbroad this volume) the pelvis provided a quantitative method for sexual determination of the mammoth population. These data are presented in the following chapter.

Femora

Metric attributes of sixteen complete and partial femora are presented in Table 24. Two-thirds of the sample are unfused, characteristic of the youth of the mammoth population, and the fusion sequence of long bones.

Table 24. Measurements of femora of *Mammuthus columbi* from Hot Springs, South Dakota (measurements in mm).

Field/Lab No.	1	2	3	4	5	6	Fusion
/221	1147	98/145	295	284	244	173	F
/244		105/199	373			189	F
76-408/289				289			N
"V"	1308	–/137	372				F
83-105/008	1274	99/163		159	172	114	F
77-20/				315			N
86-076/439	1260	176	370	334	177	105	F
/093	1317	161	319		167	88	F
76-378/					203	134	N
T3B					180	121	N
76-98/					174	104	N
76-276/MSL227					206	123	N
83-026/MSL144					185	105	N
78-040/					210	124	N
76-173/				232			N
T2B/					191	121	N

Fibulae/Tibiae

Table 25 provides the metric data for the five fibulae recovered from the site, to date. Metric data for the three tibiae are presented in Table 26.

Table 25. Measurements of fibulae of *Mammuthus columbi* from Hot Springs, South Dakota (measurements in mm).

Field/Lab No.	1	2	3	4	5	Fusion
83-086/MSL 168				94/113		F
/MSL219		5125	450			N
76-63/					60/86	N
T2F		5690	330/456			N
76-144		5750	445/500			N

Table 26. Measurements of tibiae of *Mammuthus columbi* from Hot Springs, South Dakota (measurements in mm).

Field/Lab No.	1	2	3	5	Fusion
74/115/MSL017				164/183	N
76-41/				162/184	N
T1T				165/204	N

Chapter 10

GENDER DETERMINATION OF THE
HOT SPRINGS MAMMOTHS

Adrian M. Lister and Larry D. Agenbroad

Determining the gender of proboscideans in fossil assemblages can be important both for understanding the taphonomy of the site, and for interpreting size and other features of individuals which may be affected by sexual dimorphism. Except in the very rare cases where soft tissue preservation allows examination of genitals (in some specimens from the Siberian permafrost: Garutt 1964), gender determination relies on three criteria: size and robusticity of the skeleton, dimensions of the tusks and their alveoli, and morphology of the pelvis.

Gender determination based on the size of isolated skeletal elements in proboscideans is tenuous. Male and female bones differ in mean size, giving a bimodal distribution in a large sample, but there is overlap in the ranges of the two genders so that except for very large and very small individuals, isolated bones are difficult to place. The problem is exacerbated if the assemblage covers a range of individual ages, because of the prolonged growth period and late epiphysis fusion of elephants. Females' long bones tend to fuse earlier than those of males, allowing greater height potential for the latter (Haynes 1990). Does a small femur belong to a female, or to an immature male? Bones with full epiphysis fusion must be chosen for comparison, but this reduces the sample size, and may still not give clear determination. If complete limbs or skeletons of mature animals are available, these should provide the clearest gender difference in size, as the dimorphism in the individual bones is summed. However, there is the further problem of variation in body size between populations, making it impossible to define a universal yardstick of how large or small a male or female of a particular species should be.

The dimensions of tusks and their alveoli are of greater value in gender determination. Vereshchagin and Tichonov (1986) showed that in a large sample of *Mammuthus primigenius*, there was separation between males and females in a scatter of tusk length versus basal diameter, the males having relatively more robust tusks, while those of females were both smaller overall and more gracile. This difference is also reflected in the morphology of the tusk alveoli of the skull, which tend to be broader and more divergent in males than in females. Again, the picture may be confused in assemblages containing a mixture of ages, and also by the reduction in tusk length due to distal wear during life. Nonetheless, the massive basal diameters of the majority of tusks at Hot Springs (more than three-quarters have diameters of 160 cm or above (Figure 77) suggest a predominantly male assemblage.

A third criterion for gender determination has recently been explored by Lister (in press a). Using specimens of Eurasian *M. primigenius* and *M. meridionalis*, mostly with some independent evidence of gender (genitals, tusks/alveoli and size), he found that the most reliable index for sexual identification was the ratio between the diameter of the pelvic aperture and the width of the ilium (Figure 84). Females give a higher ratio than males, the biological basis for this being: 1) a larger pelvic aperture for birthing in the female, and 2) increased robusticity of the ilium for muscle attachment in the male. Since this difference is followed in both *M. primigenius* and *M. meridionalis* (the latter being the probable ancestor of both *M. primigenius* and *M. columbi* (Maglio 1973), it seems reasonable to assume that a similar pattern would hold true in *M. columbi*. Ilium width is most reliably measured at its narrowest point, the constriction of the shaft above the acetabulum (measure 5), which is a repeatable and rarely abraded point of measurement. In complete pelves, the size of the aperture can be quantified as its maximum width (measure 3). In half pelves, an estimate of this measurement can be made, but an alternative measure, the oblique height of

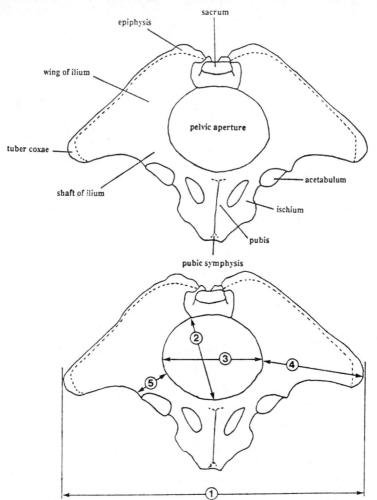

Figure 84. Measurements taken on *Mammuthus* pelves. Measures 1-5 correspond to those of Lister (in press a). the measurements used to determine gender in this study are: (2) oblique height of pelvic aperture (birth canal), from pubic symphysis to the lowest point of the sacral attachment, and (5) minimum width of ilium shaft.

the canal from the pubic symphysis to the lowest point of the sacral scar (measure 2), is preferred. It is more rigorous, and gives an equally clear separation of males and females in conjunction with ilium shaft width. Lister (in press a) found that for Eurasian *Mammuthus*, the ratio between measure 2 and measure 5 gave values ranging between approximately 1.4-2.4 in males, and 2.4-3.2 in females (Figure 85).

Table 27. Measurements on pelvic bones from Hot Springs. All measurements in milimeters. Where both left and right sides of the girdle were available, measurements were taken on both sides, and an average calculated if the two halves differed. Measurements in brackets are estimates on incomplete specimens.

Specimen	Side(s)	1	2	3	4	5	2/5	Fusion
MSL-790	L	(1580)	360	460	560	200	1.80	N
MSL-792	R	(1660)	380	480	590	245	1.55	F
MSL-113	L	(1440)	350	400	520	235	1.49	N
MSL-766	L					235		
MSL-775	R							
MSL-137	R		(340)		550	185	(1.84)	N
MSL-774	R					215		
HS-389/391	L+R				(640)			
HS-034	L		360	440		195	1.85	N
HS-441	L					(220)		N
89-046	L+R	1580	320	415	560	210	1.52	F
HS-112	L+R	(1820)	460	490	630	255	1.80	F
HS-002	R	(1600)	430	(460)	640	245	1.76	?F
HS-227	L+R	1650	380	495	570	225	1.69	F
HS-240	R	(1580)	370	(430)	550	260	1.42	N
HS-307	L	(1500)	390	(450)	540	205	1.90	F
HS-303	L	(1500)	370	(420)	530	212	1.75	N
HS-365	L+R	1460	490	540	530	210	2.33	F
HS-341	R	(1580)	400	(440)	630	245	1.63	F
HS-350						222		
unnumbered					586	234		

Table 28. Measurements on pelvic bones from Dent, Colorado.

1450-81/78	L		470			184	2.55	
1450-84	L		533			216	2.47	

Five complete pelves (left and right sides preserved) have so far been exposed in the Hot Springs bone bed, and an additional sixteen measurable half-pelves, separated because the pubis was not fused or had broken. Measurements are given in Table 27. It was not possible to take all measurements on many of the specimens, in some cases due to breakage, in others because they are exhibited *in situ* and are incompletely excavated or are overlain by other fossils. However, oblique aperture height and ilium shaft width could be obtained on fourteen pelves. Their ratio is plotted in Figure 85, in comparison with Eurasian *M. primigenius* and *M. meridionalis* samples.

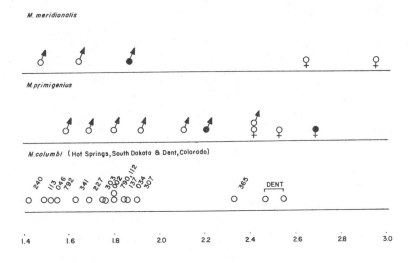

Figure 85. The ratio of pelvic aperture height (measure 2) to ilium shaft width (measure 5). Each symbol represents one specimen. The upper two lines show samples of *M. meridionalis* and *M. primigenius,* from Lister (in press a). Open symbols are specimens with some evidence of gender independent of the pelvis. The gender of one of the *M. primigenius* specimens with ratio 2.42 (Adams' mammoth from the Lena River, Siberia) is debatable (Lister in press a). The bottom line shows *M. columbi* from Hot Springs and Dent.

All except one of the Hot Springs specimens plots clearly in the male range of the spectrum. The single exception (HS-365) falls approximately at the boundary between the male and female ranges of the Eurasian sample, but in view of its clear biometric distance from the other Hot Springs pelves, and the position of its clear biometric distance from the other Hot Springs pelves, and the position of the latter towards the 'super-male' region of the Eurasian scatter, this specimen may represent the only female pelvis from the site. It is notable that this pelvis is also one of the smallest of the sample in terms of general size (measure 1). All thirteen others appear to be males.

On the basis of skeletal and tusk size, Agenbroad and Mead (1987) formed a working hypothesis that the Hot Springs mammoth assemblage comprised predominantly males. This hypothesis is supported by the pelvic data. In conjunction with dental analyses providing an age-structure of the population (Figures 66, 74), this is indicative of selective trapping of predominantly young adult males. Behavioral patterns of *Loxodonta africana* as described by Moss (1988) and other investigators are consistent with this conclusion. Young males are voluntarily or involuntarily expelled from family groups at an age of around 9-12 years, depending on the individual. Also, young adult males have little success in displacing older, breeding bulls until their mid-thirties. The result of these behavioral patterns is solitary individuals, or bachelor groups of adolescent and young adult male elephants (or mammoths, by analogy) adventurously roaming the countryside, being relatively inexperienced in life's dangers, and getting into difficult or dangerous situations. A similar explanation was posited by Coope and Lister (1987) to account for the trapping of a 28-year-old male mammoth in a late Pleistocene kettle-hole at Condover, England, and Lister (in press a) has extended this as a possible explanation for the strong predominance of males among isolated finds of *M. primigenius* skeletons in Eurasia.

One can imagine a Gary Larson cartoon depicting a group of young bachelor mammoths gathered at the edge of the Hot Springs sinkhole 26,000 years ago, daring each other to traverse the steep walls for forage or water. Any such adventurous trip—for whatever reason it was undertaken—was a one-way trip. The age analysis of the mammoth population at Hot Springs fits such a model.

An interesting comparison with the Hot Springs pelvic sample is provided by *M. columbi* material from the site of Dent, Colorado. Two incomplete adult pelves in the collection of the Denver Museum of Natural History allowed measurement of oblique aperature height and ilium shaft width. The data are shown in Table 28 and Figure 85. The specimens give ratios of 2.47 and 2.55, in the female part of the *M. primigenius* range. These results have two valuable implications. First, they corroborate, as far as a sample of two can do, the suggestion of Saunders (1980), based on skeletal size, that the Dent mammoths represent one or more matriarchal family groups. Second, considering the Dent and Hot Springs data together, the clear separation into two discrete scatters supports the validity of the pelvic sexing method, developed on samples of *M. primigenius* and *M. meridionalis*, for *M. columbi*.

ACKNOWLEDGEMENTS

We are grateful to Tom Hardy and Elise Schloeder of the Denver Museum of Natural History Museum for access to the Dent mammoths.

Chapter 11

ON THE STERNUM OF
THE COLUMBIAN MAMMOTH
(*Mammuthus columbi* [Falconer] 1857)
FROM THE MAMMOTH SITE
OF HOT SPRINGS, SOUTH DAKOTA

Dick Mol and Larry Agenbroad

PURPOSE

This is a short description, with figures, of the sternum of *Mammuthus columbi* from the Mammoth Site of Hot Springs, South Dakota, which can be used as an identification tool, and for comparison with the sternum of other extinct proboscideans.

INTRODUCTION

The Mammoth Site of Hot Springs, South Dakota has provided a number of *in situ* skeletons of the Columbian mammoth *(Mammuthus columbi)*. During the excavation of some of the skeletons, a number of isolated bones were excavated that could not be attributed to the nearly complete skeletons which remain *in situ*. In the extensive collection of bones at the Mammoth Site, nearly all skeletal parts are represented. Complete skulls, including mandibles and hyoid bones; all vertebra, including the very small, distal caudal vertebra; bones from the feet; the fore and hind limbs, ribs and sternum.

There are hundreds of publications concerning Pleistocene proboscidean skeletons, or parts of skeletons, which are described in detail, however extensive descriptions or figures of the sternum of Pleistocene proboscideans are lacking. This lack of information provides an additional reason to focus on this skeletal part.

DESCRIPTION AND MATERIAL

The sternum of the Columbian mammoth is composed of three parts: the presternum, the mesosternum, and the xiphosternum. The sternum is situated between the two humerii, just below the scapula. At the top of the presternum there is the *cartilago manubri.*

The cranial base of the sternum is larger than the caudal portion. On the presternum there are one, or two connections, on the left and right, for cartilaginous attachments to the first left and right ribs. The sternum has the shape of a keel, from the caudal to the cranial side. The mesosternum also has attachments for the cartilaginous connections to ribs 2 and 3. On the xiphosternum there are lateral connections for the 4 th through 7th rib pairs; there is also one point of connection for eight additional pairs of ribs (Figure 86 and 87).

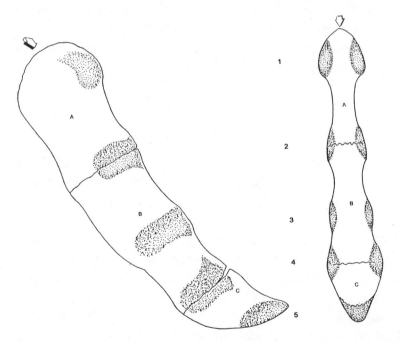

Figure 86. Diagram of a sternum, Left lateral view, right caudal view. A = Presternum, B = Mesosternum and C = Xiphosternum, Arrow = attachment for the *cartilago manubrii.* 1, 2, 3, 4, and 5 attachments for the cartilage connections with the ribs.

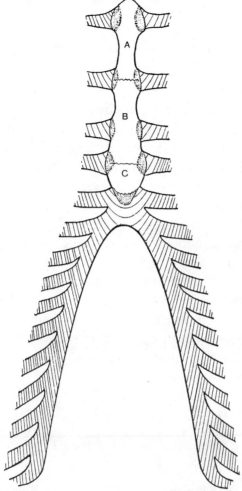

Figure 87. Diagram of a sternum with the cartilage connections with the first 15 pair of ribs. A = Presternum, B= Mesosternum, and C = Xiphosternum.

Little attention has been given to the sternum bones of mammoths. In the skeleton of the woolly mammoth *(Mammuthus primigenius)* from Pfaennerhall (Germany), described in detail by Toepfer (1957), only the presternum was found. Toepfer provided a short description and measurements of this bone. Von Koenigswald (1989) described the Poelch mammoth (Germany), also a woolly mammoth, and gave a short description and a photograph of a fused meso- xiphosternum. Unfortunately, there is no discussion, or description of Garutt's excellent book, "Das Mammut" (1964). Maccagno (1962: 68, Pl. V) described a nearly complete skeleton of

217

a male *Mammathus meridionalis* which was found in the vicinity of L'Aquila (Contrada "Madonna della Strada," Scoppito, Italia). It belongs to a very large senile individual of this mammoth-species. According to Maccagno the sternum of this skeleton consists of 4 parts. The second part was not found and was modelled to serve in a reconstruction of the skeleton, now exhibited in the Castle of L'Aquila. According to Maccagno, six pairs of ribs were connected with the sternum by cartilage. Maccagno compared the L'Aquila skeleton with *Mammuthus meridionalis* from Nogaisk (formerly USSR), in which the sternum consists of only two parts.

The Colby Site in west-central Wyoming (Frison and Todd 1986) has provided a large number of bones (463) of the Columbian mammoth, belonging to a probable maximum of 6-7 individuals. Among these bones, no sternum or portion of a sternum (Table 2.1; Frison and Todd 1986) was reported, although they excavated an articulated scapula, humerus, and rib cage.

PRESTERNUM (MSL 00138)

Figure 88. Presternum of *Mammuthus columbi*; lateral view (MSL00138).

218

This presternum is characterized by two pairs of attachments for cartilage, which forms the connection between the first and second ribs and the sternum; these attachments are situated immediately under the *cartilago manubrii*. The characteristics of this presternum indicate it belonged to a young individual. On the top of the cranial side, the suture line that also carried the cartilage *(cartilago manubri)* is visible. The presternum has the shape of a slightly curved keel. The greatest length of the cranial side is 305 mm; of the caudal side, it is 178 mm. The greatest anterior-posterior diameter, measured in the middle of the presternum, is 156 mm; the transverse diameter at the cartilage attachment for the *cartilago manubrii* is 81 mm; at mid bone it is 56 mm; at the proximal end it is 67 mm. The proximal, anterior-posterior diameter is 134 mm. In the mid portion of the cranial side, the transverse diameter is 9 mm. On the caudal side, the bone is curved.

PRESTERNUM (HS 00079)

Figure 89. Presternum of *Mammuthus columbi,* lateral view (HS 00079).

This presternum is the largest one yet recovered from the Mammoth Site at Hot Springs, South Dakota. It was found immediately adjacent to a large humerus, indicative of a large individual. This specimen is the only presternum from the site with two attachments for the cartilaginous connections with the first two pairs of ribs. The first attachment is immediately under the *cartilago manubrii*; the second is on the boundary between the presternum and mesosternum.

Table 29. Measurements for the keel shaped presternum (HS00079).

greatest cranial length	312	mm
greatest caudal length	253	
anterior-posterior diam. of the top	190	
anterior-posterior diam. of suture/mesosternum	153	
anterior-posterior diam., midshaft	172	
transverse diam., 1st rib attachment	108	
transverse diam., 2nd rib attachment	98	

A fifth presternum was discovered in the 1990 field season, and remains *in situ*. It is laying on the right lateral side, with the left lateral side exposed. It has an attachment for the cartilage connection between the 1st left rib and the presternum. the surface of this sternum is very smooth. The greatest cranial length is 289 mm; the greatest caudal length is 218 mm; the anterior-posterior diameter at midshaft is 153 mm.

PATHOLOGICAL SPECIMEN (MSL 725)

Early excavations produced a pathological presternum (MSL 725). Originally, this presternum was keel shaped, similar to MSL 000138. At the top of the specimen there is a suture line forming the egg-shaped connection with the *cartilago manubrii*. This pathological presternum has one connection for the first pair of ribs. On the lateral side and caudal side, there are additional bone growths—probably caused by infection, or a wound (Figure 90b). These extra bone growths and ossification of cartilage between the sternum and the first pair of ribs formed a rigid (non-flexible) connection. Unfortu-

220

 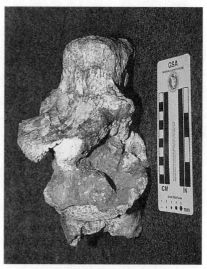

Figure 90a. *Mammuthus columbi* Pathological presternum frontal view (MSL 725).

–b: *Mammuthus columbi* Pathological presternum, cranial view (MSL 725).

nately, the first pair of ribs are broken, but their connection with the ossified cartilage is plainly visible. The bone growth is attached for 250 mm on the caudal side of the presternum, and on the entire lateral side of the bone, as well as at the top of the entire anterior-posterior diameter. On both lateral sides, there are a number of bone lesions. At the bottom of the specimen, the suture line for the mesosternum connection is preserved. No fusion between the presternum and mesosternum took place, indicating this specimen is from a relatively young individual, at the time of death.

Table 30. Measurements for the pathological specimen.

greatest length	292	mm
anterior-posterior diameter, top	153	
anterior-posterior, bottom	143	
transverse diameter @ 1st ribs	164	
transverse diameter, bottom	93	

STERNUM (HS-00388)

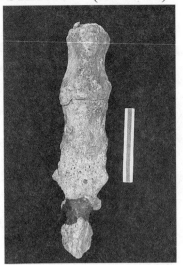 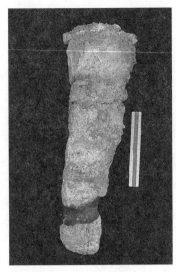

Figure 91a. *Mammuthus columbi*
Sternum, frontal view (MSL 388).

–b: *Mammuthus columbi*
Sternum, lateral view (MSL 388).

This sternum bone belongs to an old individual. It was found next to a partially excavated skeleton containing both femora, fibula, tibia, and patella, as well as bones of the hind foot. All epiphyses are fused with the diaphyses, indicative of great age. There was fusion of the presternum, the mesosternum, and the xiphosternum, which also indicates an aged individual. On the excellently preserved left, lateral side of the specimen, a small part of the suture line between the presternum and mesosternum has been preserved. Just above this suture line, on the presternum, there is an attachment for the cartilage that connects the first rib to the sternum.

The greatest length of the presternum, measured on the cranial side is 165 mm. The mesosternum is the largest of the three fused bones; its greatest length is 236 mm. In the middle of the mesosternum, just above the xiphosternum, there are connections for the cartilage attachment for the second and third ribs. The attachment for the cartilage connection of the fourth rib is situated between the caudal part of the mesosternum and the cranial part of the xiphosternum. At this point, the xiphosternum of this specimen is broken. The length of the xiphosternum is 98 mm. Its cranial portion forms the cartilage attachment for the fifth rib and a number of other ribs. In the sternum of an Asian elephant (*Elephas maximus)* in the Hot Springs Mammoth Site collection, there are ten pairs of ribs

222

which are connected, by cartilage, to the caudal portion of the xiphosternum. In the modern elephant, there are 19 pairs of ribs; four pair of which are not connected to the sternum, they are the floating ribs.

Table 31. Measurements of HS 00388 sternum.

greatest caudal length	466	mm
anterior-posterior diam.; top presternum	166	
anterior-posterior diam. bottom xiphosternum	76	
anterior-posterior diam. cartilage to 3rd rib	120	
transverse diameter, top of presternum	63	
transverse diameter, bottom xiphosternum	73	
transverse diam., cartilage to 3rd rib	79	

This complete sternum is more massive than MSL 00138. The front is keel shaped. On the caudal side, it is not rounded, in contrast to MSL 00138, but is more square in shape.

SUMMARY

At the Hot Springs Mammoth Site, the sternum consists of three parts. The location of the connections between the ribs and the sternum may vary with the individual specimen; they are not always in the same location on the sternum. The presternum population at the site consists of five specimens, one of which is fused, due to the advanced age of that individual, and one of which is pathological. The measurements of the sternum indicate the Hot Springs Columbian mammoths *(Mammuthus columbi)* were very large individuals, as compared to woolly mammoths *(Mammuthus primigenius)*, or modern Asian elephants *(Elephas maximus)*. The presternum is always keel shaped, with one or two cartilage attachments for connections to the first pair of ribs. The mesosternum is represented by a single specimen (HS 00388), and has two cartilage connections for the second and third ribs. The nearly shapeless xiphosternum has one pair of cartilage attachments for the fourth pair of ribs, and one caudal, cartilage attachment for the remaining ribs which are attached to the sternum.

Chapter 12

METAPODIALS AND SHOULDER HEIGHT OF
Mammuthus columbi
COMPARED WITH EURASIAN *Mammuthus* SPECIES

Dick Mol and Larry Agenbroad

PURPOSE

Metric analyses of the metapodials of *Mammuthus columbi* (Falconer) from Hot Springs, South Dakota, and comparisons with selected specimens from Europe and other areas.

METHODOLOGY AND DESCRIPTION OF MATERIALS

The analyses are conducted on metapodial bones of mammoth (metacarpals and metatarsals). These skeletal elements are seldom described and analyzed; often they are not recovered (Garutt 1964; Siegfried 1959; Mol 1984; Gillette1989; Frison and Todd 1986). Examples of excellent analyses of such materials include the Pfaennerhall mammoth (Toepfer 1957); the Borna mammoth (Felix 1912); the Steinheim an der Murr mammoth (Dietrich 1912); and the isolated early to late Pleistocene mammoth remains from the North Sea and the Netherlands (Mol 1984; van Essen and Mol in press). In this paper we follow the modified methodologies of these authors.

METACARPALS

Metacarpals are easily distinguished from metatarsals, in proboscideans, due to their increased length and mass characteristics resulting from the fact that the majority of the body weight is supported by the front limbs. This characteristic is just the opposite of other animals such as bovids, equids, etc. The proximal articulatory surface of metacarpals is characteristically undulatory in nature, in contrast to the planar proximal surface of metatarsals (Figure 92 and 93). Metacarpals are more robust in all characteristics, than metatarsals.

For a description of metacarpal measurements used in this analysis refer to Figure 94. Table 32 provides the material available for study at the Hot Springs Mammoth Site. These data include isolate specimens; *in situ* specimens; and articulated specimens. Table 33 lists the individual specimen numbers arranged in metacarpal I-V designations. Table 34 refers to the metacarpals of MSL 00140, an articulated, known age (AEY) individual, referred to as "Napoleon", compared to the Pfaennerhall specimen of Toepfer (1957).

Description of the metacarpals

Metacarpal I

The first metacarpal bone is the smallest of the five metacarpals in the foot. The proximal surface, which articulates with the trapezium, is oval in shape, sloping to the front and outside of the foot. The midshaft transverse diameter is one-half the anterior-posterior diameter. The distal articular surface contains a groove running from mid-point to the posterior. The articular surface indicates the presence of one sesamoid. Proboscideans with this character are "thumbless".

Metacarpal II

The second metacarpal is the next to largest metacarpal bone in proboscideans. The proximal epyphesis articulates with the trapezoid, and the magnum. Therefore, the proximal articular surface is separated into two surfaces, separated by a ridge. The higher articular surface is wider posterially, connecting with the magnum. The medial portion of the bone has a small articular surface for metacarpal

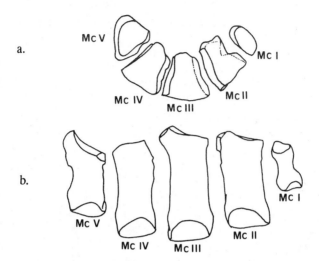

Figure 92. a-b. Diagram of the metacarpals I-V of *Mammuthus*.
   a: Proximal articulatory surfaces
   b: Frontal view of metacarpals I-V showing the characteristically undulatory shape in the proximal articulatory surfaces.

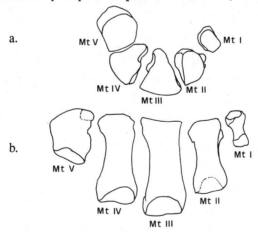

Figure 93. a-b. Diagram of the metatarsals I-V of *Mammuthus*.
   a: Proximal articulatory surfaces
   b: Frontal view of metacarpals I-V showing the characteristically undulatory shape in the proximal articulatory surfaces.

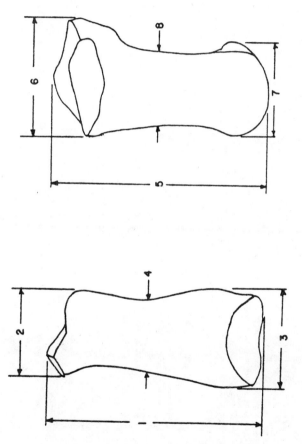

Figure 94. a. Schematic drawing of a left, third metacarpal (Frontal view) of *Mammuthus* showing measurements taken. — b. Schematic drawing of a left, third metacarpal (Lateral view) of *Mammuthus* showing measurements taken.

1=Greatest length
2=Transverse diameter distal epiphysis
3=Transverse diameter distal epiphysis
4=Transverse diameter midshaft (diaphysis)

5=Greatest length
6=Transverse diameter distal epiphysis
7=Transverse diameter distal epiphysis
8=Transverse diameter midshaft (diaphysis)

227

Table 32. Metacarpals available for this paper in the collection at the Mammoth Site of Hot Springs, S.D.

METACARPALS MAMMOTH SITE, HOT SPRINGS

Mc. I		Mc. II		Mc. III		Mc. IV		Mc. V	
lft	rt	lft	rt	lft	rt	lft	rt	lft	rt
89HS074(3)		HS00387	MSL 270	MSL 353	MSL 667	MSL 448	MSL 731	**MSL 473**	MSL 710
MSL 317		MSL 489	**MSL 378**	MSL 702	MSL 601	MSL 225	**MSL 721**	89HS071	MSL 704
MSL 033		HS00431(2)	89HS075(3)		MSL 059	**MSL 247**	MSL 495	HS00428(2)	MSL 446
					MSL 346	HS00470(2)	MSL 469		**HS00219**
					HS00530(3)		HS00479(1)		HS00081(1)
							HS00531(3)		

Notes:
(1) same individual (*in situ* in the sinkhole)
(2) same individual (*in situ* in the sinkhole)
(3) same individual (*in situ* in the sinkhole)
The bold specimens belong to the skeleton of "Napoleon" (MSL00140)
Not included in the table: a nearly complete right forefoot (HS00075) is partly excavated showing uniform, magnum, the metacarpals and the sesamoids.

Table 33. Measurements in mm of the metacarpls of the woolly mammoth (*Mammuthus primigenius*) of Pfaennerhall (Germany) and of the Columbian mammoth (*Mammuthus columbi*) (MSL 00140).

	Mc. I		Mc. II		Mc. III		Mc. IV		Mc. V	
	Woolly m. Pfannerhall (Mc. I)	Hot Springs MSL 033 (Mc. I)	Woolly m. Pfannerhall (Mc. II)	Hot Springs HS00387 (Mc. II)	Woolly m. Pfannerhall (Mc. III)	Hot Springs MSL 346 (Mc. III)	Woolly m. Pfannerhall (Mc. IV)	Hot Springs MSL 247 (Mc. IV)	Woolly m. Pfannerhall (Mc. V)	Hot Springs MSL 473 (Mc. V)
	rt	lft	rt	lft	rt	lft	rt	lft	lft	lft
Greatest length	100	123	188	208	208	237	198	202		181
Transverse diameter proximal ephiphysis	59	62	80	90	73	(±) 93	71	97		93
Transverse diameter distal epiphysis	55	67	84	109	84	115	87	105		100
Transverse diameter mid-shaft	41	49	70	76	62	79	71	83		71
Anteroposterior diameter proximal epiphysis	69	98	123	133	117	128	95	115		108
Anteroposterior diameter distal epiphysis	63	60	87	103	85	110	91	100		99
Anteroposterior diameter mid-shaft		69		74		72		72		101

II. A much larger articular surface occurs on the proximal surface (on the lateral side) of the bone for articulation with the third metacarpal (Mc III). The distal epiphysis has a smooth articular surface for the first phalanx. The posterior side has two articular surfaces, for sesamoids; the lateral one is wider than the medial.

Metacarpal III

This middle metacarpal is the longest bone of the metacarpal series. The proximal epyphesis is smaller than the distal one. Four articular surfaces are contained on the proximal surface. The medial surface is for articulation with metacarpal II (Mc II). Above it, the largest surface is for connection with the magnum. At the top of Mc III, in line with the mid-shaft, there is a connection to the unciform, and a connection to metacarpal IV (Mc IV), on the lateral side. The distal epiphysis has a smooth anterior surface for the connection to th first phalanx. On the posterior side, there are two surfaces for sesamoids; the medial one is largest.

Metacarpal IV

As seen in Mc II and Mc III, the fourth metacarpal (Mc IV) is much wider in the proximal, anterior portion. The proximal end contains three articular surfaces; the uppermost articulates with the unciform; on the medial side is an intermediate sized surface which articulates with Mc III; the smallest of the three surfaces is lateral and connects with the fifth metacarpal (Mc V).

Metacarpal V

Because of its position in the skeleton of the foot, the fifth metacarpal (Mc V) is easily recognizable from the other metacarpals. It is larger than Mc I, and intermediate with Mc II-IV. The mid-shaft anterior-posterior measurements are one-quarter larger than the transverse measurements. The proximal surface contains three articular surfaces, of which the largest, slopes to the lateral side, articulating with the unciform. The smaller articular surface, in line with the medial diaphysis, articulates with the cuniform. Metacarpal V has a large, smooth distal epiphysis for articulation with the first phalanx. There are two posterior surfaces, for sesamoids, with the lateral one being the larger.

METATARSALS:
Description of the metatarsals
Contrasted to the metapodials of the front foot, the metatarsals are considerably smaller. A characteristic of all metatarsals (Mt I-V) is that they all have planar proximal surfaces. The position of the hind foot is in a more nearly horizontal plane, as contrasted to the front foot (Sikes 1971; Garutt 1964). The front foot of elephants can be considered as a 'half' tip-toe position. Materials available for study at the Hot Springs Mammoth Site are summarized in Table 34. Special attention is given to the nearly complete hind foot (Figure 95) of *Mammuthus columbi* (HS 2500) and is summarized in Table 35.

Metatarsal I

This metatarsal is the smallest and most slender of the metatarsals. Its position is on the medial side of the skeleton. Its shape is slightly curved toward the medial portion of the body. The proximal articular surface articulates with the primary cuneiform; the lateral, proximal side also displays an articular surface, for the second metacarpal (Mt II). The diaphysis of the anterior-posterior diameter of the bone is twice as large as the transverse diameter. On the distal epiphysis the transverse diameter is one-half the width of the proximal surface. There are no articular surfaces on the distal end, for either sesamoids, or phalanges. This is a pattern which is also shown on the first metacarpal of the fore foot. Therefore, there is no first toe on mammoths.

Table 34. Metatarsals available for this paper in the collection at the Mammoth Site of Hot Springs, S.D.

	Mt.I		Mt.II		Metatarsals Mt.III		Mt.IV		Mt.V	
	lft	rt	lft	rt	lft	rt	lft	rt	lft	rt
	89HS025(2)		HS00107(1) 89HSO24(2)	**MSL 391** MSL 634 HSMS 6116	MSL 703 89HSO23(2)	**MSL 390**	MSL 714 MSL 019 HS00027(1) 89HS022(2)	**MSL 389** MSL 445 HS00033(3)	HS00927(1)	MSL 708 MSL 348 HS00033(3) HS

Notes:
Bold indicates same individual (they are glued by calcium carbonate)
(1) same individual (in situ in the sinkhole); (2) same individual (in situ in the sinkhole); (3) same individual (in situ in the sinkhole)

Table 35. Inventory and measurements in mm of the nearly complete hind foot of *Mammuthus columbi* (HS 2500) in the collection of the Mammoth Site of Hot Springs, S.D.

HSMS 2500

	Transverse diameter proximal epiphysis	Transverse diameter distal epiphysis	Transverse diameter mid-shaft	Antero-posterior diameter proximal epiphysis	Antero-posterior distal epiphysis	Antero-posterior diameter mid-shaft	Greatest length	Greatest transverse diameter	Greatest antero-posterior diameter
tibia		208			168				
fibula					136				
astragalus							232	170	154
calcaneum							44	201	113
navicular							84	154	(±) 54
cuneiform primary							46	64	93
cuneiform secondary							47	59	107
cuneiform tertiary							57	63	130
cuboid								114	
mt. I	(±) 57	75		77			135		
mt. II	72	77	60	95	66	49	154		
mt. III	67	71	62	86	76	47	142		
mt. IV	63	(±) 64	61	72	76	55	100		
mt. V	59	57	(±) 60	63	36	80	74		
phalange 1 of mt. III	63			63					
phalange 1 of mt. IV				52					

231

Figure 95. Left hind foot of *Mammuthus columbi*. Hot Springs, S.D.,
Mammoth Site collection (MSL 2500).
a) Lateral view; b) Dorsal view; c) Ventral view

Metatarsal II

The proximal portion of this bone, on the medial side, has a protruberence (knob) for connection with the lateral portion of the primary cuneiform. This is characteristic of Mt II, as contrasted to the other metatarsals. There are two proximal articular surfaces; the largest surface is medial; both articulate with the secondary cuneiform. On the lateral, proximal side, there is a small articular surface, for articulation with Mt III. The distal epiphysis is a smooth, large surface for articulation with the first phalanx; there are two posterior sesamoid surfaces, of which the medial is largest.

Metatarsal III

This is the largest metatarsal. Its proximal end articulates, for the most part, with the tertiary cuneiform, and the anterior articulation with the cuboid. For this reason, this bone is distinguished from Mt IV. The proximal anterior surface is twice as wide as the posterior portion. The distal epiphysis has a larger transverse diameter, than the width of the proximal portion. The distal epiphysis has an anterior, smooth surface for articulation with the first phalanx; two sesamoid surfaces occur posterially, of which the lateral one is the largest.

Metatarsal IV

The fourth metatarsal (Mt IV) is the most robust of the metatarsals, and is second in size. The distal portion is slightly curved laterally. The proximal portion is one planar surface, whose anterior is twice the width of the posterior. The proximal surface articulates with the cuboid. On the anterior, medial side of the proximal epiphysis, it has an articular surface for Mt III. On the posterior lateral side, there is a surface for Mt V. The distal epiphysis has a lateral curve, and an articular surface for the first phalanx. Posteriorally, it has two sesamoid surfaces, of which the medial one is the largest in transverse diameter.

Metatarsal V

The fifth metatarsal is located on the lateral side of the foot skeleton. It is a small, stout bone which is one-third shorter than the longest metatarsal (Mt III). The anterior-posterior diameter is the largest of any metatarsal. This diameter is only one-fifth smaller than the length of this bone. Its proximal side is flattened for articulation with the cuboid. On the posterior diaphysis, the material is a rugose extension of bone, extending further, posterially, than all other metatarsals. The anterior, distal epiphysis has a large articular surface for the first phalanx; the posterior has two sesamoid surfaces, of which the medial one is largest in transverse diameter.

DESCRIPTION OF THE LEFT HIND FOOT OF MSL 2500:

One of the most important discoveries from the Hot Springs Mammoth Site was made in 1978, the majority of an articulated left hind foot , for which nearly all of the skeletal parts are in articulation. Table 35 shows which skeletal parts are preserved, excluding four sesamoids. Unfortunately, it is impossible to say to which individual animal this foot belongs.

There are nineteen skeletal elements for this foot, including two sets of sesamoids which articulate with metatarsals III and IV. These elements have been cemented together by calcium carbonate, which excludes some of the measurements, for a complete metric analysis. Measurements taken are shown in Table 35. The preservation of the bones is excellent. Since there is no fusion between distal epiphyses of the tibia and fibula, it indicates this was a young animal, estimated to be between ten and twenty years of age. The distal tibia is one of the earliest points of bone epiphyseal fusion in elephants. Position of the distal tibial and fibular epiphyses with the calcaneum/navicular shows clearly the living foot position of this elephant.

This foot (MSL 2500) (Figure 95 a-c) was deposited with flesh, skin, or tendons still attached, and quickly covered by sediments, preventing the disarticulation and scatter of these small skeletal elements. Metatarsal one (Mt I) is missing, which should demonstrate no phalanx.

The maximum transverse diameter of this left hind foot, measured from the level of the cuneiform to the lateral side of the calcaneum, is 252 mm. The reconstructed maximum transverse diameter, measured in mid-shaft of the metatarsals is $\pm$ 258 mm. As far as we know, this is the most complete foot of a mammoth to be dicovered in an articulated position, excluding the frozen cadavers from Siberia.

SKELETONS OF *MAMMUTHUS COLUMBI*:

The measurement of several skeletal elements are of great importance in the calculation of the shoulder height of elephants. These elements are the humerus, radius, and ulna for the front limb; and the pelvis, femur, tibia, and fibula for the hind limb. The measurements of the skeletal parts of the feet provides information about the nature and position of the foot in the living animal.

Valuable information on the greatest length measurements and the shoulder height of mammoths from Eurasia are presented in Garutt (1964). This compilation of measurements is reproduced here, (Table 36) for comparative purposes, because this information was never presented in an English version. Early Eurasian mammoths (*Mammuthus meridionalis*) crossed the Bering Land Bridge, into North America sometime prior to 1.7 million years ago, evidenced by the dated discovery at Welsch Valley, Saskatchewan (Harington and Shackleton 1978; citing Stalker). Knowledge of the Eurasian mammoths at this early time is important in understanding the evolution of mammoths in North America, as contrasted to Eurasia. Evolution in the two hemispheres took slightly different pathways after the common ancestor, *M. meridionalis*.

Table 36. Mammoth species in Eurasia and North America.

EURASIA	NORTH AMERICA

Late PLEISTOCENE:

| *Mammuthus primigenius* | *Mammuthus primigenius**
Mammuthus exilis (pygmy)
Mammuthus columbi |

Middle PLEISTOCENE:

| *Mammuthus trogontherii* | *Mammuthus imperator* |

Early PLEISTOCENE:

| *Mammuthus meridionalis* | *Mammuthus meridionalis* |

* denotes a late Pleistocene migration across the Bering Land Bridge

SKELETON OF NAPOLEON (MSL 00140)

At the Mammoth Site of Hot Springs, South Dakota, complete skeletons are not completely excavated, but are left as an *in situ* deposit, preventing complete handling and metric analysis of the individual bones. There are several partially excavated, articulated skeletons, as of the summer field session of 1990. One animal, called "Napoleon" is the most complete (Figure 96). This male skeleton has a skull, with complete dention, necessary for age determination for the individual (Agenbroad 1990). Napoleon is calculated to be 49 years of age (AEY) as determined from Laws (1966). For comparison, we present a review of the skeletal parts and their metric attibutes, for this *in situ* specimen (Figure 97).

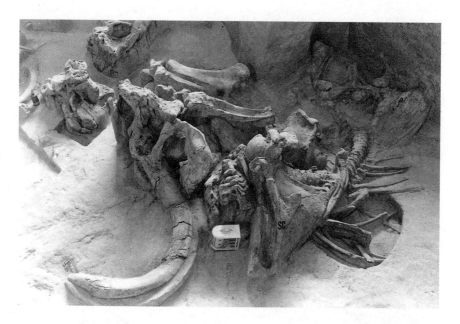

Figure 96. Skeleton of *Mammuthus columbi*, "Napoleon," *in situ* at the Mammoth Site of Hot Springs, S.D.

The Skull

Napoleon's skull is resting on its right side; the left tusk is half exposed, it is complete, and in an excellent state of preservation. The right tusk is not in evidence, but probably is still *in situ* in the unexcavated portion of the skull. The left tusk measures 1930 mm, along an outside curvilinear measurement, from the alveolus. The tusk's anterior-posterior diameter, measured at the alveolus, is 156 mm. This tusk is spirally curved; from the alveolus it is directed downward and laterally, then incurves, forming a partial circle. Also of interest in this skull is the left stylohyoid, still in life position.

Figure 97. Diagram of the skeleton of "Napoleon" (*M. columbi*). Bones in heavy outline are those known by the 1990 field season.

Dentition

The maxillary and mandibular dentition are intact in this specimen, with the maxillary M6 in complete occlusion. The anterior part of the molar is worn to the roots. The lower, right mandibular M6 is worn to the roots in the anterior part, with 11 plates in occlusion, plus three plates and a talon which are unworn. The left mandibular M6 is damaged in the anterior portion, but shows twelve plates in occlusion, plus three plates and a talon which are unworn.

Some of the cranial measurements (Agenbroad 1990) include:

greatest width over zygomatic	± 680 mm
greatest width of the left portion	340
greatest length of occipital condyles	101
greatest width of occipital condyles	240
greatest width of foramen magnum	91
greatest width of nasal foramen	443

Vertebral column

The cervical vertebra of Napoleon are in articulation; the atlas (458 mm) is separated from other cervical vertebra, followed by the axis and five cervical vertebra; then19 thoracic vertebra, with 16 articulated to ribs. Three thoracic vertebra are partially hidden by the right scapula and right humerus; there are four lumbar vertebra and one sacral vertebra. The other sacral vertebra are still unexcavated, as are the caudal vertebra. The number of rib pairs is not the same in mammoths. Some ribs are probably unexcavated, or under the scapula. The first right rib is characteristic, with the head articulating between the seventh cervical and first thoracic vertebra. The *tuberculum cos-tae* is articulated with the thoraic lateral spine.

Forelimbs

The right scapula,humerus, and articulated radius and ulna are present, *in situ*, on the upper portion of the skeleton of Napoleon. The greatest length of each bone is: scapula 1015 mm; humerus 1223 mm; radius 948 mm; and ulna 1034 mm. The left scapula, humerus, and articulated radius and ulna are only partly excavated. The left ulna is 1086 mm in length. The only unfused epiphysis in the fore-limb is the distal ulna. This is separated at the diaphysis and is parted by several centimeters, from the ulna shaft. The suture line clearly shows this epiphysis belongs to the left ulna.

Hindlimbs

The pelvis of Napoleon is nearly completely excavated. The great-est width of the left side is 901 mm. Only the proximal portions of the femora are excavated, showing the fusion of the femur heads to the femur shafts. The femur heads are in partial articulation with the pelvic acetabulum. The right tibia/fibula are still in articulation, ly-ing over the right femur; their respective greatest lengths are 813 and 786 mm. The left tibia/fibula and the bones of both hind feet have yet to be excavated. The right patella is near the proximal end of the tibial epiphysis; the left one is lying within the pelvic girdle.

SKELETON OF FT. ROBINSON SPECIMEN (NSM 1597-62-2)

A nearly complete male skeleton of *Mammuthus columbi* is on display at the Trailside Museum, Fort Robinson State Park, near Crawford, Nebraska. This specimen was excavated by citizens of Crawford in 1962, from the Moody Ranch, on Cottonwood Creek. When it was discovered there was not one, but two individuals, with their tusks locked together, the excavators were joined by a party from the Nebraska State Museum. The interlocked skulls still remain at that institution. Until now, a detailed description of the specimen has not been published. For comparitive purposes, we took measurements from the mounted skeleton (Table 36).

Skull

The skull of the mounted skeleton is replica, the original including the mandible remain in a field cast at the Nebraska State Museum, Lincoln. The cast shows both M6 of the maxilla in full occlusion. The anterior portions of the M6 is worn to the roots. According to Laws (1966) this animals age is +/- 50 AEY. The mandible also contains M6 in full occlusion.

Table 37.   Metrics Of The Ft. Robinson Mammoth: (NSM1597-62-2).

Forelimb:	left		right
Scapula	1032mm		1047mm
Humerus	m. 1045, l. 1088		m. 1045, l. 1109
Radius	823	810	
Ulna	946	955	
Foot, greatest width (top carpals)	299		303
Foot, greatest width	471		533
Mc III greatest length	194		—
Hindlimb:			
Femur	1281		1228
Tibia	728		(cast)
Fibula	(cast)		(cast)
Foot, greatest width (top tarsals)	276		340
Mt III greatest length	163		

The left and right feet are incomplete, but the original Mt I shows there were no phalanges attached to these metatarsals.
(m= medial; l = lateral)

Vertebral Column

The vertebral column contains 7 cervical vertebra; 19 thoracic vertebra; 4 lumbar vertebra; 5 sacral vertebra; and the tail is composed of 21 caudal vertebra, of which, the first 12 and # 17, 20, and 21 are original. The last two are fused. The nineteen thoracic vertebra carry 19 pairs of ribs. The shoulder height of this mounted specimen is 3190 mm. The highest point of the backbone (thoracic spine) is considerably higher, $\pm$ 3500 mm.

SKELETON OF THE LANGE-FERGUSON MAMMOTH (SDSM 12468):

A nearly complete, unmounted, adult skeleton of *Mammuthus columbi* is stored at the Geology Museum of the South Dakota School of Mines and Technology (Martin 1984). It was excavated during the period 1980-84, by L.A. Hannus, at the Lange-Ferguson Site (39SH33), a mammoth kill-butchering locality. The site is dated at 10,600 $\pm$ 300 yr B.P. and is located on the edge of a late Pleistocene pond, or marsh, in the White River Badlands of South Dakota. The site was brought to the attention of the investigators, by Les Ferguson, of Hot Springs, after he initially discovered a femur of a mammoth at the locality in 1960. There are two mammoth skeletons at the Lange-Ferguson Site, an adult and a juvenile, killed, or scavenged by Clovis hunters (Hannus 1990). For comparative purposes, we have taken some measurements of selected bones from the Lange-Ferguson mammoth; these measurements are listed in Table 38.

After re-examining and measuring the specimen, we have arrived at slightly different conclusions as to the species and age of this animal, as compared to published conclusions (Martin 1987). The written description of the tentative species assignment seems to convey the designation of *M. jeffersonii/jacksoni* as being derived as much by the age of the site as by osteological or dental characteristics of the animal. Speciation was considered using Madden's (1981) scheme for North American proboscideans.

It should be emphasized that the date is for an overlying stratum, and may post-date the fauna by several hundred years. A date on the mammoth bone should be determined.

Our conclusions, after measuring some of the bones and dentition, following Maglio (1973), is that the animal is a Columbian mammoth (*Mammuthus columbi*), and that the mandibular dentition indicates an individual age of 38 ± 2 AEY, at the time of death. We feel this age assignment is more in keeping with the epiphyseal fusion noted in the long bones of the animal. Pelvic measurements indicate the animal was a male.

Table 38. Metrics of selected bones from the Lange-Ferguson mammoth (SDSM 12468).

skeletal element	greatest length (mm)	
	left	right
scapula (damaged at the top)	977	
humerus	1261	*
ulna 1005	1014	
radius	911	928
metacarpal I		141
metacarpal II		223
metacarpal III		244
metacarpal IV		223
metacarpal V (damaged at top)	193	
femur	1372	*
tibia 842	833	
fibula	815	827

*= bones represented, but not measured.

Because of the butchering activities of the Paleoindians, not all skeletal parts are represented. A number of skeletal parts are still in field jackets, dating from the excavation period.

Skull

The skull is complete, containing the mandible. In the upper left maxilla there is an M6 containing the talon and seven plates in occlusion, with several unerrupted plates. The right maxilla contains two plates of the M5, and a M6 with a talon and seven plates in occlusion, and unerrupted plates still in the jaw. The lower jaw contains left and right M6 and partial M5 in occlusion. According to Laws (1966) this animals age is nearly 40 AEY. Both tusks are still in field jackets, but are short and relatively thick.

Vertebral column

Cervical vertebra, C1-C4 (including the atlas and axis) are present; C5-C7 are absent. Some of the thoracic vertebra are present. Lumbar, sacral, and all but two caudal vertebra are missing. There are twenty ribs, some of which are heavily damaged.

Forelimbs

The left and right forelimbs are complete. At present, only the right forefoot is prepared. It is complete, including the sesamoids, which are articulated to the caudal side of the distal epiphyses. All epiphyses are fused in the forelimbs. For measurements, see Table 38.

Hindlimbs

The pelvis is heavily damaged. Measurements taken on the pelvis are slightly in error, but calculations indicate the animal is a male. A fact that is also in accord with the stature of this individual. All epiphyses are fused, as in the forelimbs. Measurements are presented in Table 38.

SKELETONS OF *MAMMUTHUS PRIMIGENIUS:*

As a comparison of the postcranial skeletal elements for common late Pleistocene *Mammuthus columbi* and the common

Mammuthus primigenius of Eurasia, we have chosen the Pfaennerhall mammoth, from Germany, described in detail by Toepfer (1957). In addition, Table 39 provides the measurements of the larger bones of the postcranial skeleton, such as the scapula, humerus, ulna, radius, femur, tibia and fibula of mammmoths from Eurasia. This table was reproduced from Garutt (1964), an eminent Russian paleontologist specializing in woolly mammoths, whose work is not well known in English publications.

The Pfaennerhall mammoth was identified by Toepfer as a female, of ± 60 years of age, whose highest point of the backbone was 3000 mm. In accordance with the work of Laws (1966) and the published maxillary dentition of this animal, we conclude the animal's age is ±50 AEY. The highest point of the backbone of the Pfaennerhall mammoth is intermediate with the Kemel (former USSR) and the Lena (former USSR) mammoths whose respective heights are 2580 and 3200 mm (Garutt 1964).

After the 1964 publication of Garutt, additional, large, woolly mammoths have been found in western Europe. The Siegsdorf mammoth from Bavaria, FRG has a greatest shoulder height of 3880 mm. Unfortunately this nearly complete mammoth skeleton is lacking all foot bones except the right astragalus. Detailed description of this excellent specimen is, as yet, unpublished. For the reconstruction of this woolly mammoth skeleton, they sculpted part of the foot, making the length of the metapodials too long (in our opinion). We feel the shoulder height should be lowered slightly, however, this specimen is the largest woolly mammoth known from Eurasia.

COMPARISONS

Table 33 presents the measurements of the right metacarpals of the Pfaennerhall mammoth. Measurements of right and left metacarpals of 'Napoleon' from the Mammoth Site at Hot Springs, South Dakota are also presented. In both specimens we are dealing with mature, adult animals of ± 50 AEY. All epiphyses are fused, except the distal left ulna, in both specimens. Table 33 shows clearly that

Table 39. Measurements in mm of limb bones and shoulder height in mammoth skeletons from Eurasia after Garutt (1964).

Mammoth Skeletons from Eurasia

Site & Data year	Museum	Greatest length Scapula	Greatest length humerus	Greatest length ulna	Greatest length radius	Greatest length femur	Greatest length tibia	Greatest length fibula	Highest point of backbone
Woolly Mammoth									
Lena (1799)	Zoological Museum Leningrad, USSR	880	1000	770	820	1200	675	660	3200
Tura (1885)	Local Museum, Tjumen, USSR		1040	760		1294	670		2790
Beresowka (1901)	Zoological Museum Leningrad, USSR	759	850	672	702	1030	590	591	2650
Talmyr (1948)	Zoological Museum Leningrad, USSR	750	850	655	704	1055	552	558	2650
Sanga-Jurjach (1903)	Zoological Museum Leningrad, USSR		725	563	580	915			
Kemel (1899)	Geological Museum Kasan, USSR	750	910	666	645?	1050	580	590	2580
Vilnjus (1957)	Zoological Museum Kaunas, USSR		940	720	720	1170	640	659	
Borna (1908)	See Felix, 1912 (destroyed WWII)	870	1080	900	790	1150	680	680	3200
Pfaennerhall (1953)	State Museum Halle, GDR	795	1040	900?	825	1220	678	634	3000
Ahlen (1910)	Paleontological Museum Muenster, FRO	880	1030	870	793	1240	680	663	
Woolly mammoth sub-species									
Steinhelm (1910)	State Museum, Stuttgart, FRO	1090	1270	1070	955	1420	820	820	3700
Aleksejewka (1952)	Paleontological Museum, Odessa, USSR		1030	610	540?	1270	697	622	3250
Southern mammoth									
Nogaisk (1941)	Zoological Museum Leningrad, USSR	1155	1270	1100	1040	1460	980	901	4100
Georgijewsk (1960)	Local Museum Stawropol, USSR	1040	1225	885	945	1435	820	820	3960

Measurements taken from Garutt (1964: 98-99)

Napoleon's metacarpals are longer and more massive.

The longer and heavier metacarpals of North American Mam*muthus columbi* are seen to be more similar to the lower Pleistocene *Mammuthus meridionalis* of western Europe, than with the woolly mammoth (*Mammuthus primigenius*) of the late Pleistocene of Eurasia. In comparison, there are only a few milimeters difference in the measurements of the left Mc. II of Napoleon and *Mammuthus meridionalis* trawled fron the southern bight of the North Sea, between England and the Netherlands, as presented in a table by Van Essen and Mol (in press).

Measurements taken from the mounted skeleton of *Mammuthus columbi* at the Fort Robinson Trailside Museum, Nebraska give a left, third metacarpal of 194 mm for greatest length (taken on the front side); the right, third metacarpal of Napoleon measures 213 mm. The largest tranverse diameter at the metacarpals of the Fort Robinson specimen is 471 mm, indicative that the mammoth had a large, massive, front foot.

The metatarsals in the collection at the Mammoth Site of Hot Springs, South Dakota also show greater length and massiveness, comparable to those of the early Pleistocene *Mammuthus meridionalis* of western Europe. The skeletal portions of the hind feet of Napoleon are not yet excavated, and are, as yet, unavailable for comparison. The skeleton of the Pfaennerhall mammoth has only the right Mt II, left Mt IV, and a damaged Mt V as originals. When we compare these bones with the nearly complete hind foot from the Mammoth Site of Hot Springs, South Dakota (MSL 2500), belonging to a younger individual than the Pfannerhall specimen, we see a similar pattern as noted for the metapodials of the front foot. The metatarsals are longer and more massive, again signifying more similarity to the metatarsals of *Mammuthus meridionalis* described by Van Essen and Mol (in press), from the North Sea.

ON THE SHOULDER HEIGHT OF EURASIAN MAMMOTHS

The southern elephant *Mammuthus meridionalis* was one of the largest mammoth species from Eurasia, the skeleton in the Geological and Paleontological Museum at Florence, Italy, and in the Castle Museum in l'Aquila, Italy produce respective shoulder height measurements of 3800 and ± 4000 mm. Some workers (Garutt and Nikolskaja 1988) consider the middle Pleistocene steppe mammoth (Mammuthus trogontherii), a descendent of Mammuthus meridionalis, to be the largest representative of the mammoth lineage. Skeletons of the steppe mammoth in Azov (former USSR) and Edersleben (Germany) measure in at shoulder heights, respectively, of 4500 and 3500 mm.

A huge humerus from the middle Pleistocene sediments near Wiesbaden (Germany) measures 1440 mm. According to Garutt and Nikolskaja (1988) this belongs to a mammoth whose living shoulder height would have been 5000 mm (including muscles, tissue, and skin). The smallest representative of the mammoth lineage is the late Pleistocene mammoth Mammuthus primigenius (Table 39). Remains of relatively small individuals are known from Siberia and the North Sea bottom, between England and the Netherlands.

SHOULDER HEIGHT OF Mammuthus columbi

The shoulder height of the Fort Robinson Trailside Museum, Nebraska specimen measures 3190 mm. However the highest point of the backbone is even higher, estimated to be ± 3500 mm.

Assuming there is a relationship between the greatest length of the long bones of the leg and the shoulder height, or greatest height of the backbone, we can estimate the shoulder height of Napoleon, from the Mammoth Site at Hot Springs (Table 40). We have compared the greatest length of the right humerus, ulna, and tibia from Napoleon with the woolly mammoth of Pfaennerhall (Toepfer 1957); a subspecies Mammuthus primigenius fraasi (Dietrich 1912) of middle Pleistocene age from Steinheim an der Murr, Germany (Garutt 1964) and Mammuthus meridionalis from Nogaisk, formerly USSR.

Table 40. Calculated highest point of the backbone of Napoleon (MSL 00140) in comparison with several mammoths (measurements in mm).

specimen	GHB	GLH	GHB	GLU	GHB	GLT
Pfaennerhall (*M.p.*)	3000	1040	3000	900	3000	678
Napoleon (*M.c.*)	**3520**	1223	**3447**	1034	**3597**	813
Mammuthus p.f.	3700	1270	3700	1070	3700	820
Napoleon (*M.c.*)	**3560**	1223	**3576**	1034	**3668**	813
M. meridionalis	4100	1270	4100	1100	4100	980
Napoleon (*M.c.*)	**3948**	1223	**3854**	1034	**3401**	813

(GHB=greatest height of the backbone; GLH= greatest length of humerus; GLU= greatest length of ulna; GLT= greatest length of the tibia); Bold numbers are GHB values for "Napoleon".

Table 40 shows the minimum shoulder height for Napoleon to be 3401 mm, using the tibia for comparison and the greatest to be 3948 mm using the humerus, compared to *Mammuthus meridionalis*. When we compare the same bones of Napoleon, in the same way (knowing the highest point of the backbone and the greatest length of the humerus, ulna, and tibia), with the measured skeleton of *Mammuthus columbi* at the Trailside Museum at Fort Robinson, and the Lange-Ferguson mammoth we have the following calculations for the high point of the backbone (Table 41).

Table 41. Calculation of the greatest height (in mm) of Mamm*uthus columbi*.

specimen	GHB	GLH	GHB	GLU	GHB	GLT
Trailside Museum	3500	1088	3500	946	3500	728
Napoleon	**3934**	1223	**3826**	1034	**3909**	813
Lange-Ferguson	4056	1261	3718	1005	4048	842

We checked the possibility of comparison and estimation of shoulder height knowing the mounted shoulder height, compared to isolate bones. These calculations gave differing heights, even for the same animal. The comparison with other mammoths supplied considerable variation in results. The conclusion is that one must be skeptical of estimated shoulder heights made from one, or several bones, as in the case of the steppe mammoth cited by Garutt and Nikolskaja (1988), with a height of 5000 mm. The most valuable information is gained by comparisons with mounted skeletons of the same species, as in the case of the Trailside Museum specimen and Napoleon. The bones of *Mammuthus columbi* show more similarities to *Mammuthus meridionalis* of the lower Pleistocene, than of younger Eurasian species. We conclude that the highest point of Napoleon's back was between 3401 and 3984 mm. It is with great interest we await further excavations at the Mammoth Site of Hot Springs, which will yield additional skeletons of known age, for which shoulder heights can be reconstructed.

SUMMARY AND CONCLUSIONS

1. The greatest length of the metapodials are not in a predictable relationship compared to the long bones of the limbs.
2. The metacarpals are of the greatest importance in

calulation of shoulder height and maximum height of the backbone.

3. Because of the foreward orientation of the hind foot, the metatarsals are less significant in calculations of shoulder height.

4. Mammuthus *columbi* is a descendent of *Mammuthus meridionalis*, which entered North America via the Bering Land Bridge; it is much like *Mammuthus meridionalis* in shoulder height and body build (mass).

5. *Mammuthus columbi* is considerably larger in shoulder height, contrasted to *Mammuthus primigenius* of Eurasia and North America; the woolly mammoth is of a rather slender build.

6. The data presented in this paper reflect the juvenile and young- adult mammoth population of the Mammoth Site of Hot Springs, South Dakota and the Fort Robinson specimen, discovered approximately fifty miles south of the Mammoth Site, in northwestern Nebraska. Napoleon represents one of the oldest individuals known from the Mammoth Site. Other late Pleistocene *Mammuthus columbi* populations may reflect different body size, such as the Waco, Texas population (Fox *et al*. 1992) which seem to be generally smaller animals. Metric data on the Colby mammoths (Frison and Todd 1986) is not published, so could not be used for comparison. We have included selected metric data which has previously been unpublished for the geographically proximal Lange-Ferguson Site mammoths (Hannus 1990; Martin 1984).

ACKNOWLEDGEMENTS

We are indebted to the Mammoth Site Board of Directors, and staff, for access to the materials, for travel assistance for Dick Mol; to Fort Robinson Trailside Museum for permission to measure their specimen, and to the Earthwatch crews who excavated, mapped and preserved the materials. Dr. Adrien Hannus gave permission to measure the Lange-Ferguson mammoth. Photo credits belong to Phil Degginger.

Chapter 13

SKELETAL ASSOCIATIONS AND BONE MATURATION IN THE HOT SPRINGS MAMMOTHS

Adrian M. Lister

INTRODUCTION

The mammoth remains uncovered at the Hot Springs sinkhole can be divided into three categories: skeletons or partial skeletons which are in obvious anatomical association and so clearly pertain to discrete individuals; groups of bones found in close proximity which are not in anatomical order but which might represent the disarticulated remains of particular individuals; and isolated elements not obviously belonging to any bone grouping. This chapter summarizes our current state of investigation of these groupings, utilizing particularly the state of epiphysis fusion of the long bones of the skeleton.

METHODOLOGY

Elephants (family Elephantidae, including mammoths) are unusual among mammals in having a prolonged period of growth which extends into middle age or beyond. As in other mammals, the elongation of each bone or area of bone continues until its growth is finished, at which point the epiphysis fuses to the shaft. Studies of modern and fossil elephants have demonstrated that within each species there is a definite order in which the epiphyses fuse, with minor differences in order between species (Figure 98). By scoring the fusion states of a series of skeletons of known, differing ontogenetic ages (deduced from tooth eruption and wear), Roth (1984) on Asian and African elephants (*Elephas maximus* and *Loxodonta africana*)

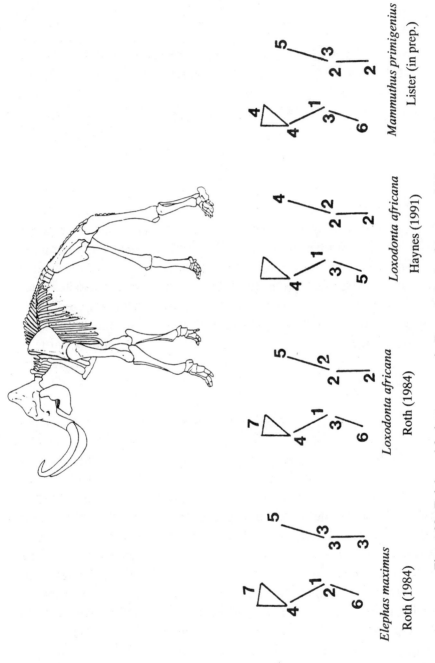

Figure 98. Epiphyseal fusion sequence in *E. maximus*, *L. africana*, and *M. primigenius*.

Elephas maximus
Roth (1984)

Loxodonta africana
Roth (1984)

Loxodonta africana
Haynes (1991)

Mammuthus primigenius
Lister (in prep.)

was able to tie the fusion sequence to the ontogenetic age scale. Further data on *L. africana* have been added by Haynes (1991), and Lister (1989 in prep.) has produced a chart of skeletal maturation versus dental progression for *Mammuthus primigenius* (Table 42). The sequences and timing are similar in the three species, the complete fusion sequence of the major limb bones being stretched over approximately 35 years in male animals. Females of each species show the same fusion sequence as males, but fusions happen at younger ages and are compressed over a shorter period of time (Roth 1984; Haynes 1991).

This extended growth period and regularity in fusion order has two potentially valuable implications for the study of fossil elephants. First, it allows the possibility of ageing skeletons where dental age determination cannot be achieved (e.g. because skull and mandible are missing). Second, it can help in the assessment of whether isolated bones may pertain to a single skeleton. For example, since distal humerus always fuses before distal ulna (Figure 98), an unfused distal humerus and a fused distal ulna cannot belong to the same individual, whereas in the reverse case, they could do so.

In the following charts, for east of assessing age and association, epiphyses are listed (from left to right) in the order in which they fuse in *Mammuthis primigenius* (Lister in prep.), this species being the nearest analogue to *M. columbi*. Fused = f, just fusing = (f), not fused = n, fusion state not entirely clear =?, not scorable =-. Dental 'ages' are estimated using Laws' (1966) scheme on African elephants as modified by Jachmann (1988), and Roth and Shoshani's (1988) scheme on Asian elephants. these two schemes are found to give very similar results on mammoth dentitions, and so dental 'ages' for the latter are estimated as an average of the two, quoted in AEY (African/Asian Equivalent Years). These 'ages' give a relative age scale for the fossil species, but cannot be assumed to represent true absolute ages, especially where the fossil species (as in *M. columbi*) was markedly larger (and with probable greater longevity) than the modern ones. This will be discussed later.

Table 42. Long bone epiphyseal fusion correlated to dental age in proboscideans.

Element	(Haynes 1991) Loxodonta africana		(Lister in preparation) Mammuthus primigenius
	Female	Male	Male (all figures in AEY ±3)
Scapula			
proximal	–	–	42
Humerus			
proximal	19-26	≥ (often 40+)	42
distal	13-14	<18	12
Radius/Ulna			
proximal	19	>32	33
distal	>24	<32 (prob. late 40s)	47
Femur			
proximal	25-32	>29 (often 40+)	45
distal	17-23	26-29	33
Tibia/Fibula			
proximal	–	28-32	28
distal	–	32?	28
Sacrum	<19	<32	–

The grid system on which bone groups are located is in meter squares, relative to a datum point in the north-east part of the site (Agenbroad and Laury 1975). Positions of the following bone groups, and of nearby skulls and mandibles, are shown in Figure 99.

RESULTS

1. Clearly associated skeletons or partial skeletons

This section includes groups of bones which are in clear anatomical association. Nearby skulls and mandibles, which may or may not be associated with them, are also listed.

(a) <u>Skeleton centered at 12N00</u>. This individual, named 'Napoleon', has been described in a previous chapter. Its skeletal fusion state is as follows:

	Dist. Hum.	Prox. Tib.	Dist. Tib.	Prox. Ulna	Dist. Fem.	Prox. Hum.	Prox. Scap.	Prox Fem.	Dist. Rad.	Dist. Uln.
right	f	f	f	-	-	f	f	f	f	f
left	-	-	-	f	-	-	-	f	f	n

This skeleton is completely fused except for the left distal ulna. It is unusual to find the distal radius and ulna of an individual in different states of fusion, and even more unusual to find a different fusion state on left and right sides of the same animal. A possible explanation for this is that the animal died just at the age when distal ulnae and radii were fusing. Alternatively, it may be that the animal had passed this stage, but for some reason the left distal ulna had failed to fuse.

Napoleon is the only skeleton found to date at Hot Springs with a definitely associated skull and mandible, i.e. found in clear anatomical connection with the postcrania. The skull (no. 140) shows M6 in middle wear, at roughly the stage which in modern elephants corresponds to an 'age' of 44 AEY. Mol and Agenbroad (this volume) have assessed this specimen as slightly older, at 49 AEY.

(b) <u>Skeleton centered at 13S23W</u>. This individual, now known as Murray, (Figure 57) comprises the following elements in clear anatomical association: complete vertebral column and many ribs, pelvic girdle, right scapula, humerus, proximal tip of radius and ulna (the rest still buried), femur, patella, tibia, fibula and some tarsals, left femur, patella, tibia, fibula and some tarsals. The fusion states of these bones are as follows:

	Dist. Hum.	Prox. Tib.	Dist. Tib.	Prox. Uln.	Dist. Fem.	Prox. Hum.	Prox. Scap.	Prox. Fem.	Dist. Rad.	Dist. Uln.
right	f	-	-	-	-	f	f	-	-	-
left	-	f	f	-	f	-	-	n	-	-

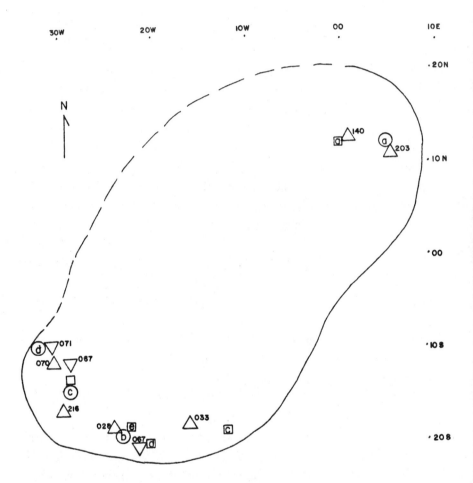

Figure 99. The position of bone groups and associated (or possibly associated) skulls and mandibles at Hot Springs. Squares (□) are clearly associated skeletons, or partial skeletons (Best Group 1). Circles (O) are possibly associated partial skeletons (Best Group 2). Triangles (Δ) are skulls; inverted triangles (∇) are mandibles. Lettering and numerical assignments are referred to in the text. Note that the mandible 067 at 20S 21W is 89-HS-067, whereas the mandible 067 at 11S28W is MSL 00067. The solid line is the proven boundary of the sinkhole, the broken line is the approximate boundary.

The unfused proximal femur implies that the distal radius and ulna, not preserved, were probably also unfused. The fusion state of the definitely associated bones also allows some deductions to be made about some other bones near to Murray which might pertain to his skeleton. The major elements missing from the articulated skeleton are the left foreleg (scapula, humerus, radius, ulna and foot), and the lower part of the right foreleg (distal radius, ulna and foot) which may be present but buried. Potential candidates among nearby bones are: left scapula 427, whose proximal epiphysis fusion state is not visible but whose size matches the right scapula of the skeleton; left humerus 076, with fused proximal epiphysis and matching in size the right humerus of the skeleton (or possibly left humerus 462, also fused but unmeasurable); and two left ulnae, 039 with unclear distal fusion state and 411 with unfused distal epiphysis. Left humerus 047 is excluded because it is smaller than the right humerus of the skeleton, and left humerus 077 because its proximal epiphysis is unfused.

There are several skulls and mandibles in the vicinity of Murray's postcrania:

mandible (83-215) 067, M5 in mid-late wear, 26-28 AEY
mandible 071, M5 in mid wear, 26 AEY
skull 070, M5 in mid wear, 26 AEY
skull (87-016) 406, M5 in mid-wear, 25 AEY

Murray is the largest skeleton found at the site so far, and the last-mentioned skull is probably the largest nearby skull (Agenbroad this volume, Table 13). The width across the occipital condyles of skull (87-016) 406 (29cm) is closely similar to that of the corresponding articular surface of Murray's atlas, suggesting that they might be associated.

(c) Hindquarters centered at 19S12W. This partial skeleton comprises the pelvic girdle, a few crushed posterior vertebrae, the left femur, patella, tibia, fibula and some foot bones, the right femur (distal half), patella, tibia and fibula. Bone fusion states are difficult to see in several cases, but appear to be as follows:

	Dist.	Prox.	Dist.	Prox.	Dist.	Prox.	Prox.	Prox.	Dist.	Dist.
	Hum.	Tib.	Tib.	Uln.	Fem.	Hum.	Scap.	Fem.	Rad.	Uln.
right	-	-	-	-	?f	-	-	-	-	-
left	-	-	?f	-	?f	-	-	(f)	-	-

This limited evidence suggests an animal just at the stage of proximal femur fusion.

The closest skull to this skeleton is no. 89HS033, with M5 in late wear indicating an 'age' of 28 AEY, although there is no direct evidence that the skull and skeleton are associated.

(d) <u>Foreleg centered at 20S20W</u>. The following bones are in articulation: right scapula, humerus, radius and ulna. Fusion states are as follows:

	Dist.	Prox.	Dist.	Prox.	Dist.	Prox.	Prox.	Prox.	Dist.	Dist.
	Hum.	Tib.	Tib.	Uln.	Fem.	Hum.	Scap.	Fem.	Rad.	Uln.
right	f	-	-	f	-	?f	f	-	?f	-

Conclusions on this limb are tentative. The proximal humerus and distal radius are encased in concretion, but as far as visible appear to be fused, which would suggest an animal with a fully fused skeleton. Near to this forelimb is a mandible, no. 89-HS-067, with M5 in mid-late wear indicating an 'age' of 27 AEY, although there is no certain evidence that it is associated with the bones.

(e) Hindleg centered at 18S22W. This comprises the left femur, tibia, fibula, and some bones of the foot. The fusion states are:

	Dist.	Prox.	Dist.	Prox.	Dist.	Prox.	Prox.	Prox.	Dist.	Dist.
	Hum.	Tib.	Tib.	Uln.	Fem.	Hum.	Scap.	Fem.	Rad.	Uln.
left	-	f	f	-	f	-	-	f	-	-

It is not excluded that this hindlimb could belong with forelimb (d) above, which was found only ca. 2m distant from it.

A skull near to this hindleg, no. 028, has M5 in mid-late wear indicating an 'age' of 26-28 AEY, although there is no definite evidence of association.

2. Possibly associated but disarticulated partial skeletons

This section includes groups of bones found in close proximity, which are not in anatomical connection, but which may pertain to disarticulated individuals.

(a) <u>Bone group centered at 12N5E</u>.

This group comprises left scapula 225, left humerus 221, associated left radius 223 and ulna 222, left femur 224, and right humerus 230. The left and right humeri are insufficiently exposed for comparative measurements. There is also one complete pelvic girdle 227, two right half-pelves 002 and 240, some ribs, and an atlas vertebra. The fusion states of the long bones are as follows:

	Dist.	Prox.	Dist.	Prox.	Dist.	Prox.	Prox.	Prox.	Dist.	Dist.
	Hum.	Tib.	Tib.	Uln.	Fem.	Hum.	Scap.	Fem.	Rad.	Uln.
right	f	-	-	-	-	-	-	-	-	-
left	-	-	-	f	-	f	-	f	f	f

These data are consistent with a single animal. If the bones are indeed associated, they would represent a fully fused individual.

In likely association with the atlas vertebra is a skull, no. 203, with M6 in early-mid wear indicating an 'age' of 44 AEY.

(b) <u>Bone group centered at 19S23W</u>.

The following bones are grouped in this area: right scapula 001, right ulna 025, right radius 022, left scapula 009, left radius 015, left tibia 024, several ribs, vertebrae and foot bones. The two scapulae correspond precisely in measurements, as do the exposed proximal ends of the radii. The bones show the following fusion states:

	Dist.	Prox.	Dist.	Prox.	Dist.	Prox.	Prox.	Prox.	Dist.	Dist.
	Hum.	Tib.	Tib.	Uln.	Fem.	Hum.	Scap.	Fem.	Rad.	Uln.

right	-	-	-	-	-	-	n	-	n	n
left	-	-	f	-	-	-	-	-	-	-

These bones would be consistent with a single animal, of skeletal stage somewhere between tibia and humerus fusion. They lie quite close to the associated hindleg numbered 1(e) above, but are unlikely to be part of the same animal. First, bone group 1(e) already has a left tibia. Second, the proximal femur epiphysis is already fused in 1(e), which is not compatible with the unfused radius and ulna of this group.

Near this grouping is a skull, no. 028, with M5 in early-mid wear indicating an 'age' of 26-28 AEY, although there is no certain evidence of association with the bone group.

(c) <u>Bone group centered at 13S28W</u>.

This group of bones is placed close to the articulated skeleton 'Murray' (see above). It can be divided into two scatters. First, a closely spaced scatter of bones lying underneath the left part of Murray's skeleton, which cannot pertain to Murray because it duplicates elements already present in the latter: right humerus 525, right femur 439, femur 054, fibula 063, tibia 064 and pelvis 441. Second, there are some more widely scattered bones some of which may pertain to Murray (see above), but which might alternatively belong with the group just listed. These are right radius 060, left scapula 427, left humeri 047, 076, 462 and 077, and left ulnae 039 and 411. The fusion states of all of these bones considered together are as follows:

	Dist.	Prox.	Dist.	Prox.	Dist.	Prox.	Prox.	Prox.	Dist.	Dist.
	Hum.	Tib.	Tib.	Uln.	Fem.	Hum.	Scap.	Fem.	Rad.	Uln.
right	-	-	-	-	-	-	n	-	n	n
left	-	-	f	-	-	-	-	-	-	-

Prox. Scap.	Prox. Fem.	Dist. Rad.	Dist. Uln.
427 -	439 f	060 u	039 -
	054 -		411 u

In theory at least, most of these bones could belong to one individual, except for the obvious fact that only one of the four left humeri and one of the two left ulnae could be included; and that the unfused proximal humerus and fused proximal femur are unlikely to belong together as the former usually fuses before the latter.

Since this bone grouping is susceptible to various possible interpretations, it is not considered of value to discuss nearby skulls.

d) <u>Bone group centered at 9S31W.</u>

This group comprises a right scapula, right humerus 485, right radius 083 associated with right ulna 088 and some carpal bones, right femur 093, left scapulae 073 and 078, left radius 484 associated with left ulna 089, pelvis 097, and a group of ribs. The bones show the following fusion states:

	Dist.	Prox.	Dist.	Prox.	Dist.	Prox.	Prox.	Prox.	Dist.	Dist.
	Hum.	Tib.	Tib.	Uln.	Fem.	Hum.	Scap.	Fem.	Rad.	Uln.
right	-	-	-	-	f	f	(f)	f	u	u
left	-	-	-	f	-	-	-	-	-	-

Of the two left scapulae, 073 has the same glenoid diameter as the unnumbered right scapula, but 078 is bigger. With the exception of the latter bone, therefore, this group is consistent with a single animal, having recently completed proximal femur fusion.

Near to this group are a skull and two mandibles:

skull 070, M5 in mid wear, 26 AEY
mandible (83-215) 067, M5 in mid-late wear, 26-28 AEY
mandible 071, M5 in mid wear, 26 AEY.

One of these mandibles (071 is most likely) could belong to the skull, although there is no certain evidence of association with the bone group.

3. Isolated bones

Up to July 1991, a total of 85 partial or complete limb bones are regarded as isolated, as they were not found in clear association with others. Some of these are still *in situ*, but most are in store. In summary, the numbers of bones showing each fusion state (n=not fused, f=fused) are as follows (note that proximal and distal fibula fuse synchronously with the corresponding epiphyses of the tibia, and so have been placed adjacent to tibia in the chart):

	Dist. Hum	Prox. Tib.	Prox Fib.	Dist. Tib.	Dist. Fib.	Prox. Ulna	Dist. Fem.	Prox Hum	Prox. Scap.	Prox. Fem.	Dist. Rad.	Dist. Ulna
n	1	3	3	9	6	1	10	8	2	18	9	1
f	6	1	-	1	-	3	-	-	1	-	-	-

The specimens scored as 'n' (unfused) comprise mostly loose epiphyses, but also some shafts with the epiphyseal surface open. Taking into account also that the above table combines left and right elements, there are doubless fewer individual animals represented than the total bone number might suggest. Nonetheless, a sizeable number of individuals must be present (MNI for proximal femurs alone is 9), and it is striking that among these 'floating' bones there is an overwhelming preponderence of unfused specimens.

DISCUSSION

Fusion sequence

The first result of this study is that, so far as the data allow, there is no evidence for any difference between the order of epiphysis fusion in *M. columbi* and that of *M. primigenius*. In the tables of clearly associated skeletons (section 1 above), the epiphyses were listed in their order of fusion in *M. primigenius*, and in none of the charts does 'n' appear to the left of 'f', which would have indicated a reversed order. Nor for any of the bone types with clear difference in the timing of proximal and distal fusion in *M. primigenius* (humerus, radius, ulna, femur: Table 42) does a single bone from Hot Springs, associated or isolated, show the reversed order of fusion.

Skeletal and dental ages

Of skulls and mandibles found near to the bone groupings, only Napoleon (group 1a) is definitely associated. the skeleton is of an animal at or after the fusion of its distal radius and ulna; the skull and mandible show M6 in mid-wear. Within limits of error, this combination, provided the radius and ulna were not long fused, is consistent with findings on modern elephants and *M. primigenius* (Roth 1984; Haynes 1991; Lister in prep.). The dental wear-stage corresponds to an 'age' of 44-49 AEY by comparison with modern elephants.

The cervical vertebrae of bone group 2(a) are positioned relative to skull 203 in such a way that they are likely to be associated. The bone group suggests a fully fused male skeleton, a stage which is not reached in *M. primigenius* until M6 has all plates in wear, corresponding to an 'age' of about 47 AEY or older. In skull 203, the molar stage is a little less advanced than this, showing an 'age' of about 44 AEY. However, within limits of error, and provided the distal radius and ulna are not long fused, the tooth and bone 'ages' could correspond to the *M. primigenius* scheme.

None of the other bone groupings is clearly associated with a skull or mandible, but it is notable that in most cases, their state of epiphyseal fusion is more advanced than would be predicted from dental ageing of nearby jaws, or indeed of the Hot Springs dental sample considered as a whole. Dental ageing of the 52 jaws currently available from the site (see chapter 9) indicates only ca. 6% of specimens with an 'age of 40 AEY or older, with ca. 85% in the 10-29 AEY category. The isolated bone finds, which are largely unfused, are consistent with this dental 'age' distribution. In contrast, the predominance of fusion among the grouped bones is unexpected. These groupings, numbered as in the previous section, have fusion states which in *M. primigenius* skeletons are associated with the following dental 'ages' in AEY (based on Lister, in prep.): 1a = 44; 1b = 42-45; 1c = 45; 1d $\geq$ 47; 1e $\geq$ 45; 2a $\geq$ 47; 2b = 28-42; 2c uncertain; 2d = 45-47. Seven of these nine skeletal groups would thus fall into the $\geq$40 AEY category according to the *M. primigenius* scheme.

There are several possible explanations for this apparent anomaly. The first is chance sampling. The grouped bones comprise only five definitely associated individuals, plus four groups which may or may not be genuinely associated. More skulls of greater relative age, or more skeletally less mature bone associations, may be uncovered as excavation proceeds. There could be traphonomic reasons why older associated skeletons but younger 'floaters' and skulls are present in the peripheral areas of the sinkhole which have been excavated to date.

Another possible explanation is that the relationship of the fusion sequence to tooth eruption is different in the Hot Springs *M. columbi* population compared to the modern elephants and Eurasian *M. primigenius* which have been used as a 'standard'. Conceivably, the Hot Springs mammoths were in an exceptionally good nutritional state, so that they completed growth and fused their epiphyses at an early age. There is limited evidence for nutritional influence on age of epiphysis fusion in living elephants (Roth 1984). Alternatively, it may be that the tooth and epiphysis sequences had a different phase relationship in *M. columbi* in general, compared to that seen in modern elephants and *M. primigenius*. One possible reason for this could be the larger body size of *M. columbi*. Typical male body weights for this species have been estimated at 10 tons, compared to 6 tons for *M. primigenius* (Roth 1990). Extrapolating from the general rule among mammals (Wootton 1987), this size difference would suggest a significantly longer lifespan for *M. columbi* compared to *M. primigenius*. Suppose, for the sake of argument, that *M. primigenius* lived to *ca.* 60 years (as in living elephants, which are of approximately the same body size), but that *M. columbi* lived to 100 years. The progression of six teeth in the larger species would then be 'stretched out' over a longer period of time, so that any given dental 'age' (in AEY) corresponded to a higher absolute age than the same dental 'age' in the smaller species. Bone growth and fusion might also be expected to occur later in the larger species, but if this 'stretching out' were less prolonged than that of the dental progression, similar stages of bone fusion would appear at earlier (apparently 'younger') dental stages in the larger species than in the smaller. This could account for the greater proportion of fused individuals at Hot Springs than would be expected from the dental 'age' distribution. Some support for this idea is given by the Lange-Ferguson mammoth described by Mol and Agenbroad (this volume). This male individual of *M. columbi* has a dental 'age' of ca. 38 AEY, but all of its limb bone epiphyses are fused, a situation which is not seen in *M. primigenius* until dental ages of ca. 47 AEY (Lister in prep.; Table 42). On the other hand, Haynes (1990 stated that his studies of *M. columbi* and *M. primigenius* indicated that "the correspondence of fusion to dental stage is nearly identical." The examination of additional *M. columbi* skeletons with associated dentitions should resolve this question.

If the hypothesis of *Mammuthus primigenius* and *M. columbi* having a different phase relationship between their dental and fusion sequences is correct, there are implications for possible associations of jaws and postcrania within the Hot Springs bone bed. In particular, the largely fused postcranial groupings whose epiphyseal stages would correspond to dental 'ages' of 40-50 AEY in *M. primigenius* could in theory be associated with jaws of *M. columbi* giving dental 'ages' of 25-35 AEY; and the largely unfused isolated bones could correspond to the jaws of dental 'age' 10-25 AEY. Between them these two categories account for around 87% of dental remains (see chapter 9). Under this hypothesis, the dental 'ages' probably underestimate true ages, by an unknown amount. Significant events in the life-cycle of the Columbian mammoth might also have been 'stretched out' relative to its woolly cousin and the living elephants. However, it should be stressed that this model is hypothetical at present, and remains to be tested. Further material may show that Columbian and woolly mammoths had an essentially similar relationship of dental eruption and bone fusion to age, and an alternative explanation may account for the data on the Hot Springs assemblage presented in this paper.

Chapter 14

Mammuthus primigenius REMAINS FROM THE MAMMOTH SITE OF HOT SPRINGS, SOUTH DAKOTA

Larry D. Agenbroad, Adrian M. Lister,
Dick Mol, and V. Louise Roth

INTRODUCTION

The late Pleistocene woolly mammoth (*Mammuthus primigenius* (Blumenbach)) is a descendent of the southern elephant (*Mammuthus meridionalis* (Nesti)), which lived in Eurasia between about 2.5 and 0.7 million years ago. The evolution of the mammoth lineage in Eurasia progressed from *M.meridionalis*, through the Middle Pleistocene steppe mammoth (*Mammuthus trogontherii (Pohlig)),* to the late Pleistocene woolly mammoth (Maglio 1973; Lister in press c; and Van Essen and Mol in press). This transition entailed reduction in body size, heightening and shortening of the skull, heightening of the molar teeth, increased number of molar plates, and reduction of enamel thickness (Maglio 1973; Lister in press c). Transitional forms between the three hominal species can be difficult to categorize taxonomically, especially on the basis of the dentition alone (van Essen and Mol in press; Lister in press c).

The transition of *M. trogontherii* to *M. primigenius* took place approximately 400,000 to 250,000 years ago (Lister in press c), but most Eurasian woolly mammoth remains date from the Weichselian Stage (*ca.* 100,000 to 10,000 yr B.P.), which is the equivalent of the Wisconsin glaciation in North America (Kurtén and Anderson 1980; Van Essen and Mol in press). Most researchers regard *M. primigenius* in the New World as a late Pleistocene (Wisconsin) migrant from

Eurasia (Maglio 1973; Guthrie 1990).

In North America, a somewhat parallel process occurred, with the evolution from *Mammuthus meridionalis* to *Mammuthus imperator* (Leidy) and *Mammuthus columbi* (Falconer) through the Quaternary. Similar morphological changes occurred, but the specialization of *M. columbi* did not progress as far as in *M. primigenius.*

SOURCE OF THE SPECIMENS

As early as the 1975 field season, the first 'formal' season of excavation at the Hot Springs Mammoth Site, we excavated an isolated molar tooth which appeared to be referable to woolly mammoth. The similarity was noted in the field log, and the specimen was mapped and recorded. The tooth (field no. 75-110; now (MSL-726)) was recovered at map grid 6N7E, on the eastern margin of the sinkhole near the edge of the spring conduit. Since it was a single tooth, we adopted a conservative approach, awaiting the recovery of further material from the bone bed before to making a positive identification of *M. primigenius* at a site dominated by remains of *M. columbi.*

Toward the end of the 1987 field season, a damaged skull was recovered at map grid 6S5W, at the current southwest limit of the central excavation. The skull, HS-369, was of small size, and the tooth appeared to be characteristic of woolly mammoth.

DESCRIPTION

Except where indicated otherwise, terminology and measurements follow Maglio (1973).

Specimen MSL-726 (75-110): right maxillary M5 or M6

This specimen (Figure 100) is an isolated fragment of a right maxillary tooth, composed of 14 plates worn in occlusion. A slight convexity of the occlusal surface, the orientation of the plates in lateral view, and the height of the fragment, indicate its maxillary deri-

Figure 100. An isolate *M. primigenius* tooth (75-HS-110/MSL 726) from the Hot Springs Mammoth Site. The tooth length is 14 cm.

Figure 101. An *in situ M. primigenius* skull (87-HS-005/MSL-369).

vation). The anterior portion of the tooth has been lost by breakage. The maximum measured width of the crown is 83 mm, to which 2.5 mm can be added because of cement abrasion on the widest plate, giving a maximum original width of 85.5 mm. In the sample of *M. primigenius* from Predmosti, Czechoslovakia (*ca.* 26,000 yr B.P.; Musil 1968), M^5 widths (including cement) range from 76.0-95.5 mm (n-29), M^6 widths from 79.5-116.5 mm (n-40) (Lister in press a and unpublished data). The dimensions of the Hot Springs tooth are therefore consistent with either an M^5 or a small M^6. The posteriormost preserved plate shows traces of the sigmoid shape (concave below, convex above), due to the emplacement of another tooth behind, which is characteristic of all molars except M^6. This would suggest that the tooth is an M^5, and that the preserved back end of the specimen is close to the natural posterior face. If this is the case, not more than three plates are likely to have been lost anteriorly and posteriorly, since M^5 in *M. primigenius* rarely possesses more than 17 plates (Musil 1968; Maglio 1973). On the other hand, if the tooth is an M^6, as many as ten plates may have been lost. The covering cementum of the tooth is worn away in many areas, exposing the enamel, but where the cementum is preserved, it is very thin. Similarly, the enamel bands on the occlusal surface are somewhat eroded, but where well preserved, are thin.

Specimen HS-369 (87-HS-005): skull with molar

This damaged skull, found in an inverted position showing the palate and occipital region, remains *in situ* in the sinkhole fill (Figure 101). A left maxillary tooth is in place, with an empty alveolus behind it; teeth are missing from the two right, maxillary alveoli.

The molar has 12.5 plates and a posterior talon preserved (Table 43); its anterior end is worn flush with the bone ahead of it. Portions of one root remain embedded anterior to the tooth, on its lingual side. If this root was (as it appears to be) the most anterior one of the molar, then because of its distance from the remainder of the tooth, and because the first root of a tooth commonly supports three or four plates, we estimate that the tooth originally was composed of approximately 17 plates, in its unworn state. From this number, and the presence of a large (approximately 260 mm long) alveolar cavity behind, we identify the tooth as an M^5.

Cementum has eroded from the buccal face of the tooth, but originally was a maximum of 2 mm thick, given the narrow space remaining between the side of the tooth and the edge of the alveolar bone that houses it. On the uneroded lingual face of the tooth, between 0 and 3 mm of cementum remains. The anterior-posterior thickness (without cementum) of plates exposed on the buccal surface ranges from 4.5 to 7 mm. The enamel bands on the occlusal surface are somewhat eroded, making measurement difficult, but where well-preserved, they are thin. The maximum measured width of the crown is 90 mm, but all cement has eroded from this widest plate, so the original width was approximately 5 mm wider, i.e. 95 mm. This is just within the range of M^5 widths in the Predmosti *M. primigenius* sample (see above), indicating a large individual for this species.

METRIC ANALYSIS

The distinction between *M. primigenius* and *M. columbi* using isolated molars is based mainly on metrical attributes. In *M. primigenius*, the number of plates in the tooth, or in a given length of tooth (lamellar frequency) is higher, and the enamel bands are thinner. In addition, *M. primigenius* teeth are generally of smaller size than *M. columbi*, and the covering of cementum around the tooth tends to be thinner, but these two attributes are considered too variable within each species for reliable identification of isolated teeth. Measurements on the two putative *M. primigenius* teeth are given in Table 43, along with those for another tooth, no. MSL-727, which will be discussed later.

In Figures 102 and 103, lamellar frequency and enamel thickness are plotted for the two putative *M. primigenius* molars, together with the same measurements on all available *M. columbi* M5's from the Hot Springs Mammoth Site. The latter form well defined scat-

Table 43. Dimensions of putative *Mammuthus primigenius* molars from the mammoth Site of Hot Springs, South Dakota. Measurements in mm, taken according to the methods described by Maglio (1973).

Specimen no.	MSL 00726	HS00369	MSL 00727
tooth	upper M^5 (or M^6?)	upper M^5	upper M^4 (?)
maximum length of plate-bearing fragment	136	168	81
maximum length to anterior of root (where separate from remainder of tooth)		176	109
maximum width[1]	85.5	95	80
maximum measureable height of worn enamel plates of tooth	113[2]	149[2]	64[2]
Ditto, incl. roots	120[2]	159[2]	119[2]
modal enamel thickness[3]	1.3	1.2	1.6
lamellar frequency	10.9	10.2	8.5[4]
plate formula[5]	0140	012.5x	06.5-

[1] where cement abraded on widest lamella, the measurement has been increased on the basis of unabraded cement width observed elsewhere on the tooth.

[2] all plates are worn in occlusion

[3] the commonest enamel thickness, of measurements taken at numerous points on the occlusal surface.

[4] less than 10 cm of plate-bearing tooth fragment; lamellar frequency extrapolated from measurements on 6 plates.

[5] x = talon

ters, from which specimens 369 and 726 are very clearly displaced. A taxonomic distinction seems justified. Data on known *M. primigenius* from other localities correspond very well to the Hot Springs specimens. On a sample of 29 upper M^5's from the Predmosti site, lamellar frequencies range from 7.70 to 11.04, and mean enamel thickness on a sample of 28 teeth ranges from 1.1 to 1.7 mm (A.M. Lister, unpublished data; cf. Figures 102 and 103). Note that even if 726 is an M^6 (see above), the taxonomic distinction still holds—indeed, is more marked—since M^6 would be expected to have if anything lower lamellar frequency and higher enamel thickness than M^5.

In maximum molar width, the two specimens are consistent not

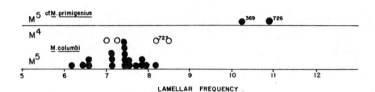

Figure 102. Lamellar frequency of upper molars from the Hot Springs Mammoth Site. LF of each specimen is averaged between four points of measurement: top and bottom of the crown, buccal and lingual.

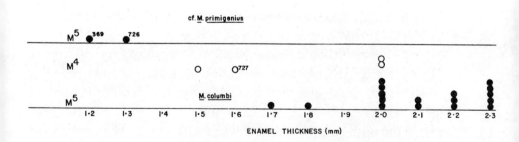

Figure 103. Enamel thickness of upper molars from the Hot Springs Mammoth Site. The value for each specimen is an average of measurements taken at various points on the tooth.

only with *M. primigenius* (see above), but also fall within the range of the *M. columbi* sample (Figure 104). This is a helpful result, as it means that the high lamellar frequencies cannot be accounted for as a compression effect due to small molar size, but is a genuine result of increased plate number (Lister and Joysey 1992).

The skull, no. 369, is unfortunately too damaged for detailed measurement or assessment of morphology. However, the appearance of the skull is small compared to the majority of the specimens at Hot Springs. One part of the skull available for measurement, which probably provides a reasonable reflection of skull size as a whole, is the region of the occipital condyles. In Table 44, height and width across the two condyles is given for skull 369, plus all other skulls from the Hot Springs Mammoth Site on which these measurements could be taken. The data on condyle width is plotted in Figure 105. The small size of the *M. primigenius* skull relative to the bulk of the *M. columbi* sample is clearly indicated. This corresponds to the generally smaller size of *M. primigenius*, whose shoulder height was on average about 1 m shorter than *M. columbi* (Mol and Agenbroad this volume). One other specimen, no. 89-HS-033, approaches 369 in small size (Figure 105). The dentition of this specimen indicates that it is unquestionably *M. columbi*. Possibly this specimen may represent one of the very rare females of the latter species occurring at the site (cf. Lister and Agenbroad this volume).

One further specimen merits discussion. This is an upper molar, no. MSL-727, discovered in 1984-85 during construction of the building now housing the mammoth site. This tooth has morphological characteristics (rather compressed lamellae, thin enamel, and thin cementum) which suggested it might pertain to woolly mammoth, and it has been displayed as such at the Mammoth Site. The specimen is the posterior-most remnant of a left molar. The relationship of the tooth to the surrounding bone suggests it had lost most of its plates in wear and had advanced to the front of the tooth row. Six and one half plates remain, the last two of which are damaged near the occlusal surface. The base of the last plate is covered with cementum that forms the natural posterior end of the tooth. The

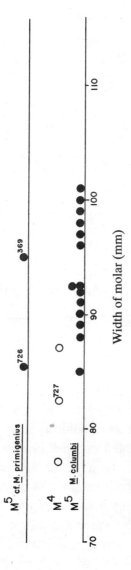

Figure 104. Maximum transverse width of upper molars from the Hot Springs Mammoth Site.

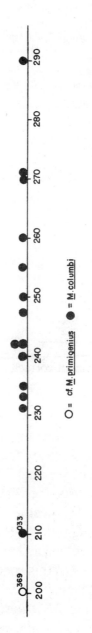

Figure 105. Occipital condyle width of mammoth skulls from the Hot Springs Mammoth Site. Closed circles: *M. columbi;* open circle: cf. *M. primigenius.*

Table 44. Occipital condyle measurements (mm) for *Mammuthus* skulls from the Mammoth Site of Hot Springs, South Dakota. Ages are given in 'African Equivalent Years' (Laws 1966).

Specimen no.	Age (AEY)	Transverse Diameter	Vertical Diameter
86-216	28	290*	121
HS-140	44-49	250	110
HS-154	24	242	109
HS-147	27	240	116
HS-203	44	271	116
HS-204	27	255	103
HS-293	28	247	111
HS-369	30	200*	103
HS-181		231	103
89-062	28	260*	116
HS-070	27	233	98
89-HS-033	28	210	97
HS-028	28	235	115
HS-205		270	
HS-146	24	240	112

*measurement corrected for distortion of fossil

posterior face of the tooth is concave, and the plates, in lateral view, angle anteriorly toward their base and follow this curvature, providing evidence of pressure from another tooth behind. In appearance, this specimen is somewhat borderline between *M. primigenius* and *M. columbi*. Metrical analysis of the tooth (Table 43 and Figures 102 - 105) suggests that it is most conformable as an M4 of *M. columbi*, rather than an M5 of *M. primigenius*. Although the sample of known M4's of this species from the site is small, specimen 727 fits well with them in size, lamellar frequency, and enamel thickness. Identification as *M. primigenius* cannot totally be ruled out, but at present we refer the specimen to *M. columbi*.

DISCUSSION

The two woolly mammoth (*Mammuthus primigenius*) specimens found to date have been located peripherally (Figure 106) and in the upper stratigraphic units of the site. This suggests a slightly younger time period in which they became victims of the sinkhole trap than the majority of other remains (predominately Columbian mammoth). The presence of a skull (HS00369) in the sinkhole fill suggests an active trap, and implies that a similar mode of entrapment operated for the woolly mammoths as for the Columbian mammoths.

A survey of North American mammoth finds (Agenbroad 1984a) reveals only one dated locality which records the presence of both species at the same site. This site, Empress, documents the presence of these species at *ca.* 20,400 yr B.P. in southeastern Alberta (Harington 1978). The ice front at *ca.* 20,000 yr B.P. was in closer proximity to Empress, Alberta than to Hot Springs, South Dakota. However, the ice front did extend into the Dakotas, at or just north of the present Missouri River. It appears that there may have been range overlap of the two species along, or proximal to, the ice front. This is also suggested by the distribution maps for the two species (Agenbroad 1984a), for which absolute dates (and therefore evidence on contemporaneity) are largely lacking.

The estimate of several hundred years for the infilling of the Hot Springs sinkhole could accommodate possible climatic perturbations, and concomitant range extensions or contractions, for both species. If the two species were incompatible in the same range, due to different requirements or to competition, a range shift caused by climatic changes could result in the presence of different species at the same locality at different times. On the other hand, it is conceivable that the two species co-existed at Hot Springs. Dated *Mammuthus primigenius* localities in the Yukon Territory and Alaska provide an antiquity for this species in the New World of over 39,000 years. Dates ranging between 30,000 and 11,000 yr B.P. are common for more southerly latitudes, so temporal contemporaneity with *M. columbi* is perfectly feasible.

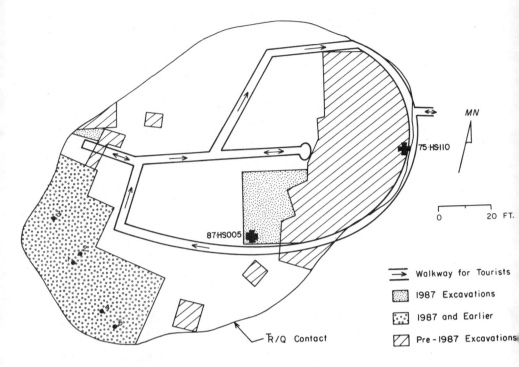

Figure 106. A location map of the two *M. primigenius* specimens.

Figure 107. A dot-map of reported occurrences of cf. *M. primigenius* localities in the north-central plains.

Based on species determinations reported in the literature, there are sparse records of *M. primigenius* in the north central Plains. Figure 107 is a dot–map of these reported localities. The Hot Springs record extends the known range of woolly mammoth by approximately 60 miles in a southwesterly direction.

The taxonomy of North American mammoths is confused (Agenbroad this volume, Table 11). Madden's (1981) unpublished dissertation states that there are no woolly mammoths (*Mammuthus primigenius*, or *M. mammonteus* in Madden's terminology) in the contiguous United States, and that they are found only in Alaska and Canada. He chose to use *Mammuthus jacksoni* for Late Pleistocene mammoth remains which had been reported as *M. primigenius* by earlier authors. Kurtén and Anderson (1980) considered *Elephas jacksoni* to be a synonym of *M. primigenius*, but suggest that animals which had been regarded as woolly mammoths south of Canada and the northeastern United States are probably to be referred to *M. jeffersoni*, a "progressive Wisconsin" form of the endemic North American mammoth line.

As a less confusing set of nomenclature, we favor Maglio's (1973) simpler scheme, in which *Elephas jeffersoni* (Osborn) is regarded as a synonym of *M. columbi*, and *Elephas jacksoni* (Mathes) as a synonym of *M. primigenius*. Maglio (1973) shows that the woolly mammoth was distributed in Alaska, Canada, and the northeastern United States.

PART III:

SITE SIGNIFICANCE, DEVELOPMENT AND FUTURE

Chapter 15

THE TAPHONOMY OF *MAMMUTHUS* REMAINS IN A CLOSED SYSTEM TRAP, HOT SPRINGS MAMMOTH SITE, SOUTH DAKOTA

Larry D. Agenbroad and Jim I. Mead

INTRODUCTION

As many as 47 mammoths (45 *Mammuthus columbi, 2 Mammuthus primigenius)* individuals, and one giant short-faced bear (*Arctodus simus*), have been exhumed in excavations at the Mammoth Site of Hot Springs, South Dakota. Dental remains from single individuals of camel, shrub ox, wolf and coyote have also been recovered; however, the lack of skeletal elements for the animals suggests the dentition may have washed into the deposit from outside the sinkhole. These animals represent remains recovered in the excavation of approximately 30% of the site's total volume. A sinkhole containing a spring fed pond created the natural trap and the sedimentary environment in which the mammoths were entombed. Postmortem processes were those contained within the geological and hydrological systems working inside this natural trap. The trap was selective for juvenile and young-adult mammoths, and at least one scavenging short-faced bear. Analyses of bone distribution, the configuration of sinkhole margins, bank caving, and the hydrologic system account for the taphonomic distribution of the faunal remains.

TAPHONOMY OF THE HOT SPRINGS MAMMOTH SITE

The study of the processes that bones go through from the death of a living animal to the final deposition and burial is known as taphonomy. Behrensmeyer (1975), Saunders (1977), Behrensmeyer and Hill (1980), and Shipman (1981), among others, have done much to trace the history and development of this aspect of paleontology. Saunders (1977) lists groupings of sedimentary environments in recent taphonomic analyses. He cites fluviatile, floodplain, deltaic, lacustrine, and upland environment and notes that prior to his publication . . . "spring environments are unrepresented in the taphonomic literature."

The Hot Springs Mammoth Site (Figure 108) represents a unique combination of spring and lacustrine environments which formed as a result of the special conditions provided by a karst feature in a particular geologic environment. The Hot Springs assemblage represents a thanatocoenosis (death assemblage) of mammoth in the unusual circumstance of an untransported, or minimally transported, accumulation in a springfed pond within a karst depression. Therefore, the Hot Springs assemblage represents an attritional thanatocoenosis of a large number of mammoths in an environment not duplicated elsewhere in the world.

Death, decomposition, disarticulation, minor downslope, subaqueous, transport and deposition took place within the confines of a small bowl-like depression with no transport mechanism available except those which occurred within that depression. Those processes were: 1) artesian spring discharge; 2) overbank flow, into the sinkhole, and 3) subaqueous gravity movements. One other factor that could account for emplacement of some elements of the assemblage would be bloating and floating of decomposing carcasses.

Data for the interpretation of the assemblage at this site are derived primarily from the detailed sedimentation and stratigraphic studies of Laury (1980) and the biological/paleontological evidence in the form of distribution, abundance, and degree of disarticulation represented in the partial recovery of the bone bed by excavation.

Origin of the Hot Spring Thanatocoenose

As Saunders (1977) has stated, "Taphonomy begins at death." In the case of the Hot Springs mammoth, death came about in one of

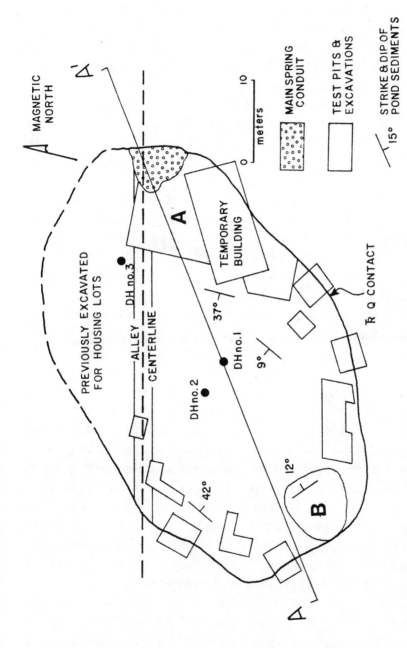

MAGNETIC NORTH

A'

PREVIOUSLY EXCAVATED FOR HOUSING LOTS

DH no.3

ALLEY CENTERLINE

DH no. 2

DH no.1

42°

37°

9°

12°

A

B

TEMPORARY BUILDING

₮ Q CONTACT

0   10

meters

MAIN SPRING CONDUIT

TEST PITS & EXCAVATIONS

15° STRIKE & DIP OF POND SEDIMENTS

A

A'

Figure 108. A plan map of the Mammoth Site at Hot Springs, indicating test pits, excavations, drill holes and a temporary structure (1979).

285

two ways: 1) by drowning or 2) by starvation.

An explanation is called for in both cases, as elephants in general are excellent swimmers. The special circumstances present at Hot Springs were in the form and nature of the trap. The wall rock of the sinkhole is the Spearfish Formation, a red, gypsiferous, sandy shale of Permo-Triassic age, from 250 to 700 feet thick (Rahn and Gries 1973). The contact between the Spearfish and the sinkhole-fill materials was observed to be no less than 60°; in some cases, such as near the conduit, the walls were overhanging. It has been estimated by various evidence that the depth of water in the sinkhole was 4 to 5 m (Laury 1980), at least in early stages in the history of the pond. A mammoth, attracted into the sinkhole by water or bankside vegetation, was trapped on entering the pond, whether the entry was made by intent, or by accident, such as by sliding the last few feet on submoistened Spearfish Shale. Once immersed, the mammoth had little or no hope of extricating itself because of the steepness of the walls and the slipperiness of the submoistened shale. The doomed animal could only swim until exhausted or position itself near the wall on whatever slump block, shelf, or sediment allowed foothold. If drowning did not claim the victim, starvation ultimately would.

This model of entrapment is supported by the distribution and condition of the faunal remains. It became apparent in the initial seasons of excavation that most of the bones were to be found within 6 meters of the Spearfish wall rock. Conversely, the central portions of the pond fill seemed to be relatively devoid of bone, as indicated by backhoe trenching and test pits dug for stratigraphic and sedimentation information and mapping. In addition, the fact that most of the bone was partially disarticulated argues for pond-side decomposition of the carcass and disarticulation of the skeleton. The bones became units within the sedimentary sequence by sliding and rolling down subaqueous sedimentary slopes, until they reached their final resting place and were covered by the sediments.

Alternatively, a case can be made for partial and completely articulated skeletal units being incorporated as units. The discovery of several articulated feet suggests deposition and burial (some in deep-water portions of the pond) as complete skeletal components. Presumably ligaments and other tissue held these small bones in articulation until after burial. In the final week of the 1979 field season, a completely articulated skeleton of a mature mammoth was discovered. The animal was in the deepest excavation area of the site (excluding drill holes and the deep trench of 1979). The skeleton was just west of the major spring conduit (Figure 108) and had apparently sunk in that location after having been afloat in the pond. The position of the skeleton (Figure 96) suggests that it sank on its back, with the skull rotating 160° to 180° to the right due to the weight of the tusks. Apparently the carcass sank in this location prior to final decomposition since small bones, such as hyoids, were still in anatomical position, and a gland stone (bile stone) was found in the approximate location of the organs in which it was produced. Test pits along the periphery of the pond-fill exposed other partially articulated specimens. In the western portion of this sinkhole, as many as six partially articulated individuals are present in close proximity (Figures 56 and 96). One animal is fully articulated, minus the skull, and deposited on top of another articulated individual (Figure 57).

Thirty-one mastodons (*Mammut americanum*) at Boney Springs, Missouri, died because of drought and nutritional deficiency, according to Saunders (1977). Based on Kurtén's population work (1953) and the age structure of the population, Saunders concludes that there was a mass mortality.

At Hot Springs the trapped animals represent young adults and mature animals (Agenbroad 1984a, 1989, 1990; Agenbroad and Mead 1986; Dutrow 1980). Scarcity of juveniles and aged animals argues against a catastrophic assemblage or a mass accumulation (Voorhies 1969) of a single herd of gregarious mammoth. The Hot Springs mammoth assemblage denotes a behavioral, or selective, death assemblage (Figure 109), a new model of natural death assemblage. The sedimentary evidence of superimposed mammoth tracks, preserved in vertical section of excavation walls, indicates continuing entrapment of occasional animals. Bones are also incorporated throughout the sedimentary sequence, which may represent several

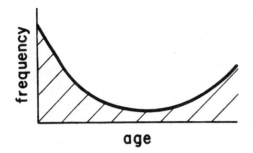

a. ATTRITIONAL
DEATH ASSEMBLAGE

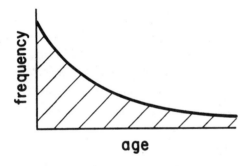

b. CATASTROPHIC
DEATH ASSEMBLAGE

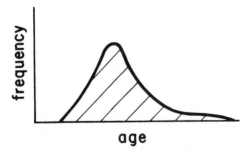

c. SELECTIVE
DEATH ASSEMBLAGE

Figure 109. Age-frequency graphs for death assemblages resulting from: a) attritional accumulation, b) catastrophic accumulation, and c) selective (behavioral) accumulation as represented by the Mammoth Site.

288

hundred years in duration.

Predation

Predators apparently played a very minor part in bone disarticulation. Although coyote, wolf, and short-faced bear have been recovered from the Mammoth Site, the minimum number of individuals represents only one animal in each case. It is quite possible, that with the exception of one short-faced bear, these remains reflect the chance accumulation of carnivore and scavenger elements as a result of overbank flow, rather than an accumulation of animals actually present in the sinkhole. It is equally possible that the decomposing carcasses did attract scavengers. The mammoth bones have not, as yet, produced evidence of carnivore action such as gnawing. It is possible that the amount of available flesh on the carcass, or the aqueous nature of the depositional site precluded major bone utilization.

At the Hot Springs Site, excavation of the remains of predators has been confined to the southwest corner of the sinkhole. In contrast, it appears that mammoth remains are scattered rather uniformly along the circumference of the sinkhole pond; as yet, the northern margin is not adequately tested. It also appears that numerous large blocks of Spearfish Shale, the sinkhole wallrock, have collapsed into the western and southwestern margins of the pond (Figures 110 and 111). These blocks may have provided a bench of relatively stable footing for those animals entrapped in the sinkhole who were attempting escape. This may also have been the area of most probable egress and ingress from the sinkhole for scavengers, although the exhumed sinkhole walls are very steep in this area.

It is likely that the southwest portion of the pond was the only bankside area that allowed partial exposure to the dead, or dying mammoths. The submerged collapse blocks may have provided a shelf, or bench in this area. Wolves, bears and other scavengers were active in this region, as contrasted to other portions of the pond, for the reasons outlined above. It is in this same area that the skeletal and dental remains of wolf and bear have been recovered. It is also the area from which wolf and bear coprolites have been retrieved. The co-occurrence of predator remains and predator fecal material (Figure 111), plus geologic and hydrologic criteria indicate that this was the area of exposure or partial exposure of victims, allowing the optimum potential for scavengers.

It is likely that multiple individuals of both species were active in the sinkhole, mainly ingesting the flesh of the most recent sinkhole victims, however occasional bone fragments are found in the coprolites. No mammoth bones from the site have yet yielded evidence of gnawing or carnivore/scavenger modification. The wolf individual recovered from the site is a very old specimen according to our analysis of the dentition. The short-faced bear was a young-adult male. It either represents a bear which was unable to negotiate an escape due to steep, slippery sinkhole walls, or it may be one individual, from a group of several bears, who suffered a fatality. That fatality could have occurred as a blow from a not-so-dead mammoth, or from competition with other scavenger/predators.

Bone Breakage

Bone from the site does give other evidence of postmortem or death processes which have been interpreted in various ways by other investigators. A small but conspicuous percentage of bones displays spiral fractures (Table 45) — usually considered to be "green bone" breaks. It should also be noted that there is an absence of evidence of subaerial bone decomposition and weathering; possible exceptions are the cases in which bones were exposed during the erosion that postdated the destruction of the trap, after it ceased to function due to infilling by sedimentary processes and the decline of hydrologic activity.

At other late Pleistocene sites Irving and Harington (1973), Stanford (1979), and others have interpreted the presence of green bone breaks of mammoth bones to be representative of human activity. Human butchering of Hot Springs mammoth is very unlikely. The spiral fractured bones from Hot Springs (Agenbroad 1989) are

290

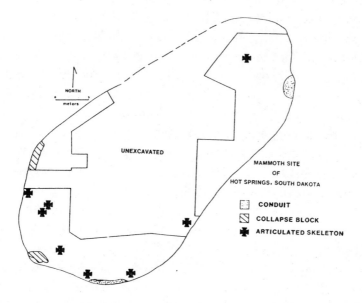

Figure 110. A location map for the articulated known skeletal remains at Hot Springs.

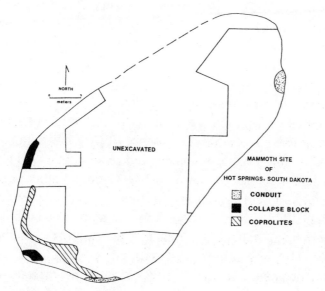

Figure 111. A distribution plot of carnivore coprolites at the Mammoth Site.

indicative of the breaking of fresh bone, or of bone broken shortly postmortem (Figure 112). The processes that would provide such breakage are limited to four categories (Table 46), exclusive of human activity. The most probable processes include: 1) torsional stress, as caused by trying to extricate a limb mired in mud, muck, or quicksand — stress possibly even enhanced by an accompanying accidental fall; or 2) the possibility of trampling of recently deceased animals by newly entrapped individuals. The intricate intermixing of bones, as evidenced in their excavation, suggests abundant opportunity for limbs to provide "anvil" associations which could have been stepped on by living animals—with the mass or an elephant—to provide sufficient force to cause spiral fractures. Sediment-loading is considered to be inconsequential as a factor in production of spiral fractures in this deposit.

Additional fracturing of bone was noted in several locations within the excavated portions of the bone bed. These fractures are a consequence of displacement of units of the fill materials due to compaction and desiccation upon the cessation of the hydrologic activity of the site or other post-depositional movements. Small fracture zones with up to several centimeters of relative displacement were observed to cut across bone accumulations adjacent to the spring conduit. In one case, a skull was fractured and the opposing elements displaced slightly (Figure 113). Several pelves and long bones, as well as tusks, displayed similar breakage in an adjacent area.

Additional postmortem agents in the distribution of faunal elements are at least twofold. The absence of long bones in sufficient quantity to match crania, scapulae, and pelvic bones (Figure 114) suggests that these elements were concentrating in other portions of the deposit. As a field hypothesis, we coined an "index of rollability," suggesting that long bones such as femora, radii, ulnae, fibula, tibia, and humeri, being rather cylindrical in shape, might roll on the steep, subaqueous slopes to come to rest in deeper, as yet unexcavated portions of the deposit. Conversely, ribs, scapulae, pelves, and so forth, which have a low rolling probability were found throughout the excavations. Skull emplacement follows a different process. Though

Table 45. Spiral fractured mammoth bone at the Hot Springs Mammoth Site, South Dakota.

Specimen No.	Bone ID	Description
74-10-24-9b	long bone (?)	distal/proximal
75-8-32	humerus fragment	medial-lateral spiral fracture diagonal to long axis of bone
76-19	long bone (?)	2 fractures directed in opposite orientations
76-34	long bone (?)	intersecting diagonal medial/lateral fractures
76-82	scapula (?)	medial lateral toward edge of blade
76-100	scapula/pelvis (?)	three fractures, producing "wedge" flake
76-364	scapula/pelvis (?)	removal of several flakes along "lunate" surface
79-11	scapula	spiral fracture across blade; hinge fracture of opposite direction
79-169	long bone (?)	two, intersecting fractures, medial-lateral
(No number)	scapula/pelvis (?)	spiral fracture near thinning edge of bone
(No number)	humerus	2 spiral fractures of "green bone" nature, with "dry bone" breakage, post-spiral fracturing

Table 46. Bone modification processes at the Hot Springs Mammoth Site.

1. Biological
   a) trampling
   b) torsion/falling
   c) carnivore

2. Hydrological
   a) spring effluent
   b) sub-aqueous down slope movement

3. Geological/Structural
   a) post-depositional movement

4. Mechanical
   a) boulder fall
   b) freezing
   c) overbank fall

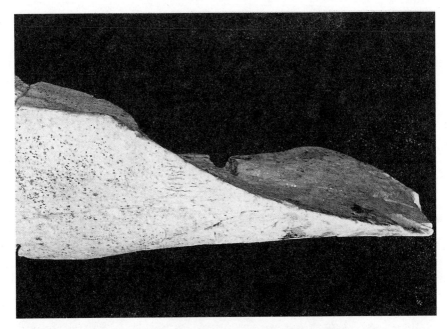

Figure 112. Spiral fractured mammoth bone (Agenbroad 1989).

Figure 113. Bone fracture by differential compaction and desiccation of the sinkhole deposits.

weighted by molars and ivory, the skull is buoyed by the cancellous material of the maxilla, nasal regions, and even the cranial vault. Visual evidence of a floating proboscidean cranium was provided on the 1979 Friends of the Pleistocene field trip to Agate Basin, Wyoming. George Frison and his crew were mascerating the skull of a recently deceased zoo elephant in a stock pond near the Agate Basin archaeological site. The skull floated in the pond and moved about in response to wind direction. Even with the attachment of weights and forced immersion, the skull continued to float in the pond. Such a mechanism could account for the abundance of skulls, tusks and mandibles located throughout the excavations (Figure 115).

Mammoth Bone Distribution

Voorhies (1969) studied skeletal element dispersal of sheep and coyotes in a stream-table experiment. His results are presented in Table 47 (a). Lag elements are those least likely to be transported and the immediate category represents those most likely to be transported. Those elements grouped between 'immediate' and 'gradual' categories indicate movement intermediate between those groups.

Taphonomic frequency in that portion of the Hot Springs bone bed that has been excavated shows a similar pattern. Figures 115, 116 and 117 show the relative abundance of selected skeletal elements of the mammoths from the Hot Springs Mammoth Site. Table 47 (b) provides a similar transport frequency for the sinkhole with an artesian spring fed pond environment at the Mammoth Site.

Todd and Frison (1986) conducted some fluvial experiments with selected bones of a mature, female, Indian elephant (*Elephas maximus*). Using their data from transport experiments in Plumbago Creek, Wyoming (especially table 2.2) they established a hierarchy of bone transport for that animal, in that hydraulic environment. Of importance, in their experiments, is a tripartate grouping of elements into: least transported; moderately transported, and most transported elements (Table 47 (c)).

Differences in placement of elements in the stream table experi-

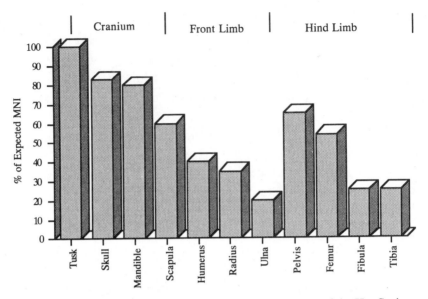

Figure 114. A relative abundance graph of selected elements of the Hot Springs mammoths. One half the tusk population is considered to be 100% of the population (MNI).

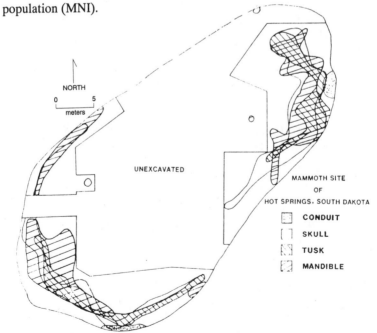

Figure 115. Cranial elements distribution map.

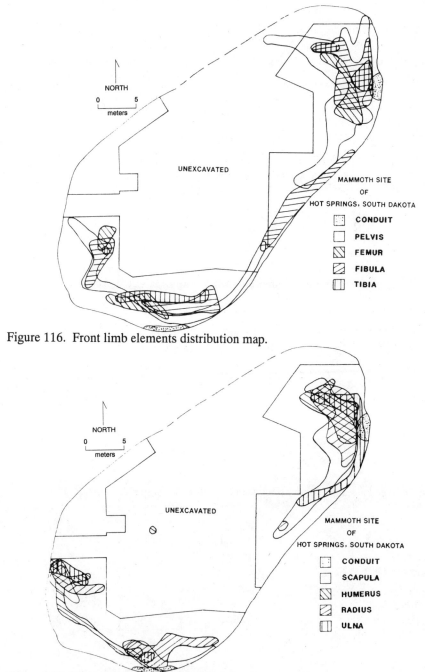

Figure 116. Front limb elements distribution map.

Figure 117. Hind limb elements distribution map.

297

Table 47. Dispersal of skeletal elements in laboratory (a) and field (b), (c).

a) Voorhies (1969) stream table transport of skeletal elements of coyote and sheep.

Immediate		Gradual	Lag
ribs		femur	skull
vertebrae	scapula	tibia	mandible
sacrum	phalanges	humerus	
sternum		metapodia	
	ulna	pelvis	
		radius	

(underlined elements equate to the selected elements studied at Hot Springs)

b) Hot Springs Mammoth Site inferred transport of selected skeletal elements of mammoths (greatest dispersal potential = highest position in column)

Immediate		Gradual		Lag
ulna		femur		tusks
fibula		humerus		skull
tibia	radius		pelvis	mandible
			scapula	

in both a) and b) those elements listed between groupings are intermediate between transport groups.

c) Selected Asian elephant bone transport in Plumbago Creek (Todd and Frison 1986)

Immediate	Gradual	Lag
vertebrae	humerus	crania
sacrum	fibula	tusk
patella	scapula	pelvis
astragalus	tibia	femur
calcaneum	metacarpals	mandible

ments and stream with semi-controlled hydraulics as compared to the sinkhole model can be explained, in part, by the hydraulic forces at work and the slope (and shape) of the confinement (stream table, stream banks, sinkhole). Figure 118 depicts a theoretical breakdown of the components of forces acting on a skeletal element in fluvial and hydro-karst environments. Case 1 is a model of deposition in a stream; case 2 is a model of deposition in a sinkhole pond, a) adjacent to, and b) removed from, the vicinity of an artesian spring conduit. Additional factors affecting bone deposition would be the size and shape of a bone, and its specific gravity, i.e. relatively flat, large area bones of the same density may settle differently than cylindrical elements. In the sinkhole environment, lateral velocity is minimal near the spring conduit. As a result, gravity is the greatest force working on bone deposition. Considering the pond floor, at least near the spring conduits, may have had an angle of ± 30° (average angle of repose) the gravity component would become a dominant force acting on bone. The current stage of taphonomic analysis of the Mammoth Site bones indicates the relative absence of lower limb elements and upper limb elements (in that order) with respect to cranial elements (Figure 114).

Plots of the distribution of selected cranial and postcranial elements (Figures 115, 116, 117) were generated for comparative distribution of elements. The figures demonstrate both similarities and anomalies of bone distribution and deposition. In general, they reconfirm the anomalous absence of lower limb bones, but they also demonstrate the differential distribution of these elements, as compared to upper limb bones and scapulae or pelves. Although all skeletal elements that have been discovered are confined to the areas of excavation thus far, there appears to be a non-random distribution of groups of elements.

Selected elements were separated into two groups (Figure 119): Group A: triangular, flat, or very curved elements and Group B: tubular elements, allows testing for distribution similarities. Voorhies (1969) experiments with skeletal element transport on a stream table resulted in three groupings of elements (Table 47). The stream table experiments were to replicate longitudinal transport of elements, as in a streambed. The Mammoth Site sinkhole hydraulics were not longitudinal, due to the configuration of the trap, yet even with a downslope movement, similarities to longitudinal stream flow should be recognizable. Voohries experiments indicate an immediate, downstream removal of scapulae and ulnae (using only those elements depicted in Figure 119) followed by removal of femorae, tibiae, humeri, pelves, and radii, leaving skulls and mandibles as lag deposits.

Within the sinkhole depositional environment, there would be several hydraulic and depositional factors that would differ as compared to stream transport and deposition. The only hydraulically active area of the sinkhole environment would be the artesian spring conduits (as contrasted to the down-gradient current in a stream), which would be reverse in direction of force (upward) contrasted to the downgradient direction of stream flow. Additionally, gravity would work as a downward, depositional (settling) force in each environment. In the sinkhole, gravity settling would be opposed by artesian pressure, in the vicinity of the spring effluent, but essentially unopposed in other areas. Another control for bone settling would be the angle of the bottom of the sinkhole pond. We have several lines of evidence that the floor of the pond was relatively steeply inclined: 1) subaqueous gravity flow structures; 2) post depositional deformation toward the center—after a decline of the hydraulic gradient; 3) the distortion of Murray's skeleton (even though some of the displacement is surely post depositional); 4) the thickness of the infilling sedimentary units toward the center of the deposit, as contrasted to the edge; and 5) the paucity of bone in the central portions of the fill, until considerable depth is reached.

If our model of bankside death and disarticulation is correct, then the downslope movement should approximate the same order of down gradient transport as Voorhies (1969) flume experiments. Examination of the bone distribution plots indicates similar patterns of deposition for scapulae and pelves —which are similar in size and shape. The scapulae are more tightly grouped, however. Skulls display a similar pattern, but are more widely distributed than pelves or

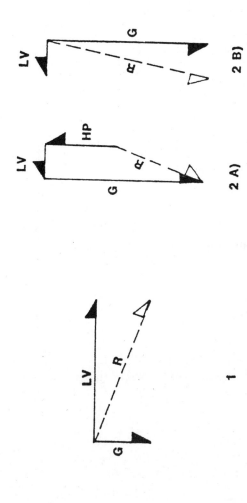

Figure 118. Relative components of stream (case 1) and sinkhole (case 2) depositional forces; G = gravity; LV = lateral velocity; P = hydraulic pressure (artesian flow); R = resultant of forces. Case 2a) represents the depositional environment adjacent to the artesian spring; 2b) represents the depositional environment distant from the artesian spring.

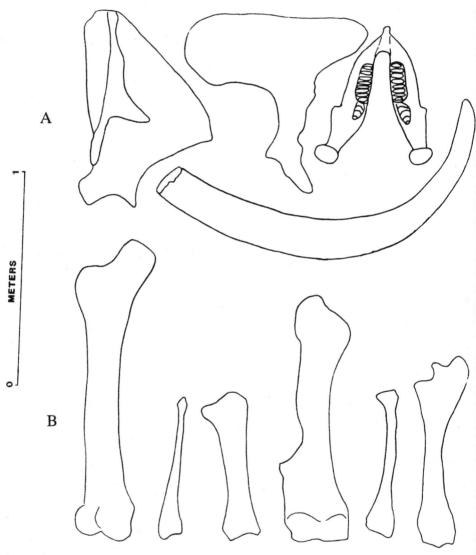

Figure 119. Apparent groupings of skeletal elements with differing transport
and depositional characteristics. The tusks, mandibles, pelves, and scapulae
form a highly represented group; the limb elements form a poorly represented
group at Hot Springs.

scapulae. Femorae and humeri display somewhat similar patterns, but radii, ulnae, fibulae and tibiae are less dispersed and are often tightly concentrated in small areas. The disproportionate number of lower limb elements, as contrasted to upper limb elements argues for additional depositional forces at work on the lower limb elements. In the front limb, considering the number of scapulae as representing 100%, there is a 34% loss in humeri, a 40% loss in radii, and a 70% loss in ulnae. Similarly, in the hind limb, considering the number of pelves as 100%, there is a 13% loss in femora, and a 62% loss in both the fibulae and tibiae.

An additional factor affecting distributional plots is the fact that several mammoth individuals, or portions of individuals are still in articulation. This articulated depositional mode reflects a different distributional effect, compared to the disarticulated remains (isolates), and would not follow the theoretical transport models.

When considering the total distributional plot of an element, as contrasted to the isolate plot of that element, differences are rapidly noted. Total distributional plots include isolates and partially articulated specimens. Elements which were deposited as part of a large unit (corpse) of an individual respond differently to taphonomic processes than do isolate bones, in the same environment. Figure 110 depicts the distribution of whole, or partially articulated (>1/4 of the animal) individuals. It will be noted that the majority (3/4) of these specimens occur in the southwestern portion of the sinkhole, coincident with the occurrence of carnivore/scavenger coprolite distribution (Figure 111) and the known occurrence of collapse blocks of Spearfish Shale, in the sinkhole. Elimination of the articulated elements from the distribution plots gives a very concentrated distribution for isolate elements.

DISCUSSION

The sinkhole environment, which has become the Mammoth Site of Hot Springs, South Dakota, was selective for juvenile and young-adult mammoths (Agenbroad 1990). The deposit also contains one giant short-faced bear). Other large vertebrates are represented by dentition from a single individual, in each case, and may represent material washed into the sinkhole from surrounding uplands. The presence of multiple coprolites assigned to wolf, plus the single wolf tooth suggests these animals were entering, and leaving the sinkhole to feed on dead and dying mammoths. Carnivore/scavenger skeletal remains and coprolites have only been recovered from the west-south-west portion of the deposit. This limited occurrence is also proximal to large bank collapse blocks of Spearfish Shale which collapsed into the sedimentary fill. We propose that the presence of these blocks gave more stable subaerial footing for entrapped mammoths than was present at other portions of the sinkhole edge. It is here that three-quarters of the articulated mammoths from the site occur. This location also provided the best opportunity for carnivore/scavenger feeding from such carcasses.

In other portions of the sinkhole pond the skeletal remains disarticulated at, or near, the pond margins. Downslope subaqueous gravity movement was the dominant depositional force acting on the disarticulated bones. It appears there was a segregation of mandible, tusks, crania, scapulae, and pelves into a "lag" group of elements. Front and hind limb bones are less well represented in comparison to the "lag" group, and appear to have been the "mobile" group of elements. The lower limb elements (fibula, tibia, radius, ulna) are particularly underrepresented in the deposit. Our conclusion is that these elements moved more quickly down the sloping floor of the pond, and will be encountered in the deposit at greater depth of excavation.

Separation of the articulated elements (deposited as the unit) from the isolate (disarticulated) elements indicates the majority of limb bones are concentrated near the north eastern spring conduit. By contrast, the cranial elements, scapulae, and pelves are widely scattered along the margins of the deposit.

Processes within the sinkhole environment were the only ones acting on the sinkhole victims. Ultimately all elements of each individual will be recovered as excavation continues. Loss of elements by erosional processes, such as those present in stream transport, are lacking in this deposit. The major depositional force within the sink-hole is gravity, as contrasted to lateral velocity combined with gravity in a fluvial system.

Dispersal (transport) of skeletal elements at Hot Springs is similar to the stream table experiments of Voorhies (1969), but the metapodials appear to disperse more rapidly in the Hot Springs environment. Tusks comprise an additional lag elements not present in Voorhies' animals.

Chapter 16

CARNIVORES FROM THE MAMMOTH SITE, HOT SPRINGS, SOUTH DAKOTA

Gennady Baryshnikov, Larry D. Agenbroad, and Jim I. Mead

INTRODUCTION

The Mammoth Site at Hot Springs (HSMS), South Dakota, is a sediment-filled sinkhole that held a spring-fed pond during the Wisconsin Glacial of the late Pleistocene (Agenbroad this volume). Details of the chronology, geology, paleontology, and paleoenvironmental reconstructions can be found in other chapters in this volume. Radiometric age assignment is approximately 26,000 years before present (Agenbroad this volume), which is equivalent to the Farmdalian interstadial elsewhere in North America. Implications from the scant pollen data are that the local environment around the sinkhole during the mid-Wisconsin was a cold steppe-grassland habitat (Mead *et al.* this volume). The temperature of the pond cannot be estimated solely on the basis of the presented pollen and molluscan record, but it seems reasonable to assume from the data at hand that temperatures were between 30° and 35° C - a "warm water oasis" (Mead *et al.* this volume).

The sinkhole acted as a natural trap accumulating remains of large animals, particularly *Mammuthus* (mammoth). Wet sieving of the spring deposits has allowed recovery of the remains of small and medium-sized vertebrates that were previously poorly known at the site and in the late Pleistocene of South Dakota generally. Apparently the "mammoth trap" acted as a death repository for other more agile vertebrates, creating a biothanosis for much of the local faunal

Table 48. Carnivores from the Mammoth Site, Hot Springs, South Dakota.

	MNI
Order Carnivora	
Family Mustelidae	
Mustela cf. *vison/nigripes* - mink/black-footed ferret	1
Taxidea taxus - badger	1
Family Canidae	
Canis lupus - gray wolf	1
Canis latrans - coyote	1
Family Ursidae	
Arctodus simus - short-faced bear	1

community. Next to proboscidians, carnivores and rodents are the most abundant mammals recovered from the Mammoth Site. This paper details the carnivores recovered from the Mammoth Site. Table 1 lists the carnivore taxa identified.

SPECIES ACCOUNT

Mustela cf. *vison/nigripes* (Schreber 1777, Audubon and Bachman, 1851) (mink/black-footed ferret) MNI = 1
Referred Material: radius. The size of the radius did not permit differentiation to species.

Postcranial skeletal variation is poorly known in wild mustelids and the sole specimen currently at hand does not permit a precise species identification. The nearness to riparian habitat of the sinkhole during Pleistocene times and the presence of fish fossils indicate fish populations that could have attracted a mink to the pond. Alternatively, the abundance of prairie dogs and ground squirrels might have attracted a black-footed ferret to the area. Other small vertebrates (Czaplewski and Mead this volume) would have provided prey for either of these mustelids, and either could be represented by the radius. Both species are known historically from the southern Black Hills region (Turner 1974).

Taxidea taxus (Schreber 1778) (badger) MNI = 1

Referred material: Left 3rd phalanx.

The 3rd phalanges are distinctive on *Taxidea* due to their aggressive digging behavior. The angle of the claw, its length and the lateral compression indicate the specimen to be *Taxidea*.

The specimen was recovered while screen washing matrix. It is assumed to be of the age of the mammoth, and not intrusive from a later age. Badgers will dig large deep holes and one therefore capable of digging down into the layers containing the mammoth remains. No such obvious intrusive holes have ever been noticed cutting into the finely laminated layers at the site. *Taxidea* lives in the Black Hills today, and apparently has done so at least for the past 26,000 years.

Canis lupus (Linnaeus 1758) (gray wolf) MNI=1

Referred material: Left M_1.

A 30% fragment of the lower first molar is from an old individual. Most of the tooth is broken so that only a portion of the buccal side preserved. Although incomplete, enough was recovered that permitted comparison with those of Pleistocene-age *Canis dirus* (dire wolf) and *C. lupus* from Rancho La Brea, California, all in equal stages of occlusal wear. The tooth proves to be smaller than any of those from *C. dirus* and therefore is assigned to the gray wolf. The gray wolf was abundant in the Black Hills but unfortunately were totally erradicated by 1934 (Turner 1974).

The length of the talonid is 8.1 mm.

Canis latrans (Say 1823) (coyote) MNI=1

Referred material: Canine. Fragment of a canine.

The slender size and shape of the canine is consistent with those from *Canis latrans*. The coyote is well distributed today throughout the Black Hills (Turner 1974).

Arctodus simus (Cope 1879) (short-faced bear) MNI=1

Referred material: Skull, left and right mandibles, atlas, axis, 3rd,

4th, and 5th cervicals, 12th and 13th thoracics, 1st, 2nd, 3rd, and 4th lumbars, left pelvis, and left tibia.

DESCRIPTION OF *ARCTODUS SIMUS*
Cranium

The cranium (83HS142) is complete and only slightly deformed (Figure 120). Both zygomatic arches are present, but both are slightly indented. Intercranially, the arch has not been completely prepared, having retained the sediments for support of the arch; the nasals, palate, and ventral cranium have not been completely prepared due to a carbonate coating.

The left and right tooth rows are present, as is the right canine. The first three premolars are missing from the maxilla, as are the incisors, left canine and two premolars of the left maxilla.

The cranium is large, as compared to the occipital condyle-basal length of the specimens from Ranch La Brea, California,and other localities of late Pleistocene age, south of Alaska, the Hot Springs specimen is larger (Agenbroad and Mead 1986). Only the crania from Alaska and the Yukon Province of Canada are larger (Table 49). This measurement is typical for males. Based on the erruption and tooth wear, plus the joining of the nasal sutures, the Hot Springs specimen is interpreted to be a young adult male. The zygomatic width is not as great as a comparison Kodiak bear (*Ursus arctos middendorfi*), or the *Arctodus simus* from Rancho La Brea (Merriam and Stock 1925). Our specimen is remarkably narrow in the palatine and the brain case. Possible compression of the Hot Springs specimen has caused slight deformation of the sides of the cranium in the region of the zygomatic arch.

The nasal rostrum is short and high in *Arctodus simus*, as compared to ursine bears. The external opening of the nasals is very large (maximum width is 77 mm). The greatest width of the external nares is measured above the middle of the opening in *Arctodus simus*, as contrasted to *Ursus arctos*, which has the greatest width at the bottom of the opening. The nasal bones are very big, but short compared

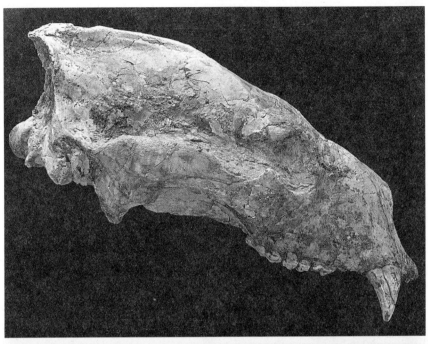

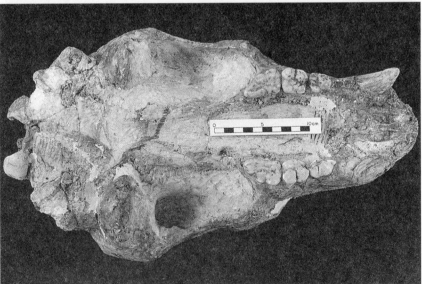

Figure 120. The cranium (83HS142) of *Arctodus simus*. (Top) right lateral view. (Bottom) ventral view.

310

Table 49. Measurements of skulls in *Arctodus simus*.

Measurements, mm [1]						Rancho La Brea							Irvington	
	Mammoth Site, S.D.	Upper Cleary River, Alaska[2]	Upper Cleary River, Alaska[2]	Gold Run Creek, Yukon[3]	Natural Trap, Wyo.[4]	McKitt-rick, Calif.[5]	Potter Creek Cave, California[2,6]	Potter Creek Cave, California[2,6]	Rancho La Brea, California[4]	Rancho La Brea, California[4]	Rancho La Brea, California[4]	Cueva Quebrada Texas[7]	Hay Springs, Neb.[2]	Irving-ton Calif.[2]
	30492	386-1076			35034	UC 33111	AMMNI 8222	UC 3001	21	22	25	TMM 41238-72	F:AM 25531	UC 40086
	M	M	M	M	F	F		F	F	F	M	F	M	M?
1	445.0	496.0	480.0	521.0	384.0	377.0	405.0	391.0	416.5	396.5		371.0	a490.0	e470.0?
2	426.0	444.0	438.0	463.0	362.0	352.0	370.0		386.0	379.0		366.0	a436.0	
3	a396.0	416.0	416.0	e440.0	338.0	331.0	345.0	345.0	360.0	348.0		343.0	a413.0	
7	259.0					226.5		220.0	237.5	216.0	295.0			
8	195.5				165.0				194.5	186.5				
9	214.0				205.0				221.1	225.3				
10	a103.5				92.5					101.9				
12	172.5				140.0					175.5				
Lengths Prosthion-level of end M2	183.5							110.0	182.0		90.1			
Lengths C1-M2 — 15	154.5				102.8				110.0	102.2	113.1			
16	112.0				58.8				60.2	61.5	63.3			
17	68.0													
18	91.5													
Lengths P4 - M2 — 23	190.0			240.0	165.4	a248.0		a167.0	185.4	165.0	206.0			
25	a90.0			89.0	71.6	98.0			76.5					
29	126.0				126.0				120.5	113.5				
30	238.0	a354.0		364.0		a150.0		241.0	245.5		334.5	246.0		
31	95.0	105.0	103.0		92.5		102.0		995.5	92.5	135.5	107.0		
32	167.0	a194.0	177.0	205.0	143.0	120.0	152.0	147.0	153.5	142.3	180.0	161.0	a184.0	122.0
33	132.0	153.0	139.0		114.5	119.0	123.0	117.0	126.0	131.5	132.3	112.0	a146.0	a124.0
34	119.0	141.0	141.0	a150.0	85.2		120.0	123.0	120.5		139.5	118.0		
35	112.0	136.0							88.0					
36	a111.0		124.0	a136.0					107.0	a108.0				
37	54.0				45.8	97.0		101.5	51.0	55.5	62.5	a101.0	a125.0	a122.0
38	132.5				112.6	116.0			124.0					

1) After von den Driesch 1976
2) Kurtén 1976
3) Lambe 1911
4) Agenbroad, Mead 1986
5) Schultz 1938
6) Merriam, Stock 1925
7) Lundelius 1984

to their width, in contrast with brown bears, which have nasals that are very long relative to their width. The frontal is flat and may include a slight deformation as small depressions are noted on the frontal and nasals. The entire frontal is very wide, with the interorbital width very large compared to ursine bears. The postorbital process is big and blunt as contrasted to the smaller, sharper process in Kodiak bears. The orbit is relatively small, with a lateral orientation, as was also noted in the material from Rancho La Brea (Merriam and Stock 1925). Our *Arctodus simus* has two open interorbital foramens on each side, in vertical placement above the middle of the anterior crown of M1; *Ursus* has only one foramen on each side.

Parietal narrowing causes a restriction of the brain case; the restriction is more posterior in *A. simus* than in *Ursus*. The saggital crest bifurcates anteriorally, forming divergent crests to the supraorbital ridges. The junction of the sagittal-orbital crest is more anterior in the arctodont bears than in the ursine bears. The sagittal crest is long, but does not overhang the occipital as far as in the ursines. The lambdoidal crest is well pronounced, with a relatively high medial crest, however the occipital is relatively narrow, as compared to the Kodiak bears (*Ursus arctos middendorfi).*

For comparison, Table 50a provides skull measurements of the Pleistocene bears *Arctodus simus* (giant short-faced bear) and *Ursus spelaeus* (Eurasian cave bear). Table 50b provides measurements for *Ursus arctos beringianus*, from Kamchatka.

Arctodus simus has a large foramen magnum. The distance from the paraoccipital process to the occipital condyle is comparable to *Ursus*. The outside bulla is broken. Mastoid processes are short and blunt, this may be due to the age of the individual specimen, however, they are short. The posterior configuration of the outside mastoid process is more vertical in *Arctodus simus*, whereas in *Ursus arctos*, it is more horizontal in orientation and the bulbous is blunter compared to *Arctodus simus*.

The glenoid fossa is deep and less closed than in *Ursus*. The interfossa width is nearly the same as the length of the tooth row. The glenoid process is more vertical than in *Ursus arctos*. There is a closer

Table 50a. Measurements (mm) of skulls of Pleistocene bears.

	Arctodus simus Alaska? U.S.N.N.H. No.V.167617 senex*	*Ursus spelaeus* Alps and Odessa[1]			
Single		n	min	max	M	SD
Total length (1)	519	4	443.0	528.0	481.5	37.2
Condylobasal length (2)	438	3	415.0	470.0	442.7	27.5
Basal length (3)	414	3	388.0	441.0	415.3	
Upper neurocranium length (7)	290	3	234.0	266.0	253.5	
Viscerocranium length (8)	209	3	220.0	237.0	228.0	
Facial length (9)	231	3	244.0	263.0	255.8	
Greatest length of the nasals (10)	95	3	103.0	113.0	109.5	
"Snout" length (12)	175	5	182.0	199.0	190.7	8.5
Median palatal length (13)	241	5	217.0	261.0	239.8	16.4
Median palatal length aboral end M2/- Prostion	182	5	177.0	211.0	192.6	13.0
Length of C1/-M2/	156	6	162.0	192.0	172.6	12.0
Length of P4/-M2/	81	5	86.0	109.0	96.4	9.0
Length of molar row M1/-M2/ (16)	62	6	70.0	83.0	76.3	5.2
Greatest mastoid breadth (23)	229	4	222.0	233.0	227.9	5.0
Greatest breadth of the occipital condyles (25)	84	5	78.0	102.0	88.8	8.5
Greatest neucranium breadth (29)	140	6	107.0	119.0	112.7	4.2
Zygomatic breadth (30)		3	265.0	290.0	281.0	13.9
Least breadth of skull (31)	106	5	78.0	90.0	83.5	4.3
Frontal breadth (32)	173	4	121.0	148.0	151.9	12.4
Least breadth between the orbits (33)	134	3	90.0	110.0	101.0	
Greatest palatal breadth (34)	142	5	107.0	120.0	114.4	4.9
Least palatal breadth (35)	121	5	76.0	87.0	81.5	4.4
Breadth at the canine (36)	125	4	99.0	118.0	106.6	8.1
Greatest inner height of the orbit (37)	60	3	63.0	65.0	64.0	
Skull height (38)	146	5	119.0	145.0	133.8	12.3

Table 50b. Measurements (mm) of skulls of Recent bears.

	Ursus arctos beringianus Kamchatka Coll. ZIN RAS*				
Single	n	min	max	M	SD
Total length (1)	12	378.0	428.0	404.3	14.3
Condylobasal length (2)	12	364.0	395.0	378.0	10.2
Basal length (3)	12	345.0	371.0	357.3	9.6
Upper neurocranium length (7)	12	211.0	243.0	228.5	9.1
Viscerocranium length (8)	12	181.0	196.0	190.4	5.9
Facial length (9)	12	193.0	221.0	208.2	8.7
Greatest length of the nasals (10)	5	102.0	116.0	108.6	5.2
"Snout" length (12)	12	144.0	160.0	151.6	5.3
Median palatal length (13)	12	187.0	209.0	199.0	5.9
Median palatal length aboral end M2/- Prostion	12	149.0	175.0	162.7	7.2
Length of C1/-M2/	12	131.0	148.0	139.4	4.9
Length of P4/-M2/	12	73.0	84.0	77.8	3.2
Length of molar row M1/-M2/ (16)	12	59.0	67.0	62.3	2.8
Greatest mastoid breadth (23)	12	177.0	219.0	200.7	11.2
Greatest breadth of the occipital condyles (25)	12	71.0	82.0	77.9	3.7
Greatest neucranium breadth (29)	12	112.0	122.0	116.1	3.7
Zygomatic breadth (30)	12	214.0	276.0	252.6	19.3
Least breadth of skull (31)	12	77.0	88.0	82.0	3.4
Frontal breadth (32)	12	116.0	167.0	137.9	14.0
Least breadth between the orbits (33)	12	80.0	106.0	91.7	7.4
Greatest palatal breadth (34)	12	94.0	106.0	99.7	4.5
Least palatal breadth (35)	12	65.0	76.0	71.3	3.2
Breadth at the canine (36)	12	82.0	105.0	91.5	6.6
Greatest inner height of the orbit (37)	12	51.0	64.0	59.7	3.9
Skull height (38)	12	109.0	132.0	117.2	6.6

* Moulage in Zoological Museum, University of Helsinki

spacing of the zygomatic and the mastoid process in *Arctodus simus*, as compared to *Ursus arctos*. The zygomatic arch is strongly restricted and narrow. The suborbital process of the jugale is pronounced. The distance between the squamosal and the suborbital process is relatively short. The front of the jugal arch projects back almost to the glenoid fossa in *Arctodus simus*, but not so far in *Ursus arctos*. The suture between the jugale and squamosale is very long (70mm). It is noted that this is similar to the canids. We interpret this long bond as a strengthening of the zygomatic arch.

Arctodus simus from the Mammoth Site of Hot Springs has a narrow palate, as compared to published arctodont specimens. The posterior of M^2 is strongly curved toward the center of the palate, peculiar to *Artodus simus*. The cranium contains a right tooth row with P^4 through M^2 and two alveoli. The left tooth row contains P^3 through M^2, with two alveoli.

There are two anterior palantine foramen. Two paired foramen lie on the back border of the foramenal opening, aligned with the center of the canine tooth. Behind these foramen there is a single foramen which is deep and wide (14.5 mm) and the back border of which is aligned with the back of the canine. In *Ursus*, the posterior foramen is very small and more anteriorly positioned. In the Hot Springs specimen the upper incisors are absent, and there is a short space between the alveolus for I^3 and the the canine; in *Ursus*, this tooth is separated by a significantly longer diastema, from the canine.

Mandibles

Both the left and the right mandibles are present, from one individual (R: 87HS004, L:92HS037); the two halves join and are from the same individual. The mandibles (Figure 121) are very large; when compared with published data for *Arctodus simus*, they are exceeded in length by only one specimen, the Hay Springs mandible (F:AM 25531 (Kurtén 1967)). The total length is similar to a large Kodiak (*Ursus arctos middendorfi*) specimen; however, the *Arctodus simus* mandible is more massive in all respects (Table 51).

The right mandible is complete, lacking only the incisors,P_1 and M_3. An alveolus for P_1 exsists, adjacent to the canine, followed by a 27mm gap to P_4. The left mandible is also complete, except for the incisors and first three premolars. The alveoli for P_1,P_2,and P_3 are present. The alveoli for P_1 and P_2 are open; the P_3 alveolus is filled with sediment.

In profile, the mandible has similar depth in all areas with a gradual increase in depth from the anterior of the tooth row to the posterior whereas in *Ursus arctos*, this is not the case. The lower border of the mandible is horizontal, to the end of the tooth row, then curves upward. There are two manibular foramen located below P_4, and slightly ahead of it. Two smaller foramen occur below M_1. The number and positon of these foramen are changeable in *Arctodus simus* (Merriam and Stock 1925:20)

The horizontal portion of the ramus is thick. The mandibular width at M_1 is 26 mm. In *Ursus americanus*, *Ursus arctos* and *Ursus spelaeus* the mandible is restricted anterior to P_4; in *Arctodus simus* this restriction is lacking (Table 51). The mandibular symphysis is short and wide—nearly equal in proportions of depth and width in *Arctodus*, whereas it is long and narrow in *Ursus*. The incisor alveoli for the right mandible are unprepared; in the left mandible the alveolus for I_3 is visible.

A great peculiarity is the character of the masseteric fossa; in *Arctodus* and in *Tremarctos* there are two deep muscle scars. The anterior one is not present in ursine bears. The forward premasseteric fossa extends to below the last molar of the tooth row. The slender border between the premasseteric and masseteric fossa is the extension of the anterior border of the ascending mandibular ramus. This crest is high and straight, while in *Tremarctos ornatus* and slightly curved in the lower part. It is more curved in Pleistocene *Tremarctos floridanus* (Gidley) from North America (Kurtén 1966:Pl. 3,8,9). The upper fossa is not as deep as the lower one.

The ascending ramus is high and has a long posterior-anterior width. The anterior border of the ascending ramus performs a smooth

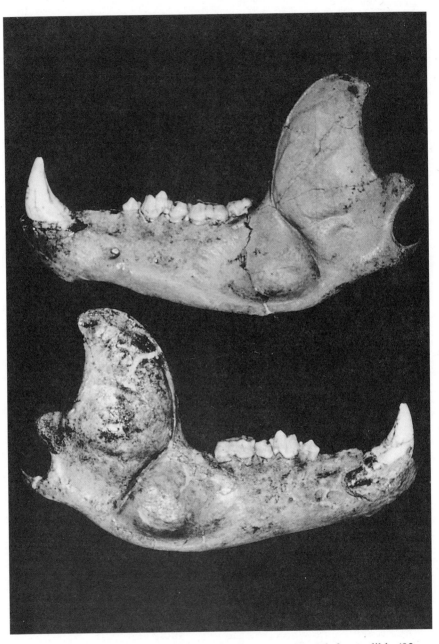

Figure 121. The mandible of HSMS *Arctodus simus.* (Top) left mandible (92-HS-037); (Bottom) right mandible (87-HS-004).

Table 51a. Measurements of the mandible in *Arctodus simus*.

Measurements, mm [1]	Mammoth Site		Frankstown Cave, Pennsylvania [2] CM 11020	Jinglebob, Kansas [2] UM 24380	Hay Springs, Neb. [2] F:AM 25531	McKittrick, Calif. [2] UC 33111	Potter Creek Cave, California [2,3]		Rancho La Brea, California [2,3]	
	Left	Right					UC 3001	UC 3003	Z6	Z53
Total length (1)	298.0	292.0					262.0			
Length from angular process to Infradentale (2)	312.0	305.0								
Length C_1 - condyle	288.0	283.0		275.0	295.0	253.0	253.0	260.0	275.0	260.0
Length C_1 - M_3	172.0	173.0								
Length P_1 - M_3 (8)	140.0	136.5								
Length P_4 - M_3	100.0	101.5	87.0	94.0	100.0	87.0	90.0	88.0	96.0	
Length M_1 - M_3 (10)	86.0	87.5					77.0		84.0	
Height of the vertical ramus (18)	149.5	147.0			163.0	121.0	121.0			145.0
Height of the mandible behind M_1 (19)	64.0	66.0								
Height of the mandible in diastema (20)	60.0	56.0	54.0	65.0	65.0	56.0	55.0	51.0	66.0	57.0

1) After vonden Driesch 1976
2) Kurtén 1967
3) Merriam & Stock 1925

Table 51b. Measurements (mm) of mandibles in *Ursus*.

Single	*U.arctos beringianus* Kamchatka Coll. ZIN RAS					*U. spelaeus* Alps and Odessa				
	n	min	max	M	SD	n	min	max	M	SD
Total length (1)	12	260.0	282.0	269.7	7.9	4	317.0	348.0	330.9	13.1
Length: the angular processes-Infradentale (2)	12	256.0	286.0	270.0	8.2	4	316.0	348.0	328.4	13.7
Length: daucal intentation-Infradentale (3)	12	252.0	274.0	258.9	6.4	4	302.0	329.0	310.6	12.4
Length: condyle process-aboral borders of canine (4)	12	222.0	243.0	231.0	6.1	7	274.0	308.0	288.1	12.4
Length C/1-M/3	12	153.0	165.0	158.8	4.6					
Length P/4-M3	12	83.0	93.0	87.7	3.7	16	97.0	114.0	106.5	4.6
Length of molar row M/1-M/3 (10)	12	69.0	77.0	72.8	2.7	17	82.0	96.0	89.7	4.5
Height of the vertical ramus (18)	12	110.0	131.0	118.0	6.1	6	120.0	168.0	147.0	16.1
Height of the mandible behind M/1 (19)	12	47.0	56.0	50.9	2.7	17	56.0	82.0	68.3	9.2
Height of the mandible in diastema (20)	12	47.0	55.0	50.7	2.6	17	53.0	73.0	63.7	6.7

curve that is more vertical than in *Ursus* and the posterior border does not dip as in ursine bears. The mandibular condyle is very thick and massive (w=66.5mm; h= 30.0 mm). This may attest to the great crushing strength of the *Arctodus* mandible. A projection of the occlusal surface of the tooth row palaces the mandibular condyle above this line in *Arctodus simus*, and below this line in *Ursus arctos*. The coronoid process is very long and projects posterially to the occipital condyle. In *Ursus arctos* this process is below the mandibular condyle.

The foramen on the lingual side of the mandible in *Arctodus simus* is small. The alveolar process is absent, while it is present in *Ursus* and other ursine bears (*Helarctos, Melursus, Thalarctos*).

DENTITION

The HSMS material has both cheek tooth rows for the upper and lower jaws, the left upper canine, both lower canines, and two isolate incisors (Table 52). Teeth in the maxilla and mandibles are fully errupted, similar in size, and are believed from one individual.

Incisors

In the maxilla, we have only alveoli. There is little difference between the I^1 and I^2 alveoli (I^1: l=12mm, w= 6mm); the alveoli for I^3 is larger (l-23mm, w=15mm). Alveolar width from the most lateral incisor alveoli is 67 mm.

I^1: An isolate right I^1 (83HS053) shows very little wear. The enamel on anterior and posterior portions of the tooth is very different; the anterior enamel is very long (rises high on the root) as compared to the posterior enamel; it is thick on both sides.

We have no comparative material from *Arctodus simus*. In *Arctodus*, there is a small vertical groove on the anterior of I^1 that is not present in the ursine bears. On the posterior, occlusal view, the enamel converges to create a small triangle; the lateral side has a small tubercle.

Table 52. Measurements (mm) of incisors and canines in *Arctodus simus*.

Specimens	Sex	I^1		C^1		I_2		C_1	
		L	W	L	W	L	W	L	W[1]
Mammoth Side, South Dakota (83-HS-142a)	M	13.2	8.5	33.2	22.8	12.5	8.3	33.7	22.0
Upper Cleary Creek, Alaska (F:AM 30492) [2]	M				25.1				
Ester Creek, Alaska (F:AM A-386-1075) [2]	M				22.1				
Gold Run Creek, Yukon [3]	M	12.5	8.0	42.0	26.0				
Frankstown Cave, Pennsylvania (CM 11020) [2]	F								18.8
Jinglebob, Kansas (UM 24380) [2]	F				19.5				20.2
Huntington Canyon, Utah (USHS 88.18.50) [4]	M			37.1	25.0				
McKittrick, California (UC 33111) [2]	F				18.6				a18.5
Potter Creek Cave, California (UC 3001) [5]	F		7.9	27.9				39.0	
Rancho La Brea, California (LACM Z1) [5]	F		8.9	29.3					
Rancho La Brea, California (LACM Z4) [5]	F			26.5					
Rancho La Brea, California (LACM Z6) [5]	F							a27.0	
Rancho La Brea, California (LACM Z8) [5]	F							a27.0	
Rancho La Brea, California (LACM Z53) [5]	F?							30.7	
Hay Springs, Nebraska (F:AM 25531) [2]	M				21.0				21.6
Irvington, California (UC 40086) [2]	M			a23.3					22.0

1) L. antero-posterior length at basale of enamel; W, maximal transverse width
2) Kurtén 1967
3) Lambe 1911
4) Gilette and Madsen 1992
5) Merriam & Stock 1925

Upper incisors from the arctodont specimen at Hot Springs are larger than the specimens from Potter Creek Cave, but smaller than the specimens from Rancho La Brea (Merriam and Stock 1925). They have a very large crown and a measured root depth of 37 mm. They are much larger than the incisors of ursine bears, with a different morphology. In *Ursus*, the anterior of the incisor is nearly cusped, with the posterior much lower and of a different shape than in *Arctodus*. In *Ursus* the posterior part of the crown has noticeable ramparts (cingulum). They also occur in *Canis* and *Crocuta,* animals that use their upper incisors to help hold prey.

Lower incisors from the right mandible are missing, and the alveolli have not yet been prepared. In the left mandible the alveolus for I_3 has a length of 10 mm and a width of 9.4 mm.

I_2: An isolate lower, right incisor (83HS261) represents a right I_2 and is a large tooth measuring 39.3 mm in depth. These incisors display little wear. The enamel on the anterior is very short compared to the posterior; a lateral crest forms a small cusp. The posterior is concave, with a medial crest which divides the tooth into two parts, lateral and medial, giving it a crenulated appearance.

Canines

Upper and lower canines are in very good condition, displaying only a small amount of occlusal wear.

C^1: Upper canines are large, robust, strong, canines, with a slight vertical ridge on the posterior surface. They measure 50.5 mm from the crown to the palate, with a transverse width of 22.8 mm, similar to Kurtén's description of a male specimen (Kurtén 1967:10).

C_1: The lower right canine (C_1) exhibits a small difference, in size, from the maxillary canine, and has a vertical crest on the anterior-lingual side. The crown height is 48.2 mm.

Maxillary cheek teeth

On the right side of the maxillary tooth row, there are alveoli for

P^1 and P^2; there is one alveolis and P^3 is present on the left side. In *Arctodus*, as in *Tremarctos*, P^1 is very large. The P^1 alveolis measures 10.0 mm in length and 6.8 mm in width. The second alveolis is 7.7 mm long and 5.6 mm wide and may be for P^2; the alveolus for the left P^3 may be bigger (length = 9.3 mm). Lambe (1911:22) states there are three alveoli, which he interprets as P^1 and a double rooted P^3. We do not agree; we feel P^1,P^2,P^3 are all single rooted teeth in the *Arctodus simus* specimen from Hot Springs. The distance between the posterior surface of the canine and the anterior of P^4 is 25 mm.

The upper tooth rows are fully occluded, robust, and massive (Table 53). The tubercles show weak wear, only on the summits. Erruption decreases posteriorly. Buccal tubercles have greater erruptive length than on the lingual side. Only P^3 shows no sign of occlusion.

P^3 : The P^3 (left) is a small, elongate tooth with one central cusp in an anterior position to P^4. The front crest (preparacriste) declines from the central cusp to the interior.

P^4 : Left and right P^4s are triangular in form, with three cusps in *Tremarctos*. P^4 is very long; the HSMS specimen has the greatest length for published *Arctodus* specimens. The alveolar length is 24.7 mm. However, this is not as large as *Arctodus bonariensis* (Gervais 1855) from South America (Kurtén 1967). This tooth is in the relative size of *Tremarctos*, a large tooth. The greatest height of the crown is 16.7 mm.

The maximum width is across the midle cusp (with *Ursus*, it is with the posterior part of the crown). There is almost no ectoflexis. The buccal side is not as vertical as in *Ursus*, it tilts toward the midpalate.

The paracone and metacone lie in a straight line. The protocone is the largest with an anterior, lingual crest, which is sharper than in *Ursus*. The metacone is long, and tends to form a shearing blade as in *Tremarctos ornatus* (Merriam and Stock 1925:12). A tubercular parastyle and metastyle are absent. The protocone has one cusp which lies opposite the notch between the paracone and the metacone. The protocone is posterior to the postcriste. There is no cingulum on the lingual side; on the outside there is only a very small shaft.

A very interesting erruption facet lies on the lingual side, along the paracone and metacone and shows wear on the lingual side. We interpret the function of the metacone as a shearing tooth (Figure122) (Merriam and Stock 1925:12). The contact with M1 is similar to the contact in flesh eating carnivores such as the hyena, and cats. We interpret the carnassials of *Arctodus simus* is for cutting flesh, and breaking small bones. In *Ursus*, P^4 is similar in shape, but exhibits wear only on the cones; evidence is lacking for P^4 functioniong as a shearing tooth in *Ursus*.

M^1: Both left and right M1's are present. The crown forms a quadrate shape; long anterior labial cusps are of approximately equal length, each forming half the labial length of the tooth. The crown is similar in proportion to *Agriotherium* (=*Hyenarctos*) from the Pliocene of North America, as stated in Merriam and Stock (1925:12). The tooth is very wide, almost as wide as it is long. The parcone and metacone are separated from the posterior cusp by a notch (ectophlexus). The anterior side of the tooth makes a near right angle with the lingual side; in *Ursus arctos* and *Ursus spelaeus* this is a curved juncture; in *Ursus americanus*, the juncture is more angular than in *Ursus arctos*.

The paracone and metacone are massive and compressed. They are of equal height. The erruption schedule for the Hot Springs specimen has allowed only the peaks of the cones to be worn by occlusion. The buccal side in *Ursus arctos* is nearly vertical; in *Arctodus simus,* it slopes steeply toward the center of the tooth. A large parastyle and very small metastyle are present.

The lingual tuberculum are nearly parallel to the crown of the paracone and metacone. The inner surface of the tooth is very steep, almost vertical. Three tuberclum, protocone, metaconule and hypocone, are present. The metaconule is large, equalling both the protocone and hypocone. The wide medial valley has differing lingual and buccal sides. It is open anteriorly and has subdued (dull) tuberculi. The posterior portion of the valley has a relatively large

Table 53a. Measurements of upper cheek teeth in *Arctodus simus*.

Specimens	P3		P4		M1		M2		
	L	W	L	W	L	W	L	Wa	Wc
Mammoth Site, South Dakota (83-HS-142a)	9.8	13.2	8.5	33.2	22.8	12.5	8.3	33.7	22.0
Upper Cleary Creek, Alaska (F:AM 30492) [2]			24.6	16.8	27.7	27.3	40.8	25.8	23.7
Ester Creek, Alaska (F:AM A-386-1075) [2]	a9.1		22.3	15.4	26.6	25.1	37.7	24.2	23.0
Gold Run Creek, Yukon [3]			22.5	17.0	27.0	25.0	37.5	25.0	
Natural Trap, Wyoming (35034) [4]					24.5	23.4	37.0	22.0	
Frankstown Cave, Pennsylvania (CM 11020) [2]			23.0	17.5	27.9	26.2	39.1	24.4	21.0
Frankstown Cave, Pennsylvania (CM 11020) [2]							36.4	22.6	21.0
Perkings Cave, Missouri (CM 123) [5]			21.7	17.0	25.5	25.0	35.8	23.5	
Perkings Cave, Missouri (CM 171) [5]							35.9	24.2	
Huntington Canyon, Utah (USHS 88.18.50) [6]			22.9	17.4	27.0	26.0			
McKittrick, California (UC 33111) [2]	8.5		21.6	15.1	23.0	22.6	34.6	22.1	19.5
Potter Creek Cave, California (UC 3091) [7]	8.5	5.0	20.5	15.0	24.0	23.0	35.0	22.0	
Rancho La Brea, California (LACM Z1) [7]	7.9	5.0	20.5	15.8	25.2	22.8	36.5	22.9	13.7
Rancho La Brea, California (LACM Z4) [7]			20.8	15.8	25.4	23.2	25.9	23.3	15.3
Rancho La Brea, California (LACM Z6) [7]			23.5	17.1	25.0	24.0	37.3	23.6	14.0
Rancho La Brea, California (LACM Z8) [7]					26.3	24.9	35.8	23.7	
Hay Springs, Nebraska (F:AM 25531) [2]	9.1		23.4	18.0	28.3	26.1	41.1	25.8	21.7
Irvington, California (UC 40086) [2]	9.6		23.9	18.0					
Irvington, California (UC 42888) [2]					26.8	25.5	38.9	24.9	22.1

1) L, length; W, width; Wa, anterior and Wc, central width
2) Kurtén 1967
3) Lambe 1911
4) Agenbroad, Mead 1986
5) After Hawksley (from Kurten 1967)
6) Gillete 1989
7) Merriam and Stock 1925

Table 53b. Measurements of upper cheek teeth in *Arctodus* and *Ursus*.

Measurements, mm and Index - 1%	*Arctodus simus* Mammoth Site		*Ursus arctos middendorfii* Kodiak Islands USFWS	*Ursus arctos horribilis* NAU 3405	*Ursus americanus* MSCC 0007
	Left	Right			
P⁴ 1. Lengths total	25.4	25.3	17.4	16.0	11.5
2. Width greatest	19.7	19.2	12.0	13.0	8.2
2:1	77.6	75.9	69.0	81.2	71.3
M¹ 1. Lengths total	27.3	27.4	22.0	22.7	16.8
2. Lengths of front half of tooth (in line paracone-metacone)	13.6	13.6	10.7	11.2	8.3
3. Width greatest	25.4	25.3	16.7	16.3	12.3
2:1	49.8	49.6	48.6	49.3	49.4
3:1	93.0	92.7	75.9	71.8	73.8
M² 1. Lengths total	41.5	41.7	37.1	34.0	25.2
2. Lengths of metacone	11.0	10.7	10.7	11.1	7.0
3. Width anterior (in across paracone)	24.8	25.1	19.3	17.9	13.5
4. Width central (in across metacone)	23.2	22.4	19.0	17.6	13.3
2:1	26.5	25.7	28.8	32.6	27.7
3:1	59.8	60.2	52.0	52.6	53.6
4:1	55.9	53.7	51.2	51.8	52.8

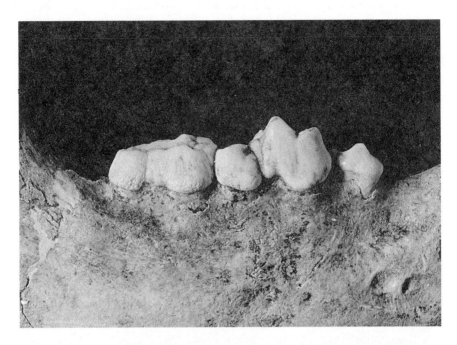

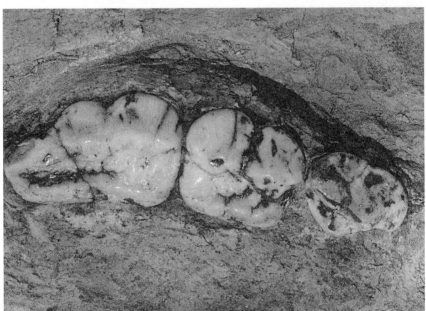

Figure 122. *A. simus* metacone as a shearing tooth.

tubercle (hypostyle) that is absent in other bears except *Tremarctos*. There is no cingulum on the lingual side, whereas in *Ursus* it is present.

M^2: Left and right M^2s are present. This tooth is relatively long as compared to the entire tooth row, (l/ln), but is relatively short in comparison with a similar ratio in *Ursus*. The ratio is less than 45% in *Arctodus simus*, which is similar to the index for *Tremarctos ornatus*. In the herbivorous *T. floridanus*, the ratio is 46% (Kurtén 1966). In omnivorous *Ursus*, the ratio is 46-49%. In herbivorous *Ursus spelaeus* from the Pleistocene of Europe, it reaches 50%.

The crown of M^2 is very wide, across the paracone, and it thins to a posterior talon. In *A. simus*, the anterior width of M^2 equals the width of M^1, whereas in *Ursus* M^2 is wider than M^1. The transverse width at the paracone is significantly greater than at the metacone. As in M^1, the buccal side of the paracone and metacone are sloped medially on the inner side of the tooth. On the buccal side there is a deep notch between the paracone and the metacone.

There is one tubercle, each, on the paracone and metacone. A parastyle is present, and therefore it is different than *Ursus*, which has no parastyle. The inner tuberculum are faint; only the hypocone is barely visible. A valley between the buccal cusps and the lingual cusps of the tooth is very wide, containing medial tuberculum between the bases of the paracone and metacone. In *Ursus*, there are no tuberculum along this line. This valley is even wider in *Tremarctos floridanus*. There is a lateral crest between the metacone and the metaconule in *Tremarctos floridanus*. (Kurtén 1966:Pl.4). It is possible this crest is a metaloph in *Tremarctos floridanus*, but absent in *Arctodus simus*. The talon from the HSMS specimen is short and narrow, it is also flat. There are no lingual cingulum which are present in *Ursus* .

Mandibular cheek teeth

Arctodus simus provides evidence for four premolars. The left mandible has the alveoli for the P_1, P_2, P_3, which are all single rooted,

327

and a small P_4. The alveolus for P_1 contacts the alveolus of C_1; the alveolus of P_2 contacts the alveolus of P_1. Between the alveolus of P_2 and P_3 there is a 6.3 mm diastema. The HSMS right mandible comprises an alveolus below P_1 and P_4. Between the P_1 and P_4 is a diastema of 27.5mm in length. The alveolus for P_1 is single rooted and contacts the alveolus for the canine; the alveolus for P_1 has a length of 8.5 mm and a width of 7.8 mm.

The cheek teeth are large (Table 54), except for P_4. Occlusal wear is displayed only on the peaks of the molars, indicative that they have not been errupted long. As in the upper teeth, there is more occlusal wear on the posterior teeth of the tooth row.

In the lower teeth, P_1 is nearly round, the alveolus measures 8.0 mm long by 7.5 mm wide; the alveolus for P_2 is more elongate and measures 9.4 x 5.3 mm; P3 is 7.7 x 6.1 mm.

P_4: (left and right). A size differential is noted in the length and width of the left P_4 (15.6mm; 8.6 mm) and right P_4 (16.6 mm; 7.8 mm). Such variation is normal in nonfunctional teeth. They have a merged, double root. In *Tremarctos* Kurtén (1966:16) indicates P_4 may possibly have two roots. The P_4 s are slightly twisted in the jaw, with the posterior of P_4 in contact with the lingual anterior of M_1. This premolar is not equal in height to the paraconid of M_1. There is no evidence of occlusion on P_4. In *Tremarctos ornatus* this tooth is not significantly lower than the paraconid of M_1. In *Ursus*, this tooth is equal in height to the M_1 paraconid, and the crest shows occlusal wear.

In the early Pleistocene *Ursus etruscans* (G. Cuvier) from Europe, four premolars are present. In *Ursus arctos*, P_1 is small, P_2 and P_3 are usually absent, P_4 is high. In *Ursus spelaeus* there are no P_1-P_3; P_4 is larger and displays molarization with many tuberculum, which is indicated as a modification to process plant food. In the highly herbivorous recent bear *Ailuropoda melanoleuca* from southern China, the anterior premolars P2-P4 are large, high, and complicated, reflecting adaptation to the mastication of bamboo shoots.

In *Arctodus simus* P_4 is approximately equal in size to P1 (Kurtén 1966; Merriam and Stock 1925). In the *Arctodus simus* specimen

Table 54. Measurements of lower cheek teeth in *Arctodus simus*.

Specimens	P4		M1				M2			M3	
	L	W	L	Lt	Wa	Wp	L	Wa	Wp	L	W[1]
Mammoth Site, South Dakota (No. (87-HS-004))	16.6	7.8	34.2	24.6	16.7	17.6	32.4	22.4	20.6		
Frankstown, Pennsylvania (CM 11020) [2]			30.8	22.0	14.1	15.4	28.2	19.2	17.6	19.8	15.6
Bat Cave, Missouri l(CM 21) [3]	12.2	8.0	31.4		14.8	16.3	30.2	19.7		20.7	16.5
Perkins Cave, Missouri (CM 123) [3]	12.2	8.0	32.1		15.9	17.8	30.5	21.1		21.6	17.2
Jinglebob, Kansas (UM 24380) [2]			a31.0				a28.0	a20.0		a21.0	16.5
McKittrick, California (UC 33111) [2]	11.8	6.5	29.9	21.8	15.1	16.5	26.4	19.1	17.9	19.6	15.0
Potter Creek Cave, California (US 3001) [4]	12.5	7.8	31.5		15.0	16.0	27.0	19.5		20.0	16.0
Rancho La Brea, California (LACM Z6) [4]			35.0		16.6	18.0	31.7	22.4			
Rancho La Brea, California (LACM Z7) [4]			31.3		15.1	16.7	30.2	21		21.4	17.0
Rancho La Brea, California (LACM Z8) [4]	13.5	7.2	32.4		16	16.7	30.8	21.4		21.3	17.2
Rancho La Brea, California (LACM Z9) [4]			32.0		15.5	17.0	30.4	21.6		21.8	17.0
Rancho La Brea, California (LACM Z10) [4]			31.7		14.5	17.2	30.4	20.8		21.9	16.9
Rancho La Brea, California (LACM Z19) [4]	13.8	8.5	32.4		16.2	17.2	31.4	21.6			
Rancho La Brea, California (LACM Z53) [4]	13.2	7.2	33.5		15.3	17.5	28.0	21.8		22.1	17.6
Rancho La Brea, California (LACM Z52) [4]			32.0		15.6	16.5	29.1	21.3		22.6	17.8
Hay Springs, Nebraska (F:AM 25531) [2]	11.7	7.9	35.0			18.4	32.5	22.8	21.7	23.5	18.6

1) L, length; W, width; Wa, anterior and Wp, posterior width; Lt, trigonid length
2) Kurtén 1967
3) After Hawksley (from Kurtén 1967)
4) Merriam and Stock 1925

from the Hot Springs mammoth site, P_4 is small, but larger than P1. The crown is a long ellipse, narrowing posteriorly; it has one central tuberculum with a posterior crest displaying a small cusp.

M_1: (left and right). *Arctodus simus* has primitive teeth, but the upper teeth are more comparable to *Ursus*, whereas the lower molars are different. The arctodont M_1 resembles the tooth of *Tremarctos* . It is more primitive in structure, and is similar to canids (canid type structure).

In *Arctodus* M_1 is a large, robust tooth, whose length is >34% of the P_4-M_3 tooth row. M_1 is longer than M_2. In *Tremarctos* these teeth are equal in length; in *Ursus* M1 is usually shorter than M_2. The M_1 is a very high tooth. The buccal height for the left tooth is 21.8 mm; for the right tooth it is 27.1 mm.

On the labial side of the *A. simus* M_1 there is a deep notch between the trigonid and the talon. The paraconid and protoconid enamel drops ventrally, toward the jaw bone. A similar, but smaller phenomenon is noted in *Tremarctos*. This may strengthen the tooth for scavenging flesh and bone. It appears to be an aid in shearing, a very interesting load characteristic. In *Tremarctos* it is not so pronounced; in *Ursus* it is missing.

The paraconid, protoconid, and metaconid produce one line of a shearing triangle in orientation as in the Pliocene *Agriotherium*. In *Ursus* the structure is completely different; the paraconid, protoconid, and metaconid give a different triangular pattern, which is better for crushing (Merriam and Stock 1925:14).

The *A. simus* paraconid has a cutting type crest on the buccal side. The crest has the paraconid displaying facets from occlusion with the upper P^4. In *Ursus*, the paraconid has a tubercle nearer on the lingual side; it is conical with no shearing evidence. The protoconid in *Arctodus simus* is large, and massive. The lingual side slopes medially. A small metaconid is located lingually and posteriorly to the protocone. Only one tuberculum is in contact with the protoconid. In *Tremarctos ornatus* the metaconid is also confined to a single cusp; however, it is more isolated from the protoconid. In *Ursus*, the metaconid is complicated and is in the same position on the lingual side that the protoconid occupies on the labial side. The ursine metaconid has 2-3 tubercles. A larger, more complicated metaconid is typical of *Ursus spelaeus.*

The talonid is relatively short and wide, with low tuberculum widely spaced within a central depression. The talonid has the aspect of a crushing platform. In *Ursus*, the talonid is longer, the tubercles are more closely spaced, with no depression between them. A small external cusp occurs on the buccal side between the trigonid and talonid as in *Tremarctos*. The talonid tubercles are located nearer the trigonid than in *Ursus*. *Ursus* has a cingulum on the buccal side, which is not present in *A. simus*.

M_2: (left and right). The M_2 is a high, wide, double crowned tooth. Its greatest width is across the proximal end, as in *Agricolarctos*. In *Ursus*, the maximum width is at the talonid (Table 55). The buccal side slopes steeply toward the labial edge.

The protoconid and metaconid are not high, with a triangular tuberculum. The inner cones of the protoconid and the metaconid form a sharp transverse crest. This crest and the anterior paraconid form a rounded, flat surface. In *Ursus*, the tooth has an anterior slope, with the transverse crest forming a ridge, for grinding food (it is especially massive in *Ursus spelaeus*).

The talonid is relatively short, but wide and weakly separated from the trigonid. The principal tuberculum of the talonid is low. A horizontal talonid surface is present, with a line of small, supplementary tubercles along the median. This is not present in *Ursus*.

M_3: (left). The third molar is not a large tooth. The posterior is raised and there is a forward tilt to this tooth, and it is much larger than in *Ursus*. The position of this tooth is similar to the Pliocene *Ursus* of Europe, and typical of bears with a short upper M^2.

Tuberculi are weakly developed on the M_3. The middle surface is marked by a number of small papillae. It is triangular in shape, with the greatest width in the anterior portion of the tooth. Differing from *Ursus,* arctdont M_3s are small in length and width, and weakly tuberculate. This is even more prounced when compared to the Eurasian cave bear (*Ursus spelaeus*). In *Tremarctos floridanus* M_3 is

Table 55. Measurements of lower cheek teeth in *Arctodus* and *Ursus*.

Measurements, mm and Index - 1%		*Arctodus simus* Mammoth Site		*Ursus arctos middendorfii* Kodiak Islands USFWS	*Ursus arctos horribilis* NAU 3405	*Ursus americanus* MSCC 0007
		Left	Right			
P_4	1. Lengths total	15.0	16.6	12.0	12.29	8.9
	2. Width greatest	8.7	7.8	7.2	7.4	4.9
	2:1	58.0	47.0	60.0	60.2	55.1
M^1	1. Lengths total	34.5	34.2	23.7	23.5	18.1
	2. Lengths of trigonid	24.8	24.6	15.4	13.3	12.3
	3. Width anterior	16.9	16.7	10.3	9.7	7.1
	4. Width posterior	17.9	17.6	11.5	11.1	8.6
	2:1	71.9	71.9	65.0	56.6	68.0
	3:1	49.0	48.8	43.5	41.3	39.2
	4:1	51.9	51.5	48.5	47.2	47.5
M_2	1. Lengths total	31.0	32.4	26.0	25.9	17.7
	2. Width anterior	22.2	22.4	15.5	15.0	10.9
	3. Width posterior	20.6	20.6	15.7	14.5	11.4
	2:1	71.6	69.1	59.6	57.9	61.6
	3:1	66.4	63.6	60.4	56.0	64.4
M3	1. Lengths total	22.6				13.1
	2. Width greatest	18.8				10.4
	2:1	83.2				79.4

also comparatively long and wide and weakly fused to the talonid. In *Ursus spelaeus*, this tooth is long and wide with many tuberculum, the talonid is easily distinguished from the anterior portion of the tooth, which is not the case in *Arctodus simus*. This appears to be a feature of the herbivorous bears of the Pleistocene of North America and Europe.

A review of the relative length and width of various forms of Pleistocene bears was undertaken. *Ursus spelaeus* was compared (Kurtén 1967) to *Ursus arctos*, and *Tremarctos floridanus* to *Tremarctos ornatus*. He showed that for herbivorous *U. spelaeus* vs, *T. floridanus* there was typically a relative increase in length of M^3 to lower M_3. This is normal, because an increase in these teeth further enhances the mastication of plant food. The comparison of *Arctodus simus* to *Tremarctos ornatus* was found to produce an inverse relationship in comparison of the P^4 to the M_1 (the carnassial teeth) (Table 56). This analysis supports our conclusion, that *Arctodus simus* is not an herbivore (see below).

VERTEBRAL COLUMN

The Recent tremarctine bear *Tremarctos ornatus* has the following vertebral formula: C 7; T 13; L 3; S 3; Ca 8-9 (Merriam and Stock 1925). Kurtén (1967) reported an analogous formula in *Arctodus*. We have recovered cervical, thoracic and lumbar vertebrae for one individual, some of which are in anatomical order (Figure 123).

Atlas

The atlas is near complete, with just the transverse processes slightly broken off (83HS124). The width and length of the occipital facets fit well with the size and shape of the occipital condyles on the skull from the Mammoth Site. We infer that this atlas and the skull are from the same individual. The ventral arch is shorter than the dorsal arch on the HSMS *Arctodus simus,* as is the case with *Ursus*

Table 56. Comparison between measurements of teeth in *Ursus spelaeus* and *U. arctos*, *Tremarctos floridanus* and *T. ornatus*, and results of analogous comparison between *Arctodus simus* and *T. ornatus*.

Measurements	Excess in U. spelaeus over U. arctos [1] %	Excess in T. floridanus over T. ornatus [1] %	Excess in Arctodus simus over T. ornatus [1] %
C_1 width Male	53.0	33.0	47.7
P_4 length	45.0	4.0	51.0
P^4 length	38.0	11.0	76.5
M_1 length	43.0	15.0	73.6
M^1 length	45.0	14.0	54.7
M_2 length	42.0	16.0	62.5
M^2 length	47.0	24.0	51.5
M_3 length	50.0	22.0	59.0

1) After Kurtén 1966 (table 2)
2) Calculated as by dates from Kurtén (1966, table 1; 1967, table 1)

Figure 123. An articulated portion of *A. simus* vertebra (83-HS-124).

americanus (black bear). This contradicts what Kurtén (1966:31) states where the ventral arch is longer than the dorsal arch on *Tremarctos*. The atlantic foramen is midway positioned in length on *Arctodus simus* and the HSMS specimen, compared to a more anterior position in *Ursus americanus*. The transverse foramen on *Arctodus simus* and the HSMS specimen is dorsally oriented whereas on Ursinae it is distinctly posterior. This positioning on *Arctodus simus* is similar to *Tremarctos* and to that on *Canis* (Merriam and Stock 1925). The adjacent posterior notch is small and insignificant on *Arctodus simus* and the HSMS specimen, whereas it is distinctly apparent on *Ursus americanus*. The angle of the atlas articulation with the axis on *Arctodus simus* is obtuse, whereas it is acute on *Ursus americanus*.

Measurements of the atlas and axis are provided in Table 57a. Comparisons of measurements of the HSMS *Arctodus simus* with a specimen from Potter Creek Cave, California, indicate that the HSMS short-faced bear was bigger.

Axis

The axis (83HS124) is complete except for one broken transverse process (Table 57b). The height relative to the length of the element is greater on *Arctodus simus* than it is in *Ursus americanus*. The dens process is long, thick, and anteriorly pointed with more vertical sides on *Arctodus*, compared to the blunt and angled dens on *Ursus*. The cranial and caudal articular facets of *Arctodus* are more horizontally oriented versus the less steep angles on *Ursus americanus*, which are similar to *Tremarctos* (Kurtén 1966). The transverse process is short and even with the posterior edge of the centrum on *Arctodus simus* compared to the longer, thinner process that proceeds distally from the centrum on *Ursus americanus*. The pedical arch support is narrower on *Arctodus simus* versus the longer (wider) arch on *Ursus americanus*. The neural spine is oriented anteriorly with a downward droop on the *Arctodus simus* from the Mammoth Site. This is not the case with *Arctodus* from Potter Creek

Table 57a. Measurements of stlas vertebrae in *Arctodus simus.*

Measurements, mm [1]	Mammoth Site	Potter Creek Cave, California [2] University of California 3035
Greatest breadth of the Facies articularis cranialis (BFcr)	95.0	87.6[3]
Greatest breadth of the Facies articularis caudalis (BFcd)	a91.5	
Greatest length from the Facies articularis cranialis to the Facies articularis caucialis (GLF)	75.0	
Length of the Arcus dorsalis median (LAd)	35.9	33.6
Greatest height (H)	64.7	

Table 57b. Measurements of axis (ephistropheus) vertebrae in *Arctodus simus.*

Measurements, mm [1]	Mammoth Site	Rancho La Brea, California [2] L.A.M. Coll. Z39
Greatest length in the region of the corpus including the dens (LCDe)	97.5	a82.0
Greatest breadth of the arch including the Processus articulares caudales (LAPa)	107.5	a80.7
Greatest breadth of the Facies articularis cranialis (BFcr)	85.0	84.6
Greatest breadth across the processus articulares caudales (BPacd)	73.5	
Smallest breadth of the vertebra (SBV)	61.8	
Greatest breadth of the Facies terminalis caudalis (BFcd)	50.5	
Greatest height (H)	109.0	

1) After von den Driesch 1976
2) Merriam and Stock 1925
3) There is presumably a transversion of Greatest width (33.6) and Least anteroposterior diameter (87.6) reported on page 20.

Cave, California (see Merriam and Stock 1925, Plate 6). On *Ursus americanus* this orientation is directly anterior without a droop. The HSMS specimen is much larger than the Rancholabrean specimen.

Cervical Vertebrae

The 3rd, 4th, and 5th cervical vertebrae are present (Table 58) (83HS124). The centrum is short as in *Ursus americanus*. The posterior dorsal notch in C3 is very wide (obtuse); not the deep, long notch as in *Tremarctos floridanus* (Kurtén 1966; Fig. 23). It may be possible that this notch angle is due to the large size of the bear, with the more obtuse angle being with the larger animals. The canal is short in relation to the height of the centraum. The pedicle of the neural arch width is narrower versus the wide arch occurring on *Ursus americanus*. The fourth and fifth cervical vertebrae are similar to the third. Overall, the length of the HSMS specimens are slightly larger than those from Potter Creek Cave, California, however the greatest breadth (C3 and C4) is much larger than that from Potter Creek Cave (Merriam and Stock 1925). The neck (cervical vertebrae) of *Arctodus simus* from HSMS is relatively short, the length of C2-C5 is 209 mm. In comparison with the lengths of the dorsal arches in the atlas, it is shorter than in *Ursus americanus*. This confirms Kurtén's (1967) indication that the neck of *Arctodus simus* was relatively shorter.

Thoracic and Lumbar Vertebrae

The thoracic 12th and 13th and lumbar 1st, 2nd, 3rd, and 4th vertebrae are articulated and heavily cemented together, therefore some measurements are only approximate (86HS079). The rib facets are readily observable on the thoracic, while the lumbar all have fragmented transverse processes. All the thoracic vertebrae "appear" shorter in length than the *Arctodus simus* thoracics from Rock Creek (Table 59). The base of the canal on the cranial face is V-shaped on lumbar on the *Arctodus simus* from HSMS, compared to the U-shaped on *Ursus americanus*. The centrum length of lumbar 4 is larger than

Table 58. Measurements of cervical vertebrae in *Arctodus simus*.

Measurements, mm [1]	Mammoth Site	Potter Creek Cave, California [2] U.S. Nat. Mus 2654
C3, No		
Physiological length of the body (PL)	39.5	36.6
Greatest length from the Processus articulares craniales to the Processus articulares caudales (GLPa)	73.0	
Greatest breadth across the Processus articulares craniales (B Paci)	72.0	59.6
Greatest breadth across the Processus articulares c audales (BPacd)	a80.0	
Greatest breadth of the Facies terminalis cranialis (BFer)	48.0	
Greatest breadth of the Facies terminalis caudalis (BFcd)	53.0	
Greatest height of the Facies terminalis ranialis (HFcr)	36.0	
Greatest height of the Facies terminalis caudalis (HFcd)	36.0	27.7
Greatest height (H)	69.0	
C4, No		
PL	38.5	37.8
GLPa	60.0	
BPacr	82.5	a68.0
BPacd	a81.0	
BFcr	52.5	
BFcd	54.0	
HFcr	37.5	
HFcd	37.0	28.8
C5, No		
PL	a37.5	37.3
GLPa	72.0	
BFcr	55.0	
HFcd	a35.0	28.5

1)   After von den Driesch 1976
2)   Merriam and Stock 1925

Table 59. Measurements of thoracic and lumbar vertebrae in *Arctodus simus*.

Measurements, mm [1]	Mammoth Site	Rock Creek, Texas [2] AMNH 12392	Lake Bonneville,Utah [3] UVP 015/4
Th 12, No			
PL	a41.0	45.6	
BFcr	58.0		
HFcr	a48.0		
Th 13, No			
PL	a43.0	47.6	
L 1, No			
PL	a45.0	50.5	
L 2, No			
PL	a46.0	51.4	66.0
BFcd	a70.0	76.0	93.0
HFcd	a45.0	49.2	66.0
L 3, No			
PL	a48.0	51.9	
BFcr	75.0		
HFcr	59.0		
H	a128.0		
L 4			
PL	a51.0	54.4	
BFcd	a82.0	75.5	
HFcd	a63.0	53.2	

1) After von den Driesch 1976
2) Kurtén 1967
3) Nelson and Madsen 1983

that of the Rock Creek specimen (AMNH 12392). The same measurements of centrum lengths for T12, 13, L1,2,3,and 4 for the HSMS specimen is 318 mm, compared to the same sum of 291 mm for the Rock Creek specimen. Again, the vertebral column is relatively shorter in the HSMS and Rock Creek *Arctodus simus* versus that of *Ursus americanus*. The thoracic seems long but that is because of the relatively short neck (see Kurtén 1967).

PELVIC GIRDLE AND HIND LIMBS

Pelvis

Left pelvis (83HS133) (Figure 124) with a partial ilium, pubis, and ischium; the acetabulum is complete (Table 60). The HSMS *Arctodus simus* ilium is thick, wide and relatively flat compared to that of *Ursus americanus* which has a more dished in area. The HSMS specimen has a short thick neck to the ilium. The saccral attachment is even with the top of the acetabulum on the HSMS *Arctodus simus* compared to the attachment being well above the acetabulum on *Ursus americanus*. The ventral edge of the ilium is lightly curved on *Arctodus simus* versus the highly curved area on *Ursus americanus*. The *Arctodus simus* from HSMS has a sacral medial attachment that is flattened, compared to the slightly raised appearance on *Ursus americanus*. The relatively large acetabulum on *Arctodus simus* is very wide, versus the distinctly smaller and more deeply cupped acetabulum on *Ursus americanus*. *Arctodus simus* has an ischium with a shorter and wider neck, compared to the long and slender ischial neck on *Ursus americanus*. Table 61 gives selected measurements for ursine bears.

Tibia

(86HS003) is a complete left tibia. The diaphysis is curved on the HSMS *Arctodus*, compared to the straight tibia in *Ursus americanus* (Merriam and Stock 1925:28). The two lines marking

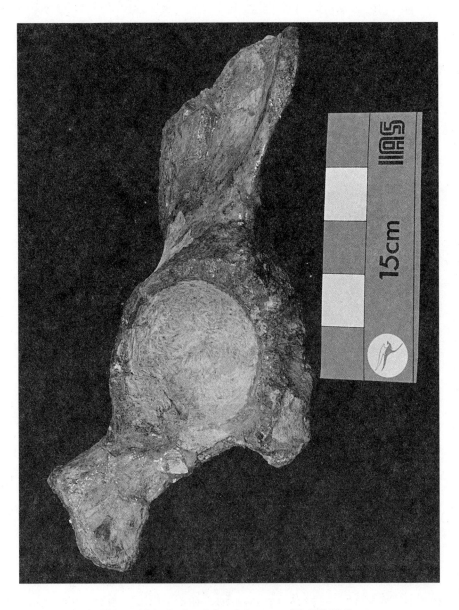

Figure 124. Left pelvis of *A. simus* (83-HS-133).

Table 60. Measurements of pelvis in *Arctodus simus*.

Measurements, mm [1]	Mammoth Site	Rancho La Brea, California [2] L.A.C.M.		Lake Bonneville, Utah [3] UVP
		251	250	015/7
Length of the acetabulum on the rim (LAR)	93.0	101.0	87.0	
Smallest height of the shaft of ilium (SB)	76.5	65.0	a78.0	84.0
Smallest breadth of the shaft of ilium (SB)	a43.0			
Least height of the neck of ischium	52.0			

1) After von den Driesch 1976; 2) Merriam and Stock 1925; 3) Nelson and Madsen 1983

Table 61. Measurements (mm) postcranial skeleton in *Ursus*.

Single	*Ursus arctos* Kamchatka coll. ZIN RAS		*Ursus spelaeus* Odessa coll. Zoological Museum, University of Helsinki				
Measurements, mm[1]	32672 male, subad. weight 215kg	32711 male, ad. weight 250kg	n	min	max	M	SD
Atlas							
BFcr	72.0	70.5	2	83.0	91.0		
BFcd	67.0	66.0	2	73.0	83.5		
GLF	59.2	66.0	2	70.8	71.0		
LAD	30.0	32.0	2	36.5	41.2		
H	49.8	49.3	2	58.5	71.5		
Axis							
LCDe	67.7	67.5	2	79.5	79.5		
LAPa	89.0	94.0	2	92.5	102.5		
BFcr	62.4	64.4	3	72.5	89.1	79.7	
BPacd	60.2	56.8	2	69.2	76.0		
SBV	46.8	50.8	3	56.0	61.0	58.5	
BFcd	38.3	40.5	2	50.0	51.5		
H	90.2	92.3	2	108.0	112.5		
Pelvis							
LAR	57.0	55.5	11	59.5	75.0	68.7	4.3
SH	47.4	53.0	8	54.0	71.5	62.7	6.0
SB	29.3	32.0					
L. height neck ischium	29.8	29.8					
Tibia							
GL	301.0	303.0	19	242.0	314.0	279.3	22.3
Bp	87.3	91.5	22	76.5	104.8	91.4	8.5
SD	28.2	28.6	22	25.5	38.3	31.3	3.5
Bd	68.0	70.0	23	65.0	88.2	75.7	6.1

1) After von den Driesch 1976

Table 62. Measurements of tibia in *Arctodus simus*.

Measurements, mm [1]	Mammoth Site	Potter Creek Cave, California [2] UC			Rancho La Brea, California [3] LACM		McKittrick, Calif. [2] LACM	Rock Creek, Texas [2] AMNH	Jinglebob, Kansas [2] UM	Hay Springs, Nebraska [2] F:AM	Lake Bonneville, Utah [4] UVP	
		3034	3722	3724	231	276	138	12392	25611	25531	015/2	015/3
Greatest length (GL)	493.0	360.0	a390.0	388.0	404.0		a375.0	389.0	a380.0	492.0	524.0	522.0
Greatest breadth of the proximal end (Bp)	162.0	107.0	a117.0	110.0	110.7			119.0		140.0	152.0	155.0
Smallest breadth of the diaphysis (SD)	50.5	33.1	35.2	37.1	40.7	43.0	39.2	38.3	38.0	50.0	50.5	50.0
Greatest breadth of the distal end (Bd)	124.0	88.0		85.5	88.4			92.5		104.0	119.0	119.0

1) After von den Driesch 1976
2) Kurtén 1967
3) Merriam and Stock 1925
4) Nelson and Madsen 1983

the attachment of the flexar digitorium muscle are further apart on *Arctodus* from HSMS compared to that on *Ursus americanus*. On *Arctodus* the outer line is distinct and extends along the posterior face to the distal end, compared to the shorter attachement on *Ursus americanus*. *Arctodus* has wide proximal and distal articular facets.

The length of the tibia from HSMS is big, but it is shorter than the specimen from Lake Bonneville (Nelson and Madsen 1983) (Table 62). However, the HSMS is wider at the greatest breadth of the epyphises, but the smallest breadth in the diaphyses is the same for both specimens.

COPROLITES

Twelve coprolites have been identified from the Mammoth Site. The coprolites are preserved in two morphological forms: 1) 11 as typical "dog dung morph" and 2) 1 as a semi-amorphous "bear pile morph". None of the coprolites is unequivocally identified to a particlular species of animal and therefore it not part of the species account above. However, we do feel that we can identify them to morphological types, which are discussed below.

Dung or coprolites of herbivores and carnivores are not typically preserved in the fossil environment. Taphonomical processes invariably destroy the fragile excrement remains, and therefore are exceedingly rare from Rancholabrean age deposits. The arid Southwest has provided an excellent record of dry-preserved herbivore dung, including mammoth, radiocarbon dating 10,000 to 40,000 yr B.P. (Agenbroad and Mead 1989; Davis *et al.* 1984; Hansen 1980; Mead and Agenbroad 1989, 1992). Carnivore dung has received less attention in North America. Most attention on carnivore coprolites has centered on the patterns of bone breakage, with less attention being paid to the identification of the producer and contents (see various articles in Behrensmeyer and Hill 1980; Bonnichsen and Sorg 1991).

The warm water that apparently filled the sinkhole at the Mammoth Site has leached most of the organics from the bones and has destroyed all plants, muscle tissue, hair, and gut contents. We do not find remnants or trace fossils that appear similar to the mammoth dung recovered from Bechan Cave, Utah (Davis *et al.* 1984; Mead *et al.* 1986). However, we have been fortunate enough to recover carnivore coprolites. Why these are preserved and herbivore dung is not, is still not fully understood. It may be that the slightly acidic nature of carnivore coprolites, permitted morphological preservation in the water. Most of the coprolites preserved contain the shape of the intestinal passage and have a slight carbonate crust coating.

"Dog Dung Morph"

All of the dung morphs were recovered in association with *Mammuthus* spp., *Canis lupus*, and *Arctodus simus* skeletal remains on the southwestern and western portions of the sinkhole. Table 63 provides the various measurements of the preserved coprolites. Measurement size of carnivore dung is highly dependent on content (vegetal, arthropod, bone, muscle residue). The coprolite of mature *Canis lupus* is typically averaging about 25 to 30 mm in diameter. Table 63a illustrates that most of the 'Dog Dung Morphs' are within the range of the wolf dung.

Scats of *Canis latrans* are extremely variable in size. *C. latrans* coprolites overlap in measurements with those of *C. lupus*, at the large end of the scale, and *Vulpes vulpes* (red fox), for the smaller scats. Some of the smaller morphs recovered could belong to *C. latrans*. Both species of *Canis* have been recovered in the sinkhole deposit.

The contents of the 'Dog Dung Morphs' are variable. Four contain bone fragments; one with a large mammal-sized bone and three with rodent bone remains, possibly *Cynonmys* (the most common rodent recovered from the sinkhole). Most samples of this morph appear to have contained meat byproducts, showing chalky remains with numerous voids and organic impressions remaining.

Table 63. Measurements of coprolites from the Mammoth Site.

a) "Dog Dung Morph"

	Length	Diameter
1.	51.7	22.3
2.	73.5	29.9
3.	58.0	33.3
4.	33.0	25.8
5.	___	21.5
6.	___	27.8
7.	67.4	26.9
8.	___	31.8

b) "Bear Pile Morph"

	Length	Diameter
1A	120.0	61.0
1B	117.0	60.0

c) "Bear Pile Morph Seeds"

Field Number	Length	Width
1. 92078	9.7	8.3
2. 92078	7.9	7.3
3. 92078	10.0	7.9
4. 92078	10.1	8.9

"Bear Pile Morph"

Only one sample is identified to this morph. It appears that at first a very liquid scat was produced, evidenced by a thin brown layer being present. Then directly on top were two piles, this time containing numerous lumps and "seeds" forming a somewhat amorphous conglomeration. The lumps contain a dark brown rind, with white chalky concentric layers within. Intermixed in the pile and between the various lumps are "seeds", which are calcareous nodules about the size of *Juniperus* seeds (Table 63b, c).

DISCUSSION

Paleoecological Adaptations

Three authors have attempted to determine the paleoecological adaptations of *Arctodus simus*. Kurtén (1967:49) states that *Arctodus simus* is very unlike bears and exhibits convergence with the great cats. He also postulates that *Arctodus simus* is predominantly carnivorous, "...the most powerful predator of the Pleistocene fauna of North America." He interprets *Arctodus simus* as being ecologically close to the brown bear (*Ursus arctos*) but notes that it is somewhat,"more exclusively flesh eating." He also indicates there is a probabiity of two subspecies , i.e. *Arctodus simus simus* for the smaller, southern form, and *Arctodus simus yukonensis* for a larger, northern form.

Emslie and Czaplewski (1985) interpret *Arctodus simus* as being,"...largely herbivorous," with characteristics of such a life style. They discuss the characteristics of the lower M_1 and noted it as being similar to the posterior premolars of hyenas and other carrion-feeding forms. These authors examine the structure of M_1 with the concept it is being used to masticate plants. At the same time, they think that M_1 had a "duality of functions for crushing plants and bone." M_2 is considered to be a broad tooth, together with M_3 to provide a broad crushing platform. These observations plus the fact that *Arctodus simus* does not have the the the tall, pointed molars such as the obligatory carnivorous *Thalarctos maritimus* (polar bear) led them to consider *Arctodus simus* as primarily an herbivore, "....with bone crushing ability." They also discuss the long limbs as characteristic of a digging animal (relative length of the proximal segment), and for use in tearing down vegetation for leaves, fruits, bark,etc. They also equate the large body size calculated by Kurtén (1967) as another herbivore characteristic. Lastly, these authors use sympatry of *Arctodus simus* and *Ursus americanus* to conclude that *Arctodus simus* was basically a herbivore (Emslie and Czaplewski 1985:15).

Based on the analysis presented in this paper, the giant short-faced bear from the Mammoth Site of Hot Springs, South Dakota, in which the entire cranium and mandible of one individual was available for analysis, we conclude that the previous conclusions are in error.

Morphological Adaptation

Our research of the skull, mandibles, and teeth of *Arctodus simus* indicates that this species was an opportunistic scavenger. In genuine scavengers (*Crocuta, Uycene, Borophagus, and Gulo*) it is typical to have wide palates, high sagittal crests, strongly developed zygomatic arch, and robust shearing (carnassial) teeth, which lie parallel to one another. *Arctodus simus* also typically exhibits wide palate (except our specimen), strongly developed zygomatic arch, and large cheek teeth. The sagittal crest is not excessively large, but great power for the mandible has developed two deep masseteric and premasseteric fossa. Also noteworthy is the morphology of the zygomatic suture, which accomodates a massive mandible with a powerful condyle. The robust cheek teeth have shearing structures on the carnassial teeth, and bone crushing posterior molars. The cheek teeth display high crowns, which are typical of scavenging carnivores. The morphology of the skull indicates features that are convergent with canids (zygomatic suture), and hyenids (dentition), which also reflect similarity to scavenging carnivores.

Our research shows that the morphology of the cheek teeth and their size correlations indicate that they are not teeth typical of herbivorous bears. Also, the cheek teeth of *Arctodus simus* are not similar to the cheek teeth of obligate carnivores such as *Thalarctos maritimus*. In the polar bear, the teeth are small, but with tall, pointed tuberculum.

Orbits in *Arctodus simus* are more laterally directed, as in *Ursus arctos*, and especially in predatory carnivores (*Canis, Panthera, Felis).* Stereoscopic vision is very important for active carnivores, but not scavengers.

Our interpretation is compatible with the proportions of the limbs (Figure 125). *Arctodus simus* was not adapted for speed, or for jumpiNg (Emslie and Czaplewski 1985). These limbs and locomotion are satisfactory for a scavenger.

The body size in *Arctodus simus* is also normal for scavengers. A weight of 620-660 kg as calculated by Kurtén (1967) is not anomalous for carnivorous bears, according to the weight of recent big bears (*Ursus arctos* from Alaska and Kamchatca (Heptner *et al.* 1967). It may be that the corpses of Pleistocene megafauna (mammoths, and other large ungulates) fed this large Pleistocene bear.

Arctodus simus was not as highly specialized a scavenger as *Crocuta* or *Canis dirus*. Their carnassials lay forward, to be effective. *Crocuta* can cut and crush bones, as shown in studies of modern and fossil assemblages (Sutcliffe 1970; Haynes 1991). *Arctodus simus* could less effectively crush small bones; big limb bones of mammoths were probably not accessible for *Arctodus*.

We interpret *Arctodus simus* to have been a large bear with a short neck and short body. It stood very high off the ground; the length of the hind leg bones indicate the animal was high in the hind quarters, not lowered as in *Ursus spelaeus*. The head was small, relative to the body size, with a short face and small, widely spaced, eyes. This was an omnivorous bear, which consumed plant foods and preyed on juvenile and sick ungulates, but primarily scavenged the carcasses of dead mammoths and other large mammals.

Arctodus simus as a Scavenger

The distribution of the species (Kurtén and Anderson 1980:181) indicates that *Arctodus simus* was adapted to a plains and grasslands habitat, whereas other earlier, smaller species (*Arctodus pristinus* Leidy 1854) indicated an adaptation as an eastern, woodland form (Figure 126). A plains and grasslands distribution negates the neces-

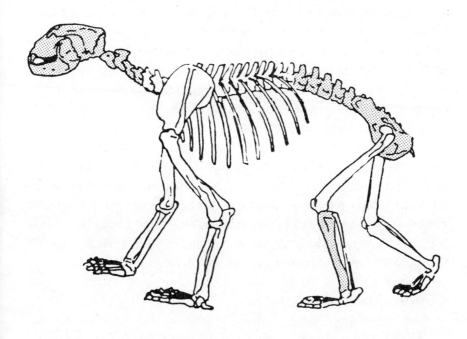

Figure 125. Skeleton of *A. simus.* Shaded portions are those bones we have
recovered from the Mammoth Site (after illustration by E. Mead *in* Agenbroad
and Mead 1986).

sity (and probability) of long limbs as an adaptation to pulling down high grass, bushes and other vegetation. It may indicate an adaptation to travel in grasslands, plus an adaptive advantage in the dismemberment of the carcasses of megaherbivores. If it is advantageous for predatory carnivores to hide in high grass, it would have been neccesary for a scavenging *Arctodus simus* to be able to see over the grass. *Arctodus simus* possibly ranged with the herds of mammoth, bison, and other large herbivores, looking for the converging of carrion-feeding birds (vultures, condors, teratorns) as a clue to carcass locations. This foraging tactic is atypical for modern bears, but it has been observed among spotted hyenas (*Crocuta crocuta*) and lions (*Panthera leo*) on the African savanna (Kruuk 1972:146; Schaller 1972:52). Such a strategy probably required a wide home range in order to exploit a sufficient number of carcasses. Information regarding the geographic distribution of late Pleistocene megaherbivores such as mammoth (Agenbroad 1984a), bison (*Bison* sp.), horse (*Equus* sp.), camels (*Camelops* sp.), and others conforms to the distribution pattern of *Arctodus simus* remains.

Arctodus simus was often associated with large accumulations of these large herbivores in death assemblages provided by natural traps, such as the sinkhole at Hot Springs, the tar seeps of southern California, or Natural Trap Cave in Wyoming (Table 64). In addition, other fauna present at these localities represent opportunistic scavengers.

If we suppose that *Arctodus simus* was a scavenger, it would be normal for it to have been sympatic with *Ursus americanus* and *Ursus arctos*. There may not have been competition for scavenging with the smaller bears, although the mighty *Arctodus simus* sometimes may have fed from the kills of the smaller bears or the big cats (*Panthera, Smilodon*).

We infer that *Arctodus simus*, like *Thalarctos maritimus* was not a hibernator. That, in fact, the time of winter stress for herbivores might be one of the more opportune feeding periods (greatest number of winter kill carcasses) for a bear adapted to a scavenging role. In contrast with these, *Ursus spelaeus,* a herbivore, has been witnessed in hibernation. Many adult and juvenile specimens of *Ursus*

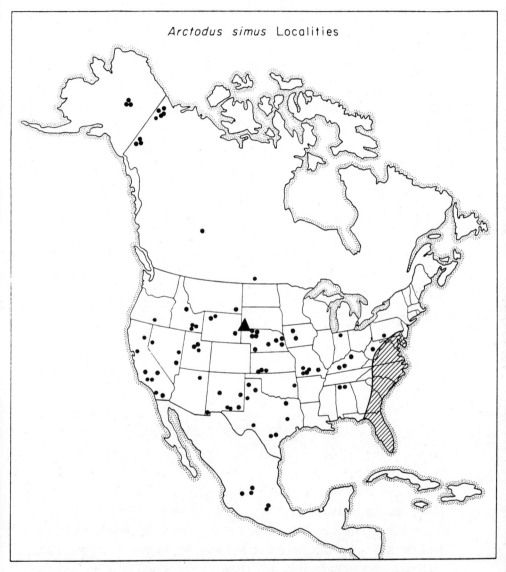

Figure 126. Distribution of reported *Arctodus simus*= ●; reported *Arctodus pristinus* distribution=▨. Map is updated and modified from Kurtén and Anderson (1980); Agenbroad and Mead (1986). Hot Springs Mammoth site is designated by ▲.

Table 64a. Herbivores associated with *Arctodus simus* in late Pleistocene in natural traps.

Hot Springs Mammoth Site, South Dakota	Natural Trap, Wyoming	Rancho La Brea, California
Mammuthus columbi	*Mammuthus* sp.	*Mammut americanum*
Mammuthus primigenius	*Equus* sp.	*Mammuthus imperator*
Camelops sp.	*Antilocarpa americana*	*Mammuthus columbi*
Euceratherium collinum	*Alces alces*	*Glossotherium harlani*
Antilocapra americana	*Cervus elaphus*	*Megalonyx jeffersoni*
	Odocoileus hemionus	*Nothrotheriops shastensis*
	Bison bison	*Camelops hesturus*
	Bootherium bombifrons	*Antilocapra americana*
	Oreamnos americanus	*Odocoileus* sp.
	Ovis canadensis	*Bison antiquus*
		Platygonus sp.
		Equus sp.
		Tapirus merriami

b. Carnivores associated with *Arctodus simus* in late Pleistocene natural traps.

Canis lupus	*Canis dirus*	*Canis dirus*
Canis latrans	*Canis lupus*	*Canis lupus*
Taxidea taxus	*Canis latrans*	*Canis latrans*
Mustela vison/nigripes	*Vulpes vulpes*	*Smilodon fatalis*
	Miracinonyx trumani	*Urus* sp.
	Panthera atrox	*Taxida* sp.
	Lynx lynx	*Lynx lynx*
	Mustela sp.	*Smilodon californicus*
	Martes nobilis	*Felis atrox*
	Gulo gulo	

spelaeus have been recovered in Europe and the Ural Mountains; these animals may have died during hibernation (Vereschagin 1982). *Tremarctos floridanus* remains are also usually recovered in cave sediments, but *Arctodus simus* remains are relatively rare in caves, except for some individual occurrences. This makes winter hibernation an unlikely adaptive role, especially in relatively flat, treeless grassland environment. Further support for this conclusion comes from the mode of occurence of *Arctodus simus* remains (Table 65).

Table 65. Some *Arctodus simus* localities and inferred environments.

1. Hot Springs Mammoth Site, South Dakota (this report)   cold steppe-grassland
2. Rancho La Brea, California (Stock 1942)   grassland
3. Cueva Quebrada, Texas (Lundelius 1984)   open grassland
4. Lake Bonneville, Utah (Nelson and Madsen 1983)   land shoreline
5. Gittin' Down-Mountain Cave, Oklahoma (Puckette 1976)   cave (den in grassland?)
6. Potter Creek Cave, California (Cope 1879)   cave (den in grassland?)
7. Labor of Love Cave, Nevada (Emslie and Czaplewski 1985)   cave (den?)
8. Lone Tree Arroyo, Kansas (Hibbard 1955b)   grassland
9. Fossil Lake, Oregon (Elftman 1931)
10. Freisenhahn Cave, Texas (Kurten 1963)   den in grassland
11. Rock Creek, Texas (Troxell 1915)
12. Trinity River, Texas (Slaughter 1962)
13. Lubbock Lake, Texas (Holiday and Johnson 1990)   grassland
14. Frankstown Cave, Pennsylvania (Peterson 1926)   cave (den?)
15. Carroll Cave, Missouri (Hawksley 1965)   cave (den?)
16. Bat Cave, Missouri (Hawksley 1965)   cave (den?)
17. Perkins Cave, Missouri (Hawksley 1965)   cave (den?)
18. Cass County, Nebraska (Barbour 1916)   grassland
19. Hay Springs, Nebraska (Mathew 1918; Hay 1924)   grassland
20. Irvine, California (Savage 1951)   grassland
21. American Falls, Idaho (McDonald and Anderson 1975)   grassland
22. Red Willow Gravel Pit, Nebraska (Corner 1986)   grassland
23. Keams Canyon, Arizona (Lindsay and Tessman 1974)   grassland
24. Little Box Elder Cave, Wyoming (Kurten and Anderson 1974)   grassland
25. Gold Run Creek, Yukon, Canada (Lambe 1911)   steppe
26. Ester Creek, Alaska (Frick 1930)   steppe
27. Cleary River, Alaska (Frick)   steppe
28. Tequixquiac, Mexico (Hibbard 1955a)   grassland

DISTRIBUTION

At the end of the Pleistocene, *Arctodus simus* was very wide-spread from central Mexico in the south, to Alaska in the north (Kurtén and Anderson 1980). No fossil remains of *Arctodus* have been found in Siberia. It is of interest to note that *Crocuta spelaea* lived in Siberia, but was not distributed in Alaska. Both species were scavengers.

Kurtén (1967) concluded there were two subspecies; *Arctodus simus yukonenesis,* and *Arctodus simus simus* based on difference in size. Emslie and Czaplewski (1985) justly noted that this problem has not been definately solved. Very large specimens of *Arctodus simus* are present in Alaska, Yukon Province, California, and Utah. Our specimen is also very large. It is possible that the size difference is simply sexual dimorphism, and that the large specimens are simply male animals. For these reason, we have not assigned a subspecies to the bear from the Mammoth Site. It is possible to document a size increase in these bears, as one goes northward (Bergman's Rule), as noted in Kurtén and Anderson (1980).

TAPHONOMY

At the Hot Springs Site, the remains of predators have been confined to the southwest corner of the sinkhole, in excavations, to date. In contrast, it appears that mammoth remains are scattered rather uniformly along the circumference of the sinkhole pond; as yet, the northern margin is not adequately tested. It also appears that numerous large blocks of Spearfish Shale, the sinkhole wallrock, have collapsed into the western margin of the pond. These blocks may have provided a bench of relatively stable footing for those animals entrapped in the sinkhole who were attempting escape. This may also have been the area of most probable egress from the sinkhole, although the exhumed sinkhole walls are very steep in this area.

It is likely that the southwest portion of the pond was the only bankside area that allowed partial exposure to the dead, or dying mammoths. The submerged collapse blocks may have provided a shelf, or bench in this area. Wolves, bears and other scavengers were active in this region, as contrasted to other portions of the pond, for reason outlined above. It is in this same area that the skeletal and dental remains of wolf and bear have been recovered, as well as being the area from which wolf and bear coprolites were retrieved. The co-occurrence of predator remains and predator fecal material, plus geologic and hydrologic criteria indicate that this was the area of exposure of victims, allowing the optimum potential for scavengers.

It is likely that multiple individuals of both carnivorous species were active in the sinkhole, mainly ingesting the flesh of the most recent sinkhole victims, however occasional bone fragments are found in the coprolites. No mammoth bones from the site have yet yielded evidence of gnawing, or carnivore/scavenger modification. The wolf individual recovered from the site is a very old specimen according to our analysis. The short-faced bear is a young-adult male. It either represents a bear which was unable to negotiate an escape due to steep, slippery sinkhole walls, or it may be one individual, from a group of several bears, who suffered a fatality. That fatality could have occurred as a blow from a not-so-dead mammoth, or from competition with other scavenger/predators.

Bears, in general, tend to be solitary except for the mating season, or in mother-cub(s) bonding. There is no reason to expect the *Arctodus simus* to behave otherwise. It may be that the Hot Springs specimen may have been the sole arctodont scavenger; it may also have been the only one, of several, to suffer fatality within the sinkhole. The distribution of the *Arctodus* skeletal elements over nearly 10 m (linearly) of the south western margin of the sinkhole suggests that trampling, during later mammoth escape efforts, scattered the decomposing carcass of the bear.

The co-occurrence of mammoth and *Arctodus* remains is normal, in North America. Scavengers are often detected in the death assemblages of mammoth and ungulates. For example, a collection of nearly 7000 bones of *Mammuthus primigenius* was found at Berelekh River in northeast Siberia. Certain bones from Berelekh contained gnaw marks of *Gulo gulo*. The remains of *Gulo gulo* were also present (Vereshchagin 1977). The most abundant collection of *Arctodus simus* remains are from Rancho La Brea, California, together with the numerous remains of other Pleistocene scavengers such as *Canis dirus, Canis lupus, Vulpes vulpes,* and vultures.

Remains of herbivorous bears are very rare, or absent in similar localities. For example, in the Transcaucasus in Binagady (located near Baku), there was a Pleistocene asphalt trap where the remains of cave bears were absent, although they are usually found in caves in the Caucasus and in Paleolithic cave sites. In this locality, the remains of scavengers (*Crocuta spelaea, Canis lupus, Vulpes vulpes*, vultures, and carnivorous crows) were numerous (Vereshchagin 1967). Also, *Tremarctos floridanus* was not found at Rancho La Brea (Kurtén 1966).

EXTINCTION

Kurtén and Anderson (1980) suggest that *Arctodus simus* became extinct during the late Pleistocene due to competition with the invasion of *Ursus arctos*. Emslie and Czaplewski (1985), having concluded that *Arctodus simus* was an herbivore with bone crushing affinities. We feel that there is a possiblity that *Arctodus simus* and *Ursus* were sympatric during the late Pleistocene. The youngest published dates for *Arctodus simus* are derived from Lubbock Lake, Texas (12,650 ± 350 yr B.P.) (Holiday and Anderson 1990) and the Provo Narrows, Utah (12,650 ± 70 yr B.P.) (Nelson and Madsen 1983).

A scavenging life style would not put *Arctodus simus* in direct competition with the carnivorous and omnivorous *Ursus*. There are only two localities south of the ice sheet where the two genera are found together (Labor of Love Cave, Nevada; Little Box Elder Cave, Wyoming), other co-occurrences are temporaly disparate. This does not support a strong case for sympatry of the species.

Rather than carnivore competition, or contemporaneity, we feel that *Arctodus simus* fell victim to the increasing scarcity of megaherbivore carcasses at, or about 11,000 yr B.P.(Mead and Meltzer 1984). Similar models have been proposed for the extinction of the saber toothed cats, and the scavenging teratorns and giant condors.

ACKNOWLEDGMENTS

We thank J.F. Hoffecker (Argonne National Laboratory) for editorial assistance.

Chapter 17

COLUMBIAN MAMMOTH: PALEONTOLOGICAL DISCOVERY OF A GLAND STONE AT HOT SPRINGS, SOUTH DAKOTA

Larry D. Agenbroad, Sandra Lash Shoshani,
and Jeheskel Shoshani

Recovery of a gland stone (probable bile stone) from the articulated remains of *Mammuthus columbi* provides the first recorded paleontological recovery of such material outside the possible recovery from frozen carcasses of the permafrost region of Alaska and Siberia. The preservation and recovery of such an object is due, in part, to the unique nature and sedimentary history of the Hot Springs Mammoth Site. X-ray comparison of the fossil material and bile stones recovered from deceased zoo animals and cropped African elephants are contrasted with water chemistry and tuffa deposits from local and distant environments.

Gland stones are not commonly recovered during the excavation of paleontological remains. Recovery of one such stone in the field season of 1979 at Hot Springs, South Dakota is unique, to our knowledge, at least in the study of sub-arctic mammoth remains. The apparent absence of such discoveries in previous investigations can be due to several causes, including: 1) infrequency of such abnormalities in the living population; 2) physical-chemical conditions of the preserving environment; 3) failure of the excavator to recognize the origin and nature of such material; 4) destruction or loss of such material in the typical mode of deposition; i.e., alluvial conditions.

Bile stones are known in African elephants, though the animals do not possess gall bladders (Sikes 1971; Buss 1990). It is also possible the stone could be a kidney stone, or a bladder stone. The specimen from the Hot Springs Mammoth Site is rounded, measuring 181 mm in its greatest dimension, 167 mm in its least. One side of the specimen is pitted and irregular, whereas the opposite side (Figure 127) is smooth and rounded. Examination of the pitted surface and X-ray of the specimen indicate concentric layers, as might be expected in a stone of this origin.

The Hot Springs Mammoth Site is unique in fossil mammoth repositories in the New World (Agenbroad 1984a, 1990, this volume). It contains a large sample (42 individuals, to date) of a local population of Columbian mammoths *(Mammuthus columbi)* and at least 2 individuals of *Mammuthus primigenius* in a sinkhole pond fed by thermal artesian water.

Deep testing, beneath the city alley right-of-way, in the northeastern portion of the deposit yielded a concentration of skulls and one articulated animal. The detailed excavation of the articulated skeleton produced the gland stone in the approximate location of the lumbar vertebrae (Figure 128). The posture of the articulated skeleton suggests a carcass that was bloated, floated on the pond surface until the paunch was deflated. The carcass sank to the pond floor, settling on its back. The weight of the tusks caused the cranium to rotate approximately 100° to the right. Since the animal was deposited on its back, the location of the stone could be actual, or it could be depositional due to deterioration of the organ which held it, such as a liver, kidney, or bladder.

The history of sedimentary filling of the sinkhole pond was in three phases (Laury 1980, 1990, this volume). Sedimentation was rapid in the initial phase, slowing progressively in the latter two. Sediments were supplied to the pond primarily by rainfall and the annual erosion of the subaerially exposed sinkhole walls and adjacent uplands. An additional source of sediment was from the high-energy spring conduit which caused sculpting, erosion, and collapse of the Spearfish Shale wall rock.

The initial phase of sedimentation was highlighted by erosion and deepening of the pond floor near the spring conduit and rapid

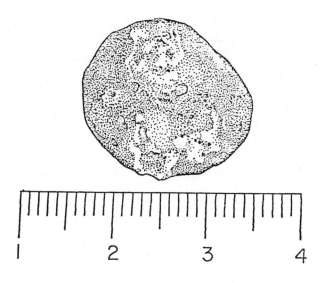

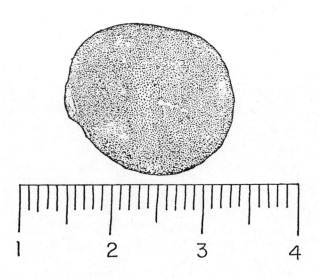

Figure 127. Ventral and dorsal views of the mammoth gland stone from the
Hot Springs Mammoth Site. Scale in cm.

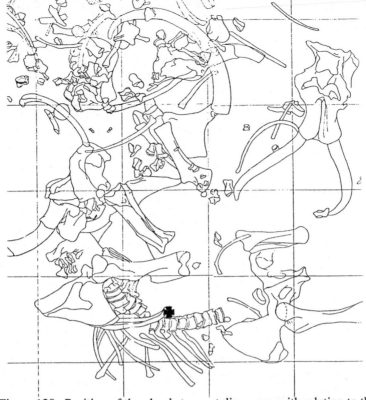

Figure 128. Position of the gland stone, at discovery, with relation to the skeleton of 'Napoleon' (MSL 140).

erosion of the over steepened, unvegetated sinkhole walls. Contemporaneous deposits of poorly sorted, matrix-rich, colluvial gravels were common along the pond margins, with thinly laminated, micrograded sands and silts in the central pond area. Progressive slowing of sedimentation rates and upward fining of the pond-margin sediments accompanied the initiation of mammoth entrapment and of mammoth induced liquefaction, slope failure, and mass flowage of steeply dipping marginal sediments. Slumpage and reworking of pond sediments and the Spearfish wallrock was common near the spring conduit.

The second phase of sedimentation probably represents the greatest time interval and exhibits the greatest frequency of mammoth entrapment. The somewhat regular encroachment of mammoth into the pond deformed sediments in the nearshore areas and triggered a variety of subaqueous sedimentation events in the nearshore areas (density currents and occasional small flows). Very little gravel or coarse grained material was supplied to the pond, with sedimentation composed of rhythmic, thinly laminated, very fine sands and clayey silts which display numerous preserved mammoth footprints. The laminations are probably not varves, but were formed by a combination of sedimentation events such as storm runoff from adjacent slopes; energy fluctuations and resedimentation events near the spring conduit; and mammoth disturbance of the slopes and pond floor. It was in phase two sediments that the skeleton and associated "stone" were deposited.

Phase three in the sedimentary history records a progressive, fairly rapid reduction in spring discharge. The results were a decrease in overall pond sediment grain size; a decrease in pond water depth; and a decrease of the areal extent of the pond surface. Ultimately, the lacustrine environment was terminated. Mammoths were able to freely traverse the remaining, water-saturated pond strata, resulting in a greatly contorted, bioturbated unit, as compared to the rhythmic laminations of phase two.

Renewed downcutting of the nearby, ancestral Fall River is believed to be responsible for the altered groundwater regime and termination of spring discharge to the sinkhole. Just when the latter happened is unknown. The mammoth bone dates of *ca.* 26,000 yr B.P. (Agenbroad 1984b, 1990, this volume) from the medial sediments of the sinkhole fill places the site in the Late Wisconsinan glacial stage. Sedimentation rates are available for several physically analogous, modern sinkhole ponds in the Black Hills which show that sinkholes similar in size to the Hot Springs Mammoth Site can be filled in less than 300-400 years. Unfortunately the paleoclimatic data needed to make such calculations for the Mammoth Site strata are presently unavailable.

Of additional importance is the discovery, based primarily on paleontological evidence, that the springs feeding the Mammoth Site pond were geothermally heated (Laury 1980, 1990; Agenbroad and Laury 1979; Mead *et al.* this volume) which kept the pond water continuously warm with an ambient temperature of at least 35°C (95°F). Springs of similar temperature and size are present nearby in the town of Hot Springs, where they emerge at the present grade of Fall River, approximately 70 m below the level of the Mammoth Site. The year-round supply of heated water to the Mammoth Site pond severely curtailed its aquatic life, except for the benthic-infauna of oligochaete worms. In addition, the presence of the heated pond would have: a) kept the pond from freezing, b) minimized or eliminated seasonality (varves) in stratification, c) increased the settling rates of suspended sediment two-fold over typical cold-water (15°C) ponds of the area—this would permit preservation of more and thinner laminae in any given time period, d) enhanced the chance for development of pond laminae, by elimination of sediment-disrupting, rooted aquatic plants, e) accelerated carcass disarticulation through greater bacterial activity, f) selectively dissolved the missing bone collagen, and g) supported a year-round flora on the heated ground marginal to the pond. As in the case of other modern areas of hot springs (e.g., Yellowstone Park), point (g) above, and the warmth of the pond atmosphere may have preferentially attracted large numbers of megafauna to the Hot Springs sinkhole, especially in winter months.

Inquiries made to zoos, veterinarians and biochemists did not produce quantitative data on gland stone compositions. Medical journals concentrated on the structure and organic composition of "gland" stones. Dr. Sylvia Sikes wrote a comprehensive book on the physiology of African elephants (Sikes 1971); she also described the occurrence of bile stones in animals she had dissected during necropsy. She provided stones collected from her sample M-117, collected in field work during the 1963-1967 field work in Africa. These stones were given to Sandra Lash. One large stone from this animal was used as a modern comparison with the fossil "stone" from "Napoleon" (MSL-140), the articulated mammoth skeleton from Hot Springs.

Analysis of the fossil "gland" stone of *Mammuthus columbi* was accomplished by a non-destructive X-ray procedure known as PIXE (proton-induced X-ray Emission) analysis. This procedure places the sample in front of an external proton beam, collecting the emitted X-ray spectra. The elements can be detected by their spectra. Figure 129 illustrates the spectral data in graphic form, with key elements indicated along the scale. It will be noted that there is striking similarity between the modern *Loxodonta africana* bile stone and the suspected fossil bile stone from *Mammuthus columbi*. As control, and a comparative standard, a bile stone recovered from the interhepatic duct of a dissected African elephant was used (Sikes personal communication). The comparison of test results indicates very close elemental profiles, even though intensities are not of the same magnitude. The bile stone from the modern animal *(L. africana)* contains phosphorus and sulphur which the fossil specimen does not contain. The fossil stone indicates minor amounts of selenium, rubidium and strontium which the modern sample does not contain. Both of these apparent anomalies can be explained by the hydrous environment of deposition and post depositional saturation at the Mammoth Site. The soluble materials such as phosphorus and sulphur could be expected to be leached from the fossil gland stone. In a similar manner, thermal spring effluent from an area with a relative abundance of radioactive minerals, carbonates, and iron could secondarily enrich a gland stone preserved in sediments deposited in and impregnated by such water.

Table 66 presents the chemical analyses of tuffa, caliche, modern and fossil gland stones. These analyses were done under two different types of laboratory procedures, an electron microprobe, and analytic chemistry. The table gives a comparison of major elements in specimens of tuffa and caliche with the biological materials. The table is an element to potassium ratio for each specimen. After calculating and comparing several ratios, all but calcium, manganese, and iron were deleted from the comparison, as these appeared to be the most diagnostic for the comparison of organic to inorganic materials. Calcium, in particular, shows the greatest similarity between the biologic stones, and is strikingly dissimilar (450X) from the geologic tuffa and caliche. Similarly, manganese composition shows no major difference, but iron seems to be more prevalent in the tuffa and caliche, although the caliche and the fossil stone

365

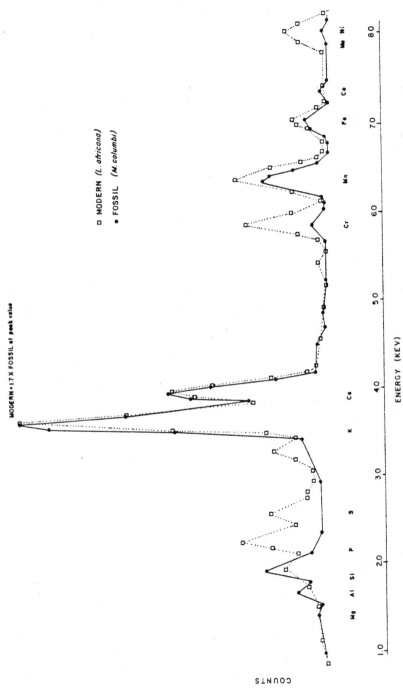

Figure 129. A graph of PIXIE compositional analyses of a modern bile stone from *L. africana* and the stone from *M. columbi*.

Table 66. Element to Potassium ratios for glandstones, tuffa, and caliche, (element/K concentration ratio).

Element	Modern "Stone"	Fossil "stone"	Cascade Cr Tuffa	Beaver Valley Caliche	Salt Lake Tuffa
Ca	.28	.29	328.80	127.85	319.80
Mn	.102	.06	.32	1.90	.23
Fe	.02	.01	10.00	4.25	27.10

are very similar in iron content.

The similarity of the X-ray elemental profiles of the bile stones is indicative that the 26,000 year old specimen and the 20 year old specimen are of similar origin. The dissimilarity between the geological specimens to the fossil specimen adds strength to the interpretation provided by the PIXIE analysis, i.e. the fossil is a mammoth bile stone.

Ground waters in the area, as assessed by artesian springs in the city of Hot Springs and at Cascade Spring, eleven miles southwest (Table 67), provide chemical information that has probably not varied greatly since the artesian system was active in the Mammoth Site sinkhole. The rationale for that statement is based on the likely source of these waters being from the Minnelusa Limestone, a regional aquifer for the Southern Black Hills. The chemistry of the water and the tuffa deposited from this source, and from nearby Cascade Spring, modern and ancient, are significantly different from that of the gland stone. The relatively spherical configuration of the fossil stone suggests it was a single stone, as multiple stones usually exhibit wear facets (W. Birkby personal communication).

In conclusion, X-ray analysis of fossil and modern specimens show remarkably similar X-ray profiles. Analysis of local thermal spring water and tuffa, plus non-local tuffa and caliche de-

Table 67. Water Chemistry of the Fall River Hydrogeologic System (Quantities in ppm). Data from Rahn and Gries (1973); Joe Muller, personal communication.

Chemistry	Evans Plunge Sec 13, T7S, R5E	Cascade Spring S20, T8S, R5E
Calcium	295.0	568.0
Magnesium	49.1	92.0
Sodium	99.1	60.0
Silica	16.0	22.0
Iron	1.1	0.3
Fluoride		0.9
Carbonate	123.0	0.0
Bicarbonate		235.0
Sulfate	736.3	1540.0
Chloride	120.0	62.0
Ph	6.8	7.0
Hardness ($CaCO_3$)	680.0	—
Total Dissolved Solids	1553.0	2530.0

posits indicate a different composition for the geologic materials, ruling out concretions, water worn-tuffa, and other possibilities, as an origin for the Mammoth Site specimen. The Hot Springs trap and depositional environment are unique in that they have deposited and faithfully preserved elements such as bile stones from an extinct species of proboscidean, *Mammuthus columbi*.

Chapter 18

THE SIGNIFICANCE OF THE MAMMOTH SITE OF HOT SPRINGS

Larry D. Agenbroad

SITE SIGNIFICANCE: FAUNA AND FLORA

The geological nature of the Hot Springs Mammoth Site has been described in some detail in previous publications (Agenbroad 1984b, 1985, 1990, this volume; Agenbroad and Laury 1979; Laury 1980, 1990 this volume) and will not be repeated here.

The Hot Springs Mammoth Site is the largest primary repository of mammoth in the New World. By "primary," we mean an *in situ* depositional occurrence, i.e., the remains are where the animals were trapped and died (thanatocoenosis), as contrasted to fluvial transport and deposition, as would be the case of bones accumulating on a sandbar, beach, or along a major stream. This distinction means that all skeletal remains are present within the elliptical confines of the sinkhole.

The sinkhole (doline) itself is a unique hydrologic-geologic trap and preservation environment. Collapse of subterranean solution caverns—probably in the Minnelusa Formation—was expressed upward as a breccia pipe, above the collapse, and as a sinkhole at the surface being formed, locally, in the Spearfish Shale. Artesian springs utilized the zone of weakness and filled the depression with a pond to an estimated five meters (fifteen feet) depth (Laury 1980, 1990 this volume). Exhumed walls of the sinkhole reveal banks steeper than 60° to overhanging, in all areas of the circumference that have been tested. The slope, plus the submoistening above the pond level, of the gypsiferous Spearfish Shale would result in a steep, extremely slippery sinkhole wall from near the water level, to an estimated two to two and a half meters (6–8 feet) upslope. Once an animal with the bulk of a mammoth reached that submoistened zone, it would be a one-way trip into the pond. Once trapped, there was little chance for escape for a large graviportal animal (mammoth) with non-grasping feet. The victim(s) could only attempt escape until exhaustion allowed them to drown, or starvation accomplished a similar demise.

It appears that most of the animals died, decomposed, and disarticulated at, or near the pond edge, on whatever slump block, or shelf provided footing. The remains were subjected only to processes that occurred within the confines of the sinkhole, i.e., spring activity, bank caving/slumpage, scavenging, trampling, overbank flow into the sinkhole from upslope surficial deposits, subaqueous down-slope movement, and the sedimentary processes present in that environment. A few individuals appear to have reached their post-mortem depositional positionals by 'bloat-and-float' mechanisms (Figure 56). These individuals are the most articulated animals within the deposit, as evidenced by the excavation of ± 30% (volume) of the deposit, to date.

This large population of mammoths provides a statistically valid sample of a local (non-transported) mammoth population. An age-structure analysis of ± 80% of the exhumed animals at the site indicates the trap was most effective for the sub-adult and young adult male animals of the local populations (Agenbroad 1984b, 1990, this volume; Agenbroad and Mead 1987, 1989). Age determinations indicate that greater than 80% of the individuals are in the 10-29 year age bracket with a peak in the 20-29 age set. It is also believed that only single individuals, or a few animals per year (or decade) were trapped, over a period of several hundred years, as concluded from the sedimentation rates and the incorporation and burial of mammoth remains.

The mammoth population at this site allows a detailed metric analysis of a local population. Several individuals remain articulated allowing metrics of post-cranial material to be correlated to the age of the individual, as determined from dental criteria (Laws 1966; Jackman 1988). With these data, element size versus age charts for various elements can be constructed, which may aid in estimates of individuals represented by only post-cranial material in other pale-ontological localities, or archaeological sites with man-mammoth accumulations.

Taphonomic analyses utilizing three-dimensional grid diagrams generated by computer are currently underway. Each bone in the bone bed has x, y, z coordinates, which have been entered into the computer (Autocad) and will yield such data presentations—not only for the entire bone bed, but for individual elements, or groups of elements. These data sets will allow taphonomic interpretations of natural causes of bone distribution, which can be contrasted to other localities with suspected human-caused distributions of bones of mammoths or mastodons.

The analyses of not only the mammoth, but the associated fauna—both vertebrate and invertebrate—allow us to reconstruct a portion of the biotic community in the southern Black Hills during mid-Wis-consin times. Adding the limited palynological information helps us to estimate the paleoecological conditions from deposits within the Black Hills physiographic province, rather than attempt to extrapo-late data from further east (or west). We envision a cold steppe-grasslands environment (with hot springs and their associated mi-cro-environments) inhabited by herbivores such as mammoth, cam-els, antelope, horses, bison, shrub-oxen and micromammals adapted to steppe-grassland, plus associated carnivores such as coyote, wolf, and bear. The spring/pond habitat reflects mollusks, amphibians, fish, and water adapted microfauna such as mink.

Paleontological Significance

It all began, as referred to in Chapter 1, with an evening discus-sion between myself and Phil Anderson, at the newly exposed bone bed in 1974. Phil Anderson deserves great credit for being a contrac-tor who appreciated the scientific potential of the site—more than potential financial gain by his original plans for development of the area. That spirit was further displayed when he sold the property—at his cost—to the newly formed Mammoth Site Board. In that evening conversation, Phil caught the vision of an *in situ* exhibit for the public, and he has been a faithful supporter of that concept and its development since that time, as has his entire family.

The remains of mammoths and associated fauna provided the first record of Quaternary fossils within the Black Hills physiographic province. Initially, we knew we had mammoth remains and bear incisors. Since that 1974 salvage paleontological season the list of Pleistocene first occurrences has increased for the Mammoth Site, as well as other Quaternary localities within the southern Black Hills. Research efforts in natural traps within Wind Cave National Park has not only extended the faunal range, it has greatly extended the temporal range. In addition, a ranch in another drainage, near Hot Springs has recently produced additional Pleistocene fauna.

Table 68 lists thirty species of Pleistocene animals discovered in the southern Black Hills since the discovery of the Mammoth Site bones in 1974. It is our firm conviction that additional sites and new species remain to be discovered, not only in the southern Black Hills, but throughout the entire province.

Significance as an Interpretive Center

One of the visions that grew on us, from an early stage, was the concept of the Site becoming a Research Center for Quaternary Studies of the Black Hills and surrounding region. Of course, the paleontological aspects of the deposit itself are obvious, but the impact of the site, its complexity, abundance, and paleoecological importance set a focus on the paucity of Quaternary research within the region. Initial, and expanded research and evaluation of some small deposits within Wind Cave National Park gave us new faunal and temporal information for the southern Black Hills. Additional information derived from a nearby ranch and Holocene deposits investigated within the Wind Cave National Park boundaries (Martin *et al.* 1987,

Table 68. First occurrences of Pleistocene fauna within the Black Hills physiographic province. (HSMS=Mammoth Site; NW=ranch near Hot Springs, WICA=Wind Cave National Park).

Scientific name and common name	Locality	Reference
Osteichthyes (bony fish)		
Order Cypriniformes		
Genus *et* species indeterminate	HSMS	Czaplewski and Mead 1990, this volume; Mead this volume
Amphibia (Amphibians)		
Order Anura (frog/toad)		
Bufo cognatus		
Bufo cf. *woodhousei*	HSMS	Mead this volume
Aves (birds)		
Order indeterminate	HSMS	Agenbroad 1984b; Czaplewski and Mead this volume
Mammalia (mammals)		
Order Insectivora (insectivores)		
Family Talpidae (moles)		
Scalopus aquaticus (eastern mole)	HSMS	Czaplewski and Mead 1990, this volume
Order Lagomorpha (pikas, rabbits, hares)		
Family Leporidae (hares and rabbits)		
Sylvilagus sp. (cottontail rabbit)	HSMS	Czaplewski and Mead 1990, this volume
Lepus cf. *townsendii* (white-tailed jackrabbit)	HSMS	Czaplewski and Mead 1990, this volume
Order Rodentia (rodents)		
Family Sciuridae (squirrels)		
Spermophilus cf. *elegans/richardsonii*	HSMS	Czaplewski and Mead 1990, this volume
(Wyoming/Richardson's ground squirrel)		
Spermophilus cr. *tridecemlineatus*	HSMS	Czaplewski and Mead 1990, this volume
(13 lined ground squirrel)		
Cynomys (Leucocrossuromys) sp. (white-tailed prairie dog)	HSMS	Czaplewski and Mead 1990, this volume
Cynomys sp.	WICA	Mead *et al.* in preparation
Family Geomyidae		
Thomomys cf. *talpoides* (northern pocket gopher)	HSMS	Czaplewski and Mead 1990, this volume
Family Cricetidae (hamsters and voles)		
Peromyscus cf. *maniculatus* (deer mouse)	HSMS	Czaplewski and Mead 1990, this volume
Neotoma cf. *cinerea* (bushy-tailed woodrat)	HSMS	Czaplewski and Mead 1990, this volume
*Phenacomys*s cf. *intermedius* (heather vole)	HSMS	Czaplewski and Mead 1990, this volume
Microtus sp. (vole)	HSMS	Bjork 1978; Czaplewski and Mead 1990, this volume

Order Carnivora (carnivores)
Family Mustelidae (weasels)
    Mustela cf. *vison* or *nigripes* (mink or   HSMS   Czaplewski and Mead 1990, this
    black-footed ferret)   volume
    Taxidea taxus (badger)   HSMS   Mead this volume
Family Canidae (dogs
*   *Canis dirus* (dire wolf)   WICA   Mead *et al.* in preparation
    Canis lupus (gray wolf   HSMS   Czaplewski and Mead 1990, this
   volume

    Canis latrans (coyote   HSMS   Czaplewski and Mead 1990, this
   volume

Family Ursidae (bears)
*   *Arctodus simus* (giant short-faced   HSMS   Agenbroad and Mead 1986;
    bear)   Baryshnikov *et al.* this volume
Order Perissodactyla
Family Equidae (horses
    Equus cf. *spp.* (horse)   WICA   Mead *et al.* in preparation
Order Artiodactyla
Family Camelidae (camels)
*   *Camelops* sp. (camel)   WICA   Mead *et al.* in preparation
*   *Camelops* cf. *hesternus* (camel)   HSMS   Czaplewski and Mead 1990, this
   volume; Mead and Agenbroad this
   volume

Family Antilocapridae (pronghorns)
    Antilocapra americana (pronghorn)   HSMS   Mead and Agenbroad this volume
Family Bovidae
    Bison sp.   NW   Agenbroad and Mead in preparation
*   cf. *Euceratherium collinum* (shrub ox)   HSMS   Mead and Agenbroad this volume
Order Proboscidea
Family Elephantidae
*   *Mammuthus columbi* (Columbian   HSMS/   Agenbroad 1984b, 1990 this volume
    mammoth)   NW   Agenbroad and Laury 1979
*   *Mammuthus primigenius* (woolly   HSMS   Agenbroad *et al.* this volume
    mammoth)

* = extinct species

374

1988, 1993; Benton 1991) plus our own investigations have generated a more complete picture of the last 253,000 years in the Southern Hills. It is as if the Mammoth Site and its development served as a catalyst for additional, related investigations which complement and reinforce each other.

Early efforts at Hot Springs were salvage and exploratory in nature. Once the site significance and potential was recognized, it began to serve as a Quaternary research center and to serve as a model for the development of other sites—paleontological and archaeological—in the region. In varied capacities, the Mammoth Site helped similar efforts in *in situ* exhibits and visitor centers. Some examples would include the Lubbock Lake Site in Texas, and the Ashfall Fossil Bed in Nebraska. Other sites which are currently being developed are the Hudson-Meng Bison Kill in Nebraska, The Vore Buffalo Jump in Wyoming, and the Hell Gap archaeological site in Wyoming.

The growth of the expansion and development of the Mammoth Site went through most of the problems and financial burdens that can be encountered in a project that had a volunteer initial season, a $500 budget for a second season, and finally attracted National Geographic Society and Earthwatch support. I think one of the most powerful testimonies that the Mammoth Site gives is what can be accomplished by a literal "grass roots movement" in a small, rural community in a rural state. A development, and a movement carried out by local citizens, without the financial aid or intervention of state or federal agencies.

The "watershed year" for the Mammoth Site was 1985, when in September, we held an open house for a $1.1 million building enclosing the bone-bearing sinkhole. We made the quantum leap from a meager tour and exhibit area contained in a small, temporary, plywood building with add-ons, to a world class structure. That has been continuously upgraded through an expansion to allow exhibits and retail, to improved and expanded exhibits, interpretations, and tour facilities with the site building. We are currently in the initial phases of a fund raising effort to add a state-of-the-art laboratory/

repository addition to the original structure.

Educational Significance

This natural trap is unique in the New World in that it has been preserved as an *in situ* paleontological exhibit and working excavation that exposes mammoth remains and leaves the bones where they were deposited. The public is able to visit the site year-round; the chance to interact with the guides and staff, and the excavation crew (during the excavation period each year) allows an informational, educational interaction between lay persons, technical staff and excavators that is also unparalleled. The Mammoth Site of Hot Springs South Dakota was selected as one of the exemplary paleontological sites in North America open to public visitation (McDonald and Skwara 1989) on a multi-criteria basis for evaluation. Public visitation, information, interpretation, and education have been some of the major goals in the development of this site. The Board of Directors for the Mammoth Site also utilizes public funding, generated through admissions and sales, to expand and improve the facilities for both public and scientific endeavors.

It has become an educational resource, hosting in-service workshops, regional and international symposia, and hands-on experience for students and teachers. It has also produced video-tapes, scientific publications for scientists and lay-public, and education materials and instruction for state, regional, and national education programs and educators.

Most children have a "dinosaur-fixation" and currently dinosaur toys, models, books, etc. are probably more prevalent than the reptiles were at any given point in time. That is all a positive manifestation of one aspect of human inquisitiveness and fascination with extinct fauna and environments. Humans and dinosaurs only coexist in our imagination, or through such fantasies as Orson Welles books (later movies), Japanese "monster" films, comic and television creations such as "Alley Oop," or the "Flintstones," etc. What dinosaurs and dinosaur fans miss, however, is the actual human coexistence with the extinct creature, such as the evidence that exists for human-mammoth contemporaneity, interaction, and utilization. This portion of pre-history is only 11,000 years distant in the past. Abundant evidence remains in the form of art, ornaments, housing, tools, and kill-sites to document the man-mammoth interrelationship in the northern hemisphere of our planet. The Mammoth Site is one non-archaeological locality in which the public can begin to realize the excitement of this much more recent prehistory. It also provides a memorable introduction to the recreation of a portion of the most recent "ice-age," in the Black Hills region.

Construction of a laboratory facility will merge with, and enhance a newly initiated education and curriculum effort being produced by the Mammoth Site. We have chosen to make the science and science activities of the Site a vehicle to give regional schools an opportunity to incorporate the Site with classroom and field trip educational experiences.

A "Junior Paleontologist" program, in cooperation with the National Geographic Society allowed 8-16 year old youngsters a chance for hands-on excavation of fiberglass replicas of mammoth bones. They learn to excavate, pedestal, identify, and map bones using similar techniques and equipment to what is being done professionally, immediately adjacent to them, in the Site. The initial success of the program has led to an expanded program for future years. Concurrently, we began to develop curriculum projects, using the Site as a focus, to teach a wide variety of educational skills and subjects. We have initiated agreements with several agencies to allow future development of multi-media educational programs which have the potential of being carried by satellite to even the most remote rural school systems. In another educational realm, the Mammoth Site has been used as a catalyst for in-service teacher training.

As an outgrowth of these activities, it has become involved in a publication series. Initially, a symposium volume was generated. Success in that regard has led to a series of publications, with several requests to publish materials of Quaternary nature, for entities and agencies outside South Dakota. The primary goal of Mammoth Site publications is the rapid, affordable, dispensation of knowledge about the Site, the region, and Quaternary research in a broader view.

With expansion of the original building for exhibits and retail, we initiated efforts to create a bookstore featuring Quaternary period literature for scientific, lay reader, and children audiences. The enterprise covers everything from fiction to introductory science, to scientific methodology, site reports and monographs. Our next major endeavor in this realm is for curriculum materials and teacher's guides dealing with Quaternary subject matter.

Additionally, the Site has served as a training facility for an increasing number of crew members, staff, and students. The crews are comprised of persons from every age and walk of life who— through Earthwatch, of Watertown, Massachusetts—become the excavators under the instruction and training of a watchful eyed staff of university and college graduate and undergraduate students.

We have received some criticism in regard to using "amateurs" as excavators on a site of this importance. I have been involved in nearly every method of crew selection that exists, from academic major, to letters of recommendation, to post-secondary grade point averages, etc. My experience with Earthwatch participants has shown me that, with rare exceptions, they have been as good as the best of crews picked by criteria referred to above, and better than the worst of crews picked under those criteria. One thing Earthwatch participants never fail to bring (unless they are individuals who have been "sent to camp" by family members who don't want to have them around) is enthusiasm!! Closely akin, is a fear they will damage something due to lack of prior formal training. Everyone has an "Indiana Jones" personality hidden somewhere within themselves. However, due to financial responsibility, family responsibility, vocational choice, etc. that adventuresome part of their spirit has often been suppressed, in some cases until after retirement. Earthwatch allows them to pursue an interest area—in our case, paleontology— and become their own version of "Indiana Jones" (or "Jonesette") for two weeks, in an active, educational, research environment. They can contribute, in many ways, to a project and share in the discoveries, interpretations, and development of research at that locality.

The Site also provides continual training and upgrading for the staff—from guides through preparators, office and management, Board of Directors, to the field research team. One way we have contributed to this is to initiate a visiting scientist program. Through this endeavor, we bring international researchers, scholars, and scientists to the Mammoth Site, to interact with all the personnel of the Site, as well as the public, and to apply their expertise, interests, methodologies to mutually beneficial research during their field season tenure.

Similarly, foreign documentaries have been produced that feature the Mammoth Site as part of their product. National and international symposia and publications also feature the Site or aspects of the research produced here.

Last, but certainly not least, the public have become enthusiastic visitors, supporters, and interested students of the Site and what it has to tell them about the past, present, and future. From our initial concept, the Mammoth Site has been devoted to becoming an active research center and an *in situ* exhibit for the public. The public, in turn, has allowed us to continually expand and upgrade exhibits and interpretations and printed material by which they can expand their knowledge and interest. Admission fees are turned back into development of the Site. Each person who buys a ticket has also become a part of the Site, a contributor to the continued enhancement of the Mammoth Site of Hot Springs, South Dakota.

ACKNOWLEDGMENTS

The excavations and interpretations contained in this volume are the products of numerous individuals and organizations. Funding was derived from The Geological Society of America: Penrose Grant; The National Geographic Society; Earthwatch (Center for Field Research); Northern Arizona University, and Chadron State College. The building housing the Site was completed in 1985 and was constructed using funds generated by the Board of Directors of the Mammoth Site of Hot Springs, South Dakota, Inc.; donations from private individuals, and groups; The South Dakota Economic Development Program; Major funding by the Bush Foundation; a USEDA grant from the government; and a loan from Norwest Bank, First Bank, and First Federal Bank.

Many hours of volunteer labor, guides, camp guards, etc. were donated by the original Board of Directors, and members of the Hot Springs community and surrounding region. Guides and the Mammoth Site staff were hired locally. The Board of Directors began within the Hot Springs community, and grew to include the surrounding region. Crew members came from all over the world, via Earthwatch. Staff members included former students and former Earthwatch participants. The people of Hot Springs contributed in many ways—including picnics for every crew.

Maxine Campbell generated portions of the initial, and the final draft of the entire manuscript. Finn Agenbroad generated portions of the initial manuscript.

Photo Credits

Authors provided most of the photographs and figures. Photo credits for Figures 88-91 belong to Paula Jansen; Figures 60, 95 and 96 were taken by Phil Degginer; Dan Boone provided Figure 61; Figures 120, 122, and 124 were taken by D. Nations; Figures 100, 101, and 121 were provided by the staff of Hot Springs Mammoth Site. The frontispiece was provided by EROS Data Center, Sioux Falls, South Dakota.

REFERENCES CITED

Agenbroad, L.D.
  1978a   Excavations at the Hot Springs Mammoth Site: a Pleistocene
           animal trap. *Transactions of the Nebraska Academy of Sci-
           ences* 6:127-130
  1978b   The Hudson-Meng Site: An Alberta bison kill in the Nebraska
           High Plains. University Press of America. Washington, D.C.
           230 p.
  1982   A Mammoth-Selective Natural Trap in Hot Springs, South
           Dakota. *Abstracts XI INQUA Congress* 1:7. Moscow, USSR.
  1984a   New World Mammoth Distribution. *In* "Quaternary Extinc-
           tions: A Prehistoric Revolution" (P.S. Martin and R.G. Klein,
           Eds.), pp. 90-108, University of Arizona Press, Tucson, Ari-
           zona.
  1984b   Hot Springs South Dakota: Entrapment and Taphonomy of
           Columbian Mammoth, *In* "Quaternary Extinctions: A Prehis-
           toric Revolution" (P.S. Martin, and R.G. Klein, Eds.), pp.113-
           127. University of Arizona Press, Tucson.
  1985   The Hot Springs Mammoth Site, South Dakota: from salvage
           paleontology to *in situ* exhibit and research center. *In* "Fossil-
           iferous Cenozoic Deposits of Western South Dakota and north-
           western Nebraska" (J.E Martin, Ed.), *Dakoterra* 2:121-139.
  1989   Spiral Fractured Mammoth Bone from Non-Human
           Taphonomic Processes at Hot Springs Mammoth Site, South
           Dakota. *In* "Proceedings of the First International Bone Modi-
           fication Conference." (R. Bonnichsen, Ed.). University of
           Maine, Orono. pp. 139-147.
  1990   The mammoth population of the Hot Springs Site; and associ-
           ated megafauna, *In* Megafauna and Man: Discovery of
           America's Heartland" (L.D. Agenbroad, J.I. Mead and L.W.
           Nelson, Eds.), *Scientific Publications of Hot Springs Mam-
           moth Site* No. 1:32-39.
Agenbroad, L.D., and Barton, B.R.
  1991   North American Mammoths: an annotated bibliography: 1940-
           1990. *Scientific Papers of the Mammoth Site of Hot Springs,
           South Dakota, Inc.* 2. 118p
Agenbroad, L.D., and Laury, R.L.
  1975   Geology, paleontology, paleohydrology, and sedimentology
           of a Quaternary mammoth site, Hot Springs, South Dakota:
           1974-1979 excavations. National Geographic Society Reports
           16:1-32.

1979   Excavation and sedimentology of the Mammoth Site of Hot Springs, South Dakota. *National Geographic Society Research Reports*, 1976-1978.

1984   Geology, Paleontology, Paleohydrology, and Sedimentol ogy of a Quaternary Mammoth Site, Hot Springs, South Dakota: 947-79 Excavations, *In National Geographic Research Reports* (H. Oehser, S. Lea, and N.L. Powars, Eds.), **16**:1-32.

Agenbroad, L.D. and Mead, J. I.

1986   Large carnivores from Hot Springs Mammoth Site, South Dakota. *National Geographic Research.* **2**: 508-516.

1987   Age Structure Analysis of *Mammuthus columbi*, Hot Springs, South Dakota. *Current Research in the Pleistocene.* **4**:101-102.

1989   Quaternary Geochronology and Distribution of Mammuthus on the Colorado Plateau. *Geology* **17**:861-864.

Agenbroad, L.D., Laury, R.L., Dutrow, B.L., Mead, J.I., and Bjork, P.R.

1979   Excavation of the Hot Springs Mammoth Site: Field seasons 1974-1977. *Guidebook and Roadlogs for the Rocky Moun tain-Plains Field Conference: Friends of the Pleistocene, July 29-30, Hot Springs South Dakota.*

Agenbroad, L.D., Lister, A.M., Mol, D. and Roth, V.L.

(this volume) *Mammuthus primigenius* remains from the Mammoth Site of Hot Springs, South Dakota. *In* "The Hot Springs Mammoth Site: a decade of field and laboratory research in paleontology, geology, and paleoecology" (L.D. Agenbroad and J.I. Mead, Eds.), Hot Springs, South Dakota: Mammoth Site Inc.

Agenbroad, L.D., Mead, J. I., and Martin, P. S.

1984   Chronology and diet of *Mammuthus* from Eurasia and temperate North America. *Abstracts of the XXVII International Geological Congress*, Moscow.

Agenbroad, L. D., Mead, J. I. , and Nelson, L. W. (eds.)

1990   Megafauna and Man: Discovery of America's Heartland. *Scientific Publications of the Hot Springs Mammoth Site* **1**:32-39.

Armstrong, D.A.

1972   Distribution of mammals in Colorado. *University of Kansas Museum of Natural History, Monograph* **3**:1-415.

Ashley, G.M.

1975 Rhythmic sedimentation in Glacial Lake Hitchcock, Massachusetts-Connecticut, *In* "Glaciofluvial and Glaciolacustrine Sedimentation" (A.V. Jopling and B.C. McDonald, Eds.), *Society of Economic Paleontologists and Mineralogists Special Publication* **23**:304-320.

Backalowitz, M. J., Ford, D. C., Miller, T. E., Palmer, A. N., and Palmer, M. V.
1987 Thermal genesis of dissolution caves in the Black Hills, South Dakota. *Geological Society of America* Bulletin **99**:729-738.

Baker, R.G., and Waln, K.A.
1985 Quaternary pollen records from the Great Plains and Central United States. *In* "Pollen records of late-Quaternary North American sediments" (V. Bryant and R. Holloway, Eds.), pp. 191-203. American Association of Stratigraphic Palynologists Foundation, Dallas.

Bailey, V.
1926 A biological Survey of North Dakota. I. Physiography and life zones. II. The mammals. *North American Fauna* **49**:1-226.

Barbour, E.H.
1916 A giant Nebraska bear, *Dinarctotherium merriami*. *Bulletin Nebraska Geological Survey* **4**:349-53.

Beden, M.
1979 Les Eliphants (*Loxodonta* et *Elephas*) d'Afrique Orientale: systimatique, phyloginie, intirit biochronolozique. Unpublished doctoral dissertation, l'Universite de Poitiers. 567 p.

Behrensmeyer, A.K.
1975 The taphonomy and paleoecology of Plio-Pleistocene vertebrate assemblages east of Lake Rudolph, Kenya. *Harvard Museum of Comparative Zoology Bulletins.* **146**:473-578.

Behrensmeyer, A.K. and Hill, A.P.
1980 Fossils in the Making. University of Chicago Press, Chicago. 338 p.

Benton, R.C.
1991 "The paleoecology of the Early and Middle Archaic section of the Beaver Creek Shelter (39CU779), Wind Cave National Park, Custer County, South Dakota." Unpublished M.S. Thesis, S.D. School of Mines.

Berner, R.A.
1971 "Principles of Chemical Sedimentology." McGraw-Hill, New York.

Birkeland, P.W., Crandell, D.R. and Richmond, G.M.

1971   Status of correlation of Quaternary stratigraphic units in the western coterminous United States. *Quaternary Research* **1**: 208-227.

Bjork, P.R.
1978   A Preliminary Report on the Microvertebrates of the Mammoth Site. *Guidebook and Roadlogs for Rocky Mountain-Plains Field Conference: Friends of the Pleistocene.* Hot Springs, South Dakota, pp. 37-38.

Black Hills Conservancy Sub-District
1973   "Comprehensive Water Quality Management Plan for the Black Hills Region." Publication 7, Appendix A, Lake Management Data, Rapid City, South Dakota.

Blinn, D.W.
1976   Aquatic environmental study on biotic and physio-chemical responses to elevated temperatures in Cholla Lake, Arizona. *Third Annual Report of the Department of Biological Sciences to Arizona Public Service*, Northern Arizona University.

Bloom, A.L.
1978   "Geomorphology." Prentice-Hall, New York

Bonnichsen, R.
1979   Pleistocene Bone Technology in the Beringian Refugium. *National Museum of Man, Mercury Series, Archaeological Survey of Canada*, Paper No. **89**. Ottawa. 297 p.

Bonnichsen, R., and Sorg, M.
1991   Bone modification. Center for the study of the first Americans. Orono.

Bowles, C.G., and Braddock, W.A.
1963   Solution breccias of the Minnelusa Formation in the Black Hills, South Dakota and Wyoming. *In* "Short Papers in Geology and Hydrology". *U.S. Geological Survey Professional Paper.* **475**:C91-C95.

Brink, A.B.A., and Partirdge, T.C.
1965   Transvaal karst: some considerations of development and morphology, with special reference to sinkholes and subsidence in the Far West Rand: *South African Geographic Journal*, **47**:11-34.

Brinkhurst, R.O., and Cook, D.G.
1974   Aquatic earthworms. In"Pollution Ecology of Freshwater Invertebrates" (C.W. Hart, Jr., and S.L.H. Fuller, Eds.), pp. 1453-156. Academic Press, New York.

Brock, T.D.
1978   "Thermophylic Micoorganisms and Life at High Temperatures." Springer-Verlag, New York.

Brock, T.D., and Brock, M.L.
  1971   Life in the geyser basins: Wyoming, Yellowstone Library and Museum Association. 31 p.
Brown, Donald L., and Brown, D. L.
  1987   Wrench-style deformation and paleostructural influence on sedimentation in and around a crantonic basin, *In* "Williston Basin: anatomy of a cratonic oil province" (J.A.Peterson, D.M. Kent, S.B. Anderson, R.H. Pilatzke, andM.W. Longman, Eds.), pp. 57-90. Denver, Rocky Mountain Association of Geologists.
Brues, C.T.
  1932   Further studies on the fauna of North American hot springs. *Proceedings of the American Academy of Arts and Sciences* **67**: 186-303.
Bull, W.B.
  1979   Threshold of critical power in streams. *Geological Society of America Bulletin* **90**:453-464.
Burns, J.A., and McGillivray, W.B.
  1989   A new prairie dog, *Cynomys churcherii* from the late Pleistocene of southern Alberta. *Canadian Journal of Zoology* **67**:
Buss, I.O.
  1990   Elephant life: fifteen years of high population density. Iowa State University Press. Ames. 191p.
Carleton, M.D.
  1985   Macroanatomy. *In*"Biology of New World *Microtus*" (R.H. Tamarin, Ed.), American Society of Mammalogists, Special Publication **8**:116-175. Lawrence, Kansas.
Carlston, C.W.
  1963   Drainage density and streamflow: *U.S. Geological Survey Professional Paper* **422-C**:C1-C8.
Chomko, S.A.
  1982   Late Pleistocene-Holocene faunal successions in the northern Bighorn Mountains, Wyoming. *Program and Abstracts, American Quaternary Association* **7**:80.
Chorn, J., Frase, B.A., and Frailey, C.D.
  1988   Late Pleistocene pronghorn, *Antilocapra americana*, from Natural Trap Cave, Wyoming. *Transactions of the Nebraska Academy of Sciences* **16**:127-139.
Clarke, A.H.
  1973   The freshwater molluscs of the Canadian Interior Basin. *Malacologia* **13**:1-509.
Cook, H.J.

1922   Basic Tertiary conglomerate of the Black Hills: *Pan American Geologist* **37**:421-424.

Cooke, H.B.S.
1947   Variation in the Molars of the Living African Elephant and a Critical Revision of the Fossil Proboscidea of South Africa. *American Journal of Science* **245**:434-517.
1960   Further Revision of the Fossil Elephantidae of Southern Africa. *Palaeontologia Africana* **8**:46-58.

Coope, G.R., and Lister, A.M.
1987   Late-glacial mammoth skeletons from Condover, Shropshire, England. *Nature* **330** 472-4.

Cope N.R.
1879   The Cave Bear of California. *American Naturalist* **13**:791.

Corner, R.G.
1986   The giant short-faced bear (*Arctodus simus*) in the Pleistocene of Nebraska. *Proceedings of the Nebraska Academy of Sciences* **106**:48.

Czaplewski, N.J., and Mead, J.I.
1990   Small mammals from Hot Springs Mammoth Site, South Dakota. *In* ""Megafauna and Man (L. Agenbroad, J. Mead, L. Nelson, Eds.), *The Mammoth Site of Hot Springs South Dakota Scientific Papers* **1**:40-41.

Dalquest, W.W.
1988   Fossil prairie dogs (*Cynomys*) from Texas. *Texas Journal of Science* **40**:3-10.

Darton, N.H.
1901   Preliminary description of the geology and water resources of the southern half of the Black Hills and adjoining regions in South Dakota and Wyoming: *U.S. Geological Survey 21st Annual Report*. pp. 489-599

Darton, N.H., and Paige, S.
1925   Central Black Hills folio, South Dakota: U.S. Geological Survey Atlas **219**:34 p.

Davis, O.K., Agenbroad, L. D., Martin, P.S., and Mead, J.I.
1984   The Pleistocene dung blanket of Bechan Cave, Utah. *In* "Contributions in Quaternary vertebrate Paleontology: A volume in memorial to John E. Guilday. (H.H. Genoways and M.R. Dawson, Eds.), Carnegie Museum of Natural History Special Publication **8**:267-282.

Davis, O.K., Mead, J.I., Martin, P.S., and Agenbroad, L.D.

1985   Riparian plants were a major component of the diet of mammoths of southern Utah. *Current Research in the Pleistocene* **2**:81-82.

Delcourt, P.A., and Delcourt, H.R.
1981   Vegetation maps for eastern North America: 40,000 yr BP to present. *In* "Geobotany II" (R. Romans, Ed.), pp. 123-166. New York, Plenum Publishing.
1983   Late-Quaternary vegetational dynamics and community stability reconsidered. *Quaternary Research* **19**:265-271.

Delcourt, P.A., Delcourt, H.R., Brister, R.C., and Lackey, L.E.
1983   Quaternary vegetation history of the Mississippi Embayment. *Quaternary Research* **13**:11-132.

Delcourt, H.R., Delcourt, P.A., and Webb, T.
1983   Dynamic plant ecology: the spectrum of vegetational change in space and time. *Quaternary Science Reviews* **1**:153-175.

Dial, K.P.
1984   Four sympatric species of *Neotoma*: ecological aspects of morphology, diets, and behavior. Unpublished Ph.D. dissertation, Northern Arizona University, Flagstaff.

Dietrich, W. O.
1912   *Elephas primigenius fraasi*, eine schwaebische Mammutrasse. *Jahrb. Ver. Naturk.* Wuerttemberg. **68**:42-106.

Dorn, R.D.
1977   "Flora of the Black Hills." Cheyenne, Wyoming.

Douglas-Hamilton, I. and O.
1975   Among the Elephants. Viking Press, New York. 284 p.

Dutrow, B.
1977   Preliminary Post-cranial metric analysis of mammoths from the Hot Springs Mammoth Site, South Dakota. *Transactions of the Nebraska Academy of Sciences* **4**:223-227.
1980   "Metric Analysis of a late Pleistocene mammoth assemblage, Hot Springs, South Dakota." Unpublished M.S. thesis. Southern Methodist University. Dallas. 164 p.

Eardley, A.J.
1962   Structural geology of North America: 2nd ed., New York, Harper and Row, New York. 743 p.

Elftman, H.O.
1931   Pleistocene mammals of Fossil Lake, Oregon. *American Museum Novitates* **481**:1-21.

Emslie, S.D., and Czaplewski, N.J.

1985   A new record of giant short-faced bear, *Arctodus simus* from western North America with a re-evaluation of its paleobiology. *Natural History Museum of Los Angeles County. Contributions in Science* **371**:1-12.

Eshelman, R.E.
1975   Geology and paleontology of the early Pleistocene (late Blancan) White Rock fauna from north-central Kansas. *University of Michigan Museum of Paleontology, Papers on Paleontology* **13**:1-60.

Essen, Van H. and Mol, D.
(in press)Plio-Pleistocene proboscideans from the southern bight of the North Sea and Eastern Scheldt (the Netherlands). *In "The Proboscidea: Trends in Paleoecology and Evolution"* (J. Shoshani and P. Tassy, Eds.), Oxford University Press.

Fagerstone, K.A.
1982   Ethology and taxonomy of Richardson's ground squirrel (*Spermophilus richardsonii*). Unpublished Ph.D. dissertation, University of Colorado, Boulder. 198 pp.

Fenneman, N.M.
1931   Physiography of western United States: New York, McGraw Hill Book Co., Inc., 543 p.

Felix, I.
1912   Das Mammuth van Borna. *Veroffentlichungen des Staedtischen Museums fuer Voelkerkunde zu Leipzig.* **4**:1-55, plates I-VIII. Leipzig

Fillman, L.
1929   Cenozoic history of the northern Black Hills: *University of Iowa Studies in Natural History* **13**:1-48.

Fisher, D.C.
1981   Evidence of mastodon butchery in Southeastern Michigan. *Geological Society of America, Program Abstracts.* **13**:452.

1984a   Mastodon butchery by North American Paleo Indians. *Nature* **308**:271-272.

1984b   Bone Modification at the Lake Pleasant Mastodon Site, Southeastern Michigan. *Abstracts: First International Conference on Bone Modification.* Carson City, Nevada. p. 12.

Folk, R.L.
1974   "Petrology of Sedimentary Rocks." Hemphill Publishing Co., Austin, Texas.

Fox, J., Smith, C., and Wilkins, K.
1992   "Proboscideans and Paleoindian Interactions." Baylor University Press. Waco.

Frick, C.
1930   Alaska's frozen fauna. *Natural History* **30**:70-80
Frison, G.C., and Todd, L.C.
1986   "The Colby Mammoth Site: taphonomy and archaeology of a Clovis kill in northern Wyoming." University of New Mexico Press, Albuquerque. 238p.
Froiland, S.G.
1978   "Natural history of the Black Hills." The Center for Western Studies, Augustana College, South Dakota.
Frye, J.C., and Leonard, A.B.
1957   Ecological interpretations of Pliocene and Pleistocene stratigraphy in the Great Plains Region: *American Journal of Science* **255**:1-11.
1959   Correlation of the Ogallala Formation (Neogene) in western Texas with type localities in Nebraska: University of Texas, *Bureau of Economic Geology, Report of Investigations* **39**:46 p.
Gable, D.J., and Hatton, T.
1983   Maps of vertical crustal movements in the coterminous United States over the last 10 million years: *U.S. Geological Survey Miscellaneous Investigations.* Map I-1315.
Garutt, W. E.
1964   Das Mammut, *Mammuthus primigenius* (Blumenbach). Die Neue Brehm-Buecherei. A. Ziemsen Verlag. Wittenberg-Lutherstadt. 140 p.
Garutt, W. E., and Nikolskaja, V. N.
1988   Ueber das skelett vom Steppenelefanten aus Edersleben. *Spengler Museum* **9**:3-13. Sangerhausen.
Geisler, F.
1945   A study of pollen grains of thirty-two species of grasses. *Butler University Botanical Studies* **7**:65-73.
Gilbert, B.M., and Martin, L.D.
1984   Late Pleistocene fossils of Natural Trap Cave, Wyoming, and the Climatic models of extinction. *In* "Quaternary Extinctions" (Martin, P. S. and R. G. Klein, Eds.), pp. 138-147.
Gilbert, B.M., Martin, L.D., and Chomko, S.A.
1978   Paleontology and paleoecology of Natural Trap Cave, Wyoming: 20,000-10,000 B.P. *Program and Abstracts, American Quaternary Association,* 5.
Gillette, D.
1989   The Huntington Mammoth: The last holdout? *Canyon Legacy* **2**:3-8.

Giterman, R.E., Sher, A.V., and Matthews, J.V.
    1982   Comparison of the development of tundra-steppe environments in west and east Beringia: pollen and macrofossil evidence from key sections. *In* "Paleoecology of Beringia" (D.M. Hopkins *et al.*, Eds.), pp. 32-73. Academic Press, New York.

Goodwin, T.H.
    1989   Late Pleistocene zooeography of prairie dogs (*Cynomys*). *Journal of Vertebrate Paleontology* **9** Supplement.

Gott, G.B., and Schnabel, R.W.
    1963   Geology of the Edgemont NE Quadrangle, Fall River and Custer Counties. *U.S. Geological Survey Bulletin* **1063-E**:127-190.

Graham, R.W.
    1981   Preliminary report on late Pleistocene vertebrates from the Selby and Dutton archaeological/paleontological sites, Yuma County, Colorado. *Contribution to Geology* **20**:33-56.

    1986   Description of the dentitions and stylohyoids of *Mammuthus columbi* from the Colby Site. *In* "The Colby Mammoth Site: taphonomy and archaeology of a Clovis kill in northern Wyoming" (G.C. Frison and L.C. Todd, Eds.), pp. 171-190. University of New Mexico Press, Albuquerque.

Graham, R.W., and Semken, H.A., Jr.
    1987   Philosophy and procedures for paleoenvironmental studies of Quaternary mammalian faunas. *In* "Late Quaternary mammalian biogeography and environments of the Great Plains and prairies" (R.W. Graham, H.A. Semken, Jr., and M.A. Graham, Eds.), *Illinois State Museum Scientific Papers* **22**:1-17. Springfield.

Graham, R.W., Semken, H.A., Jr., and Graham, M.A. (eds.).
    1987a   "Late Quaternary mammalian biogeography and environments of the Great Plains and prairies." *Illinois State Museum Scientific Papers* **22**, Springfield.

Graham, M.A., Wilson, M.C., and Graham, R.W.
    1987b   Paleoenvironments and mammalian faunas of Montana, southern Alberta, and southern Saskatchewan. *In* "Late Quaternary mammalian biogeography and environments of the Great Plains and prairies" (R.W. Graham, H. A. Semken, Jr., and M. A. Graham, Eds.), *Illinois State Museum Scientific Papers*, Springfield. **22**:410-459.

Green, M., and Gries, J.P.
    1963   A possible Pliocene deposit in the Black Hills: *South Dakota Academy of Science Proceedings.* **42**:54-56.

Gregory, K.J., and Walling, D.E.
1973   Drainage basin form and process: New York, John Wiley and Sons, Halsted Press, 456 p.

Gries, R.
1983   North-south compression of Rocky Mountain foreland structures. *In* "Rocky Mountain foreland basins and uplifts" (J.D. Lowell, and R. Gries, Eds.), pp. 9-32. Denver, Rocky Mountain Association of Geologists.

Gries, J. P., and Crooks T. J.
1968   Water losses to the Madison (Pahasapa) Limestone, Black Hills, South Dakota. *Wyoming Geological Association Guidebook*, 20th Field Conference. p. 209-214.

Guilday, J.E., and Parmalee, P.W.
1972   Quaternary periglacial records of voles of the genus *Phenacomys* Merriam (Cricetidae: Rodentia). *Quaternary Research* **2**:170-175.

Guilday, J.E., Hamilton, H.W., and Adam, E.K.
1967   Animal remains from Horned Owl Cave, Albany County, Wyoming. *University of Wyoming Contributions to Geology* **6**:97-99.

Guthrie, R.D.
1984   Mosaics, allelochemics and nutrients. *In* "Quaternary extinctions. A prehistoric revolution" (P.S. Martin and R. G. Klein, Eds.), pp. 259-198. University of Arizona Press, Tucson.

1990   "Frozen Fauna of the Mammoth Steppe: The Story of Blue Babe." Chicago: University of Chicago Press, 323 pp.

Hall, E.R.
1981   "The Mammals of North America." 2 vols. John Wiley and Sons, New York.

Hall, R.D.
1976   Stratigraphy and origin of the surficial deposits in sinkholes in south-central Indiana. *Geology* **4**:507-509.

Hannus, L.A.
1982   Evidence of mammoth butchering at the Lange/Ferguson (29SH33) Clovis Kill site. *Program and abstracts, Society for American Archaeology* **47**:52.

1990   The Lange-Ferguson Site: A Case for Mammoth Bone Butchering Tools. *In* "Megafauna and Man: Discovery of America's Heartland" (L. Agenbroad, J. Mead and L. Nelson, Eds.). *Scientific Papers of the Mammoth Site of Hot Springs, South Dakota, Inc.* **1**:86-99.

Hansen, R.M.
1980   Late Pleistocene plant fragments in the dungs of herbivores at Cowboy Cave. *In* "Cowboy Cave" (J.D. Jennings, Ed.), University of Utah, *Anthropological Papers* **104**:179-189.

Harington, C.R.
1978   Quaternary vertebrate faunas of Canada and Alaska and their suggested chronologic sequence. *Syllogeus* **15**:1-105.

Harington, C.R., and Shackleton, D.M.
1978   A Tooth of *Mammuthus primigenius* from Chestermere Lake near Calgary, Alberta and the distribution of mammoths in Southwestern Canada. *Canadian Journal of Earth Sciences* **15**:1272-1283.

Harington, C.R., Tipper, H.W., and Mott, R.J.
1974   Mammoth from Babine Lake, British Columbia. *Canadian Journal of Earth Science* **11**:285-303.

Harksen, J.C.
1969   The Cenozoic history of the southwestern South Dakota, *in* Harksen, J.C., and MacDonald, J.R. (eds.) Guidebook to the major Cenozoic deposits of southwestern South Dakota: South Dakota Geological Survey, Guidebook **2**:11-28.

1974   Radiocarbon dating of terraces along Bear Creek, Pennington County, South Dakota: *South Dakota Geological Survey Report of Investigations* **108**, 7 p.

Harksen, J.C., and MacDonald, J.R.
1969   Guidebook to the major Cenozoic deposits in southwestern South Dakota: South Dakota Geological Survey, Guidebook **2**, 103 p.

Harris, A.H.
1985   "Late Pleistocene Vertebrate Paleoecology of the West." University of Texas Press, Austin. 293 p.

Haury, E.W., Sayles, E.B. and Wasley, W.W..
1959   The Lehner Mammoth Site, Southeastern Arizona. *American Antiquity* **25**:2-34.

Hawksley, O.
1965   Short-faced bear (*Arctodus*) fossils from Ozark caves. *Bulletin National Speleological Society* **27**:77-92.

Hay, O.P.
1924   The Pleistocene of the Middle Region of North America and its vertebrated animals. *Carnegie Institute Washington Publication* **322A**:1-385.

Haynes, G.

1990   The Mountains that fell Down: Life and Death of Heartland Mammoths. *In* "Megafauna and Man: Discovery of America's Heartland" (L.D. Agenbroad, J.I. Mead, L.W. Nelson, Eds.). *Scientific Papers Mammoth Site of Hot Springs South Dakota, Inc.***1**: 22-31.

1991   Mammoths, Mastodonts, and Elephants: Biology, Behavior and the Fossil Record. Cambridge University Press, Cambridge.

Hayward, H.E.
1928   Studies of plants in the Black Hills of South Dakota. *Botanical Gazette* **85**:353-412.

Hemmings, E.T.
1970   Early Man in the San Pedro Valley, Arizona. Ph.D. dissertation, University of Arizona, Tucson.

Henderson, J.
1927   Some South Dakota mollusca. *Nautilus* **41**:19-20.

Heptner, V.G., Naumov, N.P., Yurgenson, P.B., Sludskyi, A.A., Chirikova, A.F., and Bannikov, A.G.
1967   Mammals of Soviet Union T.2, Part 1. Sirenia and Carnivora. Moskau:Vsshaya Shkola. 1004p.

Herrington, H.B.
1962   A revision of the Sphaeriidae of North America (Mollusca:Pelecypoda). *Miscellaneous Publications, Museum of Zoology* **118**:1-81. University of Michigan .

1965   Corrections of sphaeriid nomenclature. *Nautilus* **79**:42-45.

Heusser, C.J.
1983   Vegetational history of the northwestern United States including Alaska. *In* "Late-Quaternary environments of the United States" (H.E. Wright, Ed.), pp. 239-258. "The late Pleistocene" (S.C. Porter, Ed.), Minneapolis, University of Minnesota Press.

Hibbard, C.W.
1955a   Pleistocene vertebrates from the Upper Becerra (Becerra Superior) Formation, Valley of Tequixquiac, Mexico, with notes on other Pleistocene forms. *Contributions Museum Paleontology, University of Michigan* **12**:47-96.

1955b   The Jinglebob interglacial (Sangamon?) fauna from Kansas and its climatic significance. *Contributions Museum Paleontological, University of Michigan* **12**:179-228.

1965   Quaternary mammals of North America. *In* "The Quaternary of the United States." (H.E. Wright and D.G. Frey, Eds.), pp. 509-525. Princeton, Princeton University Press.

Hoffman, R.S., and Jones, J.K., Jr.
    1970   Influence of late-glacial and post-glacial events on the distri-
                 bution of Recent mammals on the northern Great Plains. *In*
                 "Pleistocene and Recent environments of the central Great
                 Plains." (W. Dort and J.K. Jones, Jr., Eds.), pp. 355-394.
                 University of Kansas Press, Lawrence.

Hoffmeister, D.F.
    1986   "Mammals of Arizona." University of Arizona Press and
                 Arizona Game and Fish Department, Tucson and Phoenix.

Holliday, V.T., and Johnson, E.
    1990   An overview of the cultural chronology of the Lubbock Lake
                 Landmark. *In* "Fifty years of Discovery: The Lubbock Lake
                 Landmark" (V.T. Holiday and E. Johnson, Eds.). *Lubbock*
                 Lake Landmark Quaternary Research Center Series **2**:19-54.

Holman, J.A.
    1969   Herpetofauna of the Pleistocene Slaton local fauna of Texas.
                 Southwestern Naturalist **14**:203-212

    1977   America's northernmost Pleistocene herpetofauna (Java, North-
                 Central South Dakota). *Copeia* 1977:191-193.

Hubricht, L.
    1985   The distribution of the native land mollusks of the eastern
                 United States. *Fieldiana (zoology)* **24**.

Indeck, J.
    1987   "Sediment analysis and mammal faunal remains from Little
                 Box Elder Cave, Wyoming." Unpublished Ph.D. dissertation,
                 University of Colorado, Boulder.

Inuzuka, N., Hasegawa, Y., Nogariya, H., and Kamei, T.
    1975   On the stylohyoid bone of Naumann's elephant (*Elephas*
                 naumanni Makiyama) from Lake Nojirri. *Memoirs of the*
                 Faculty of Science, Kyoto University, Series of Geology and
                 Mineralogy, **41**.

Irving, W.N., and Harington, C.R.
    1973   Upper Pleistocene radio-carbon dated artefacts from the North-
                 ern Yukon. *Science* **79**:335-340.

Jachmann, H.
    1988   Estimating age in African elephants: a revision of Laws' molar
                 evaluation technique. *African Journal of Ecology* **26**:51-56

Jennings, J.N.
    1971   "Karst." Massachusetts Institute of Technology. Press, Cam-
                 bridge, Massachusetts.

Jones, J.K., Jr.

1964   Distribution and taxonomy of mammals of Nebraska. *University of Kansas Publications, Museum of Natural History* **16**:1-356.

Jones, J.K., Jr., Armstrong, D.M. Hoffman, R.S., and Jones, C.
1983   "Mammals of the northern Great Plains." University of Nebraska Press, Lincoln.

Jones, M., and Newell, L.C.
1948   Size, variability and identification of grass pollen. *Journal of the American Society of Agronomy* **40**:136-143.

Kempton, P.D.
1980   "Quaternary terrace development along the Fall River, Hot Springs area, South Dakota." Unpublished M.S. thesis, Southern Methodist University, Dallas, Texas.
1981   Quaternary terrace development along the Fall River, Hot Springs area, South Dakota: *Geological Society of America Abstracts with Programs* **13**:201.

Koenigswald, W. von
1989   Das Mammut von Polch bei Mayen (Eifel). *Eiszeitalter Gegenwart* **39**:87-97. *Hannover.*

Kruuk, H.
1972   The Spotted Hyena: A Study of Predation and Social Behavior. Chicago and London: The University of Chicago Press. 335pp.

Küchler, A.W.
1964   "The potential natural vegetation of the coterminous United States." Special Publication of the American Geographical Society. 1-37 pp. and map, 1:3,157000 scale.

Kurtén, B.
1953   On the variation and population dynamics of fossils and recent mammal populations. *Acta Zoologica Fennica* **76**:1-122.
1963   Fossil bears from Texas. *Pearce Sellards Series Texas Memorial Museum* **1**:1-15.
1966   Pleistocene bears of North America, I: Genus *Tremarctos*, spectacled bears. *Acta Zoologica Fennica* **115**:1-120.
1967   Pleistocene Bears of North America II. *Acta Zoologica Fennica* **17**:1-58.

Kurtén, B., and Anderson, E.
1974   Association of *Ursus arctos* and *Arctodus simus* (Mammalia: Ursidae) in the late Pleistocene of Wyoming. *Breviora* **426**:1-6.

1980   "Pleistocene Mammals of North America." Columbia University Press, New York.

Lambe, L.M.
1911   On *Arctotherium* from the Pleistocene of Yukon. *Ottawa Naturalist* **25**:21-26

Lane, E. W.
1955   The importance of fluvial morphology in hydraulic engineering. *American Society Civil Engineering Proceedings* 81, *Paper* **745**:1-17.

LaRocque, A.
1967   "Pleistocene Mollusca of Ohio." *Department of Natural Resources, Division of Geological Survey* **62**:113-356.
1970   "Pleistocene Mollusca of Ohio." *Department of Natural Resources, Division of Geological Survey.* **62**:555-800.

Laury, R.L.
1980   Paleoenvironment of a late Quaternary Mammoth-bearing Sinkhole Deposit, Hot Springs, South Dakota. *Geological Society of America Bulletin* Part 1, **91**:465-475.
1990   Geologic history of the Mammoth Site and surrounding region, Hot Springs Area, Fall River and Custer Counties, South Dakota: an overview. *In* "Megafauna and Man" (L.D. Agenbroad, J.I. Mead and L.W. Nelson, Eds.). *The Mammoth Site of Hot Springs, South Dakota, Inc. Scientific Papers* **1**:15-21.

Laury, R.L., and Kempton, P.D.
1980   Late Quaternary landscape evolution of the southern Black Hills, South Dakota (Abstract): *American Quaternary Association Sixth Annual Meeting Abstracts*, **6**:126

Laury, R.L., Agenbroad, L.D., and Dutrow, B.L.
1978   Sedimentology of Late Quaternary mammoth-bearing sinkhole deposits, Hot Springs, South Dakota. *American Association of Petroleum Geologists Bulletin.* **62**:535-536.

Laws, R.M.
1966   Age criteria for the African elephant, *Loxodonta a. africana. East African Wildlife Journal* **4**:1-37.

Lehmkuhl, D.M.
1974   Thermal regime alteration and vital environment signals in aquatic organisms. *In* "Thermal Ecology" (J.W. Gibbons and R.R. Sharitz, Eds.), 670 p. U.S. Atomic Energy Commission.

Lemke, R.M.Laird, W.M., Tipton, M.J., and Lindvall, R.M.
1965   Quaternary geology of northern Great Plains. *In* "The Quaternary of the United States." (H.E. Wright and D.G. Frey, Eds.), pp. 15-27. Princeton, Princeton University Press.

Leonard, A.B.
    1982   Ecological and climatic implications of fossil mollusks at the Lange/Ferguson (39SH33) Clovis Kill site. *Program and abstracts, Society for American Archaeology* **47**:64.

Leonard, A.B., and Frye, J.C.
    1954   Ecological conditions accompanying loess deposition in the Great Plains region of the United States. *Journal of Geology* **62**:399-404.

Leopold, L.B., Wolman, M.G., and Miller, J.P.
    1964   "Fluvial Processes in Geomorphology." San Francisco, W.H. Freeman, 522 p.

Lindsay, E.H., and Tessman, N.T.
    1974   Cenozoic vertebrate localities and faunas in Arizona. *Journal of the Arizona Academy of Science* **9**:2-34.

Linneaus, 1758
    1758   *Systema naturae per regina tria naturae, secundum classes, ordines, genera, species cum characteribus, differenteus; synonymis, locis* (edito decima, reformata, I. Laurentii Slavii, Holmiae).

Lisenbee, A. L.
    1978   Laramide structure of the Black Hills uplift, South Dakota-Wyoming-Montana. *Geological Society of America Memoirs* **151**:185-196.

    1985   Tectonic map of the Black Hills Uplift, Montana, Wyoming, and South Dakota: Geological Survey Wyoming, Map Ser. **13**.

Lister, A.M.
    1989   Pelvic sexing and skeletal maturation in the mammoth. Abstracts of Papers and Posters, Fifth International Theriological Congress, Rome, p. 152.

Lister, A.M.
    (in press a) Sexual dimorphism in the mammoth pelvis: an aid to gender determination. *In* "The Proboscidea: Trends in Evolution and Paleoecology" (J. Shoshani and P. Tassy, Eds.). Oxford University Press.

    (in press b) Evolution of mammoths and moose: the Holarctic perspective. *In* "Morphological Change in Quaternary Mammals of North America" (R.A. Martin and A.D. Barnosky, Eds.). Cambridge University Press, New York.

    in press c) The evolution of the mammoth in Eurasia. *In* "The Proboscidea: Trends in Paleoecology and Evolution (J. Shoshani and P. Tassy, Eds). Oxford Press.

(in prep) Postcrainial epiphysis fusion and age determination in the wooly mammoth, *Mammuthus primigenius* (Blum.). (to be submitted to *Journal of Vertebrate Paleontology*)

Lister, A.M., and Agenbroad, L.D.
(this volume). Gender determination of Hot Springs mammoths. *In* "The Hot Springs Mammoth Site: a decade of field and laboratory research in paleontology, geology, and paleoecology" (L.D. Agenbroad and J.I. Mead, Eds.). Hot Springs, South Dakota: Mammoth Site Inc.

Lister, A.M., and Joysey, K.A.
1992   Scaling effects in elephant dentitions: the example of Eurasian *Mammuthus*. *In* "Proceedings of the 1989 *Dental Morphology Symposium*" (P. Smith and E. Tchernov, Eds.). Jerusalem: Freund.

Long, C.A.
1965   The mammals of Wyoming. *University of Kansas Publications, Museum of Natural History* **14**:493-758.

Lundelius, E.L.
1984   A Late Pleistocene Mammalian Fauna from Cueva Quebrada, Val Verde County, Texas. *In* "Contributions in quaternary Vertebrate Paleontology: A Volume in Memorial to John E. Guilday" (H. Genoways and M. Dawson, Eds.) *Special Publication of the Carnegie Museum of Natural History* **8**:456-481.

Lundelius, E.L, Jr., Graham, R.W., Anderson, E., Guilday, J., Holman, J.A., Steadman, D.W., and Webb, S.D.
1983   Terrestrial vertebrate faunas. *In* "Late-Quaternary environments of the United States" (H.E. Wright, Ed.), pp. 311-353. "The Late Pleistocene" (S.J. Porter, Ed.), Minneapolis, University of Minnesota Press **1**.

MacAndrews, J.H., Berti, A.A. and Norris, G.
1973   Key to the Quaternary Pollen and Spores of the Great Lakes Region. *Royal Ontario Museum Life Science Miscellaneous Publication*.

Maccagno, A.M.
1962   L'*Elephas meridionalis* Nesti di Contrada "Maddonna della Strada" Scoppito (L'Aquila). Atti dell'Accademia della Scienze fisiche e matematiche di Napoli. p. i-vii and 1-132, XI Pls.

McDonald, H.G., and Anderson, E.
1975   A late Pleistocene fauna from southeastern Idaho. *Tebiwa* **18**:19-37.

McDonald, J.N., Neusius, S.W., and Clay, V.L.

1987   An associated partial skeleton of *Symbos cavifrons* (Artiodactyla:Bovidae) from Montezuma County, Colorado. *Journal of Paleontology* **61**:831-843.

McDonald, J.N., and Ray, C.E.

1989   The autochthonous North American musk oxen *Bootherium, Symbos,* and *Gidleya* (Mammalia; Artiodactyla: Bovidae). *Smithsonian Contributions to Paleobiology* **66**.

McDonald, J.N. and Skwara, T.

1989   Publicly accessible and interpreted vertebrate fossil localities in Canada and the United States. *Abstracts of Papers: Journal of Vertebrate Paleontology* **9** (Supplement to No. 3):32A.

McFarlane, R.W., Moore, B.C., and Williams, S.E.

1976   Thermal tolerance of stream cypriniid minnows. *In* "Thermal Ecology II" (G.W. Esch and R.W. McFarlane, Eds.), pp. 141-144. Technical Information Center, Energy Research and Development Administration.

Mackin, J.H.

1948   Concept of a graded river. *Geological Society of America Bulletin* **59**:465-511.

Madden, C. T.

1981   "Mammoths of North America." Unpublished Ph.D. dissertation, University of Colorado, Boulder. 271 p.

Madole, R.F., Bradley, W.C., Loewenherz, D.S., Ritter, D.F., Rutter, N.W., and Thorn, C.E.

1987   Rocky Mountains. *In* "Geomorphic systems of North America" (W.L. Graf, Ed.), *Geological Society of America, Centennial Special Paper* **2**:211-257.

Maglio, V. J.

1973   Origin and Evolution of the Elephantidae *Transactions of the American Philosophical Society* **63**:Part 3.

Martin, J.

1965   Quelques types de depressions karstiques du Moyen Atlas central. *Reveue de Geographie du Maroc* **7**:95-106.

Martin, J.E.

1982   Vertebrate fossils from the Lange/Ferguson (39SH33) Clovis Kill site. *Program and Abstracts, Society for American Archaeology* **47**:67.

1984   Fossil vertebrates and the paleoenvironment of the Lange/Ferguson Clovis Kill site in the Badlands of South Dakota. *Current Research* **1**:69-71.

1987   Paleoenvironment of the Lange/Ferguson Clovis Kill Site in the Badlands of South Dakota. *In* "Late Quaternary Mammalian Biogeography and Environments of the Great Plains and Prairies" (R.W. Graham, H.A. Semkens, Jr., M.A. Graham, Eds.). Illinois State Museum Scientific Papers **XXII**:314-332.

Martin, J.E., and Abbott, J.P.
1987   New discovery of an archaeological and paleontological site in Wind Cave National Park, South Dakota. *Proceedings South Dakota Academy of Science* **65**:28-29.

Martin, J.E., Alex, R.A., and Benton, R.C.
1988   Chronology of the Beaver Creek Shelter, Wind Cave National Park, South Dakota. *Proceedings North Dakota Academy of Science* **42**:16.

Martin, J.E., Alex, R., Abbott, J., Benton, R., and Miller, L.
1993   The Beaver Creek Shelter (39CU779): A Holocene Succession in the Black Hills of South Dakota. *Plains Anthropologist* **38**:17-36.

Martin, L.D., Gilbert, B.M., and Chomko, S.A.
1979   *Dicrostonyx* (Rodentia) from the late Pleistocene of northern Wyoming. *Journal of Mammalogy* **60**:193-195.

Matthew, W.D.
1918   Contributions to the Snake Creek Fauna with notes on the Pleistocene of western Nebraska. *Bulletin American Museum Natural History* **38**:183-229.

Maughan, E.K., and Perry, W. J., Jr.
1987   Lineaments and their tectonic implications in the Rocky Mountains and adjacent plains region. *In* "Paleotectonics and sedimentation in the Rocky Mountain region, United States" (J.A. Peterson, Ed.). *American Association of Petroleum Geologists Memoir* **41**:41-53.

Mead, J.I.
1978   Freshwater Moluscs from the Hot Springs Mammoth Site, South Dakota. *Guidebook and Roadlogs for Rocky Mountain Plains Field Conference: Friends of the Pleistocene*, Hot Springs, South Dakota, p. 32-36.

Mead, J.I., and Agenbroad, L.D.
1989   Pleistocene Dung and the Extinct Herbivores of the Colorado Plateau, Southwestern USA. *Cranium* **6**:29-44. Rotterdam
1992   Isotope Dating of Pleistocene Dung Deposits from the Colorado Plateau, Arizona and Utah. *Radiocarbon* **34**:1-19.

Mead, J.I., and Meltzer, D.J.
    1984   North American late Quaternary extinctions and the radio-
            carbon record. *In* "Quaternary Extinctions" (P.S. Martin
            and R.G. Klein, Eds.), pp. 440-450. University of Arizona
            Press, Tucson.
Mead, J. I., Agenbroad, L. D., Martin, P. S., and Davis, O. K..
    1986   Dung of *Mammuthus* in the arid Southwest, North America.
            Quaternary Research **25:**121-127.
Mead, J. I., Hevly, R. H., and Agenbroad, L. D.
    1990   Late Pleistocene invertebrates and plant remains, Mammoth
            Site, Black Hills, South Dakota. *In* "Megafauna and Man:
            Discovery of America's Heartland" (L.D. Agenbroad, J. I.
            Mead, and L. W. Nelson, Eds.). *Scientific Papers* **1:**9-11.
Merriam, J.C. and Stock, C.
    1925   Relationships and Structure of the Short-Faced Bear,
            Arctotherium, from the Pleistocene of California. Papers
            Concerning the Paleontology of the Pleistocene of California
            and the Tertiary of Oregon. *Contributions to Palaeontology*,
            Carnegie.
Meyerhoff, H.A., and Olmstead, E.W.
    1937   Cenozoic leveling in the Black Hills (abstract). *Pan American
            Geologist* **68:**306.
Michener, C. F., and Koeppl, J.W.
    1985   *Spermophilus richardsonii. Mammalian Species* **243:**18.
Middleton, G.V., and Hampton, M.A.
    1973   Sediment gravity flows: mechanics of flow and deposition. *In*
            "Turbidites and Deep Water Sedimentation," pp. 1-38. Society
            of Economic Paleontologists and Mineralotists Pacific Section
            Short Course.
Mol, D.
    1984   Over de hand van de mammoet en een byzonder
            middenhandsbeen van dit dier. *Cranium* **1:**11-19.
Mol, D., and Agenbroad, L.D.
    (this volume). Metapodials and shoulder height of *Mammuthus columbi*
            compared with Eurasian *Mammuthus* species.
Mol, D., and Kerkhoff, N.
    1991   Nieuwe tongbeenfragmenten van pleistocene zoogdieren.
            Cranium **8:**15019.
Morlan, R.E.
    1984   Proboscidean Limb Bone Fracture. *Program with Abstracts;
            Society for American Archaeology, 49th Annual Meeting.* Port-
            land, Oregon. p. 81.

Morisawa, M.E.
    1957   Accuracy of determination of stream length from topographic maps. *American Geophysical Union Transactions* **38**:86-88.
    1968   "Streams, their Dynamics and Morphology." New York, McGraw Hill Book Co. 175 p.

Moss, C.
    1988   Elephant Memories. Wm. Morrow & Co., New York. 336 p.

Musil, R.
    1968   Die Mammutmolaren von Predmosti. *Palaontologische Abhandlung* **A** **3**:1-192.

Nadler, C.F., Hoffmann, R. S., and Greer, K.R.
    1971   Chromosomal divergence during evolution of ground squirrel populations (Rodentia: *Spermophilus*). *Systematic Zoology* **20**:298-305.

Nelson, M.E., and Madsen, J.H., Jr.
    1983   A Giant Short-faced Bear (*Arctodus simus*) from the Pleistocene of Northern Utah. *Transactions of the Kansas Academy of Science* **86**:1-9.

Neuner, A.M.
    1975   "Evolution and distribution of the *Spermophilus richardsonii* complex of ground squirrels in the middle and late Pleistocene: a multivariate analysis." Unpublished M.A. thesis, University of Kansas, Lawrence.

Neuner, A.M., and Schultz, C.B.
    1979   *Spermophilus* from the "Citellus Zone" of the late Quaternary of the central Great Plains. *Transactions of the Nebraska Academy of Sciences* **7**:101-104.

Nie, N.H., Hull, C.H., Jenkins, J.G., Steenbrenner, K., and Bent, D.H.
    1975   "Statistical package for the social sciences." McGraw Hill Book Co., New York. 675 p.

Noble, J.A.
    1952   Structural features of the Black Hills and adjacent areas developed since the Precambrian time. Billings Geological Society 3rd annual conference, pp. 31-37.

Nowak, R.M.
    1979   North American Quaternary *Canis*. *Monograph of the Museum of Natural History, University of Kansas* **6**. 153 p. Lawrence.

O'Gara, B.W.
    1978   *Antilocapra americana. Mammalian Species* **90**:1-7.

Olsson, I.U., El-Daoshy, M.F., Abd-El-Mageed, A.I., and Klasson, M.

1974   A comparison of different methods for pretreatment of bones, I. *Geologiska Foreningens i Stockholm Forhandlingar* **96**:171-181.
Osborn, H.F.
1942   "Proboscidea, Vol. II." American Museum Press, New York, pp. 805-1675.
Osterkamp, W.R., Fenton, M.M., Gustavson, T.C., Hadley, R.F., Holliday, V.T., Morrison, R.B., and Toy, T.J.
1987   Great Plains ed. *In* "Geomorphic Systems of North America" (W.L. Graff, Ed.), pp. 163-210. *Geological Society of America Centennial Special Volume 2*.
Over, W.H.
1915   Mollusca of South Dakota. *Nautilus* **29**:79-87, 90-95.
Parmalee, P.W., and Klippel, W.E.
1981   A late Pleistocene record of the heather vole (*Phenacomys intermedius*) in the Nashville Basin, Tennessee. *Journal of the Tennessee Academy of Science* **56**:127-129.
Patrick, R.
1974   Effects of abnormal temperatures on algal communities. *In* "Thermal Ecology" (J.W. Gibbons and R.R. Sharitz, Eds.), pp. 335-349. U.S. Atomic Energy Commission.
Peterson, O.A.
1926   The fossils of the Franskstonn Cave, Blair County, Pennsylvania. *Annals of the Carnegie Museum* **16**:249-315
Pettingill, O.S., and Whitney, N.R.
1965   Birds of the Black Hills. *Special Publication* 1, Cornell Laboratory, Ithaca, New York.
Phillips, W.S.
1963   Vegetational changes in northern Great Plains. University of Arizona, *Agricultural Experiment Station* **214**:1-185.
Picard, M.D.
1971   Classification of fine-grained sedimentary rocks. *Journal of Sedimentary Petrology* **41**:179-195.
Pilsbry, H.A.
1948   Land Mollusca of North America. *Academy of Natural Sciences of Philadelphia* **2**:521-1113.
Pinsof, J.D.
1985   The late Pleistocene vertebrate localities of South Dakota. *Dakoterra* **2**:233-264.
Plumley, W.J.,

1948 Black Hills terrace gravels, a study in sediment transport. *Journal of Geology* **56**:526-577.

Powers, W.A.
1953 A new roundness scale for sedimentary particles. *Journal of Sed. Petrology* **23**:117-119.

Puckette, W.L.
1976 Notes on the occurrence of the short-faced bear (*Arctodus*) in Oklahoma. *Proceedings of the Oklahoma Academy of Sciences* **56**:67-68.

Rahn, P.H., and Gries, J.P.
1973 Large Springs in the Black Hills, south Dakota and Wyoming. *South Dakota Geological Survey Report of Investigations* **107**, 46 p.

Repenning, C.A.
(In press) The fossil record of Arborimus and Phenacomys. *In* "Tree voles of the Old Growth Forest" (M.L. Johnson and C. Maser, Eds.) Chapter 2, *American Society of Mammalogists, Special Publication.* Provo, Utah.

Repenning, C.A., and Grady. F.
1988 The microtine rodents of the Cheetah Room fauna, Hamilton Cave, West Virginia, and the spontaneous origin of *Synaptomys*. *U.S. Geological Survey Bulletin* **1853**:1-32.

Repenning, C.A., Browers, E.M., Carter, L.D., Marincovich, L., Jr., and Ager, T.A.
1987 The Beringian ancestry of *Phenacomys* (Rodentia: Cricetidae) and the beginning of the modern Arctic Ocean borderland biota. *U.S. Geological Survey Bulletin* **1687**:1-31.

Rhodes, R.S.
1984 Paleoecology and regional paleoclimatic implications of the Farmdalian Craigmile and Woodfordian Waubonsie mammalian local faunas, southwestern Iowa. *Illinois State Museum Reports of Investigations* **40**.

Ritter, D.F.
1967 Terrace development along the front of the Beartooth Mountains, southern Montana. *Geological Society of America Bulletin.* **78**:467-484.

1986 "Process Geomorphology." Dubuque, Iowa, Wm. C. Brown Co., Publishers. 579 p.

Robinson, J.W., and Hoffmann, R.S.
1975 Geographical and interspecific cranial variation in big-eared ground squirrels (*Spermophilus*): a multivariate study. *Systematic Zoology* **24**:79-88.

Roosevelt, O., and Burden, J.W.
    1934   A new species of antilocaprine, *Tetrameryx onusrosogris*, from a Pleistocene cave deposit in southern Arizona. *American Museum Novitiates*. **754**:1-4.

Roscoe, E.J.
    1954   Terrestrial gastropods from the Black Hills, Lawrence County, South Dakota. *Utah Academy of Sciences, Arts, and Letters*. **31**:67-72.

Roth, V.L.
    1984   How elephants grow: heterochrony and the calibration of developmental stages in some living and fossil species. *Journal of Vertebrate Paleontology*. **4**:126-145.
    1990   Insular dwarf elephants: a case study in body mass estimation and ecological inference. *in Body size in mammalian paleobiology: estimation and biological implications,* Damuth, J. & MacFadden, B.J. (eds.), pp.151-179. Cambridge: Cambridge University Press.

Roth, V.L., and Shoshani, J.
    1988   Dental identification and age determination in *Elephas maximus*. *Journal of Zoology* **214**:567-588.

Saunders, J.J.
    1970   "The distribution and taxonomy of *Mammuthus* in Arizona." Unpublished M.S. thesis; University of Arizona, Tucson.
    1977   Late Pleistocene Vertebrates of the Western Ozarks Highland, Missouri. *Illinois State Museum Reports of Investigations* **33**, Springfield. 118 p.
    1980   A model for man-mammoth relationships in Late Pleistocene North America. *Canadian Journal of Anthropology,* **1**:87-98.

Savage, D.E.
    1951   Late Cenozoic vertebrates of the San Francisco Bay region. *University California Publication Bulletin Department Geo logical Sciences* **28**:215-314.

Schaller, B.
    1972   "The Serengeti Lion: A Study of Predator-Prey Relations." Chicago and London: The University of Chicago Press. 480 pp.

Schultz, C.B., and Stout, T.M.
    1948   Pleistocene mammals and terraces in the Great Plains. *Geological Society of America Bulletin* **59**:553-588.

Shultz, J.R.

1938   A late Quaternary mammal fauna from the tar seeps of McKittrick, California. *Carnegie Institution, Washington Contributions to Paleontology* **487**:111-125.

Schumm, S.A.

1956   Evolution of drainage systems and slopes in badlands at Perth Amboy, New Jersey. *Geological Society of America Bulletin* **67**:597-646.

1971   Fluvial geomorphology: the historical perspective and channel adjustment and river metamorphis. *In* "Fluvial geomorphology in river mechanics" (H.W. Shen, Ed.), pp. 4-1 to 5-20. Water Resources Publication, Fort Collins, Colorado; reprinted *In* "River Morphology" (S. A. Schumm, Ed.), 1972, pp. 365-417. Dowden, Hutchinson and Ross, Inc. Stroudsburg, PA,

Selley, R.C.,

1982   "An Introduction to Sedimentology." New York, Academic Press. 417 p.

Semken, H.A., Jr.

1966   Stratigraphy and paleontology of the McPherson *Equus* beds (Sandahl local fauna), McPherson County, Kansas. *Contributions of the Museum of Paleontology, University of Michigan* **20**:121-178.

Semken, H.A., Jr., and Falk, C.R.

1987   Late Pleistocene/Holocene mammalian faunas and environmental changes on the northern plains of the United States. *In* "Late Quaternary mammalian biogeography and environments of the Great Plains and prairies." (R.W. Graham, H.A. Semken, Jr., and M.A. Graham, Eds.), *Illinois State Museum, Scientific Papers* **22**:176-313. Springfield.

Shipman,

1981   "Life history of a fossil: an introduction to taphonomy and paleoecology." Harvard University Press, Cambridge. 222 p.

Siegfried, P.

1959   Das Mammut von Ahlen. *Palaeontologisches Zeitschrift* **33**: 172-184. Stuttgart.

Sikes, S.

1971   "The natural history of the African elephant." Weidenfeld and Nicolson. London.

Skinner, M.F.

1942   The fauna of Papago Springs Cave, Arizona, and a study of *Stockoceros*: with three new antilocaprines from Nebraska and Arizona. *Bulletin of the American Museum of Natural History* **80**:143-220.

Slaughter, B., Crook, W.W., Jr., Harris, R.K., Allen, D.C., and Seifert, M.
    1962   The Hill-Shuler local faunas of the Upper Trinity River, Dallas and Denton Counties, Texas. University Texas Bureau Eco nomic Geology Report Investigation **48**:1-75.

Sneed, E.D., and Folk, R.L.
    1958   Pebbles in the lower Colorado River, Texas: a study in particle morphogenesis. *Geology* **66**:114-150.

Soffer, O.
    1985   "The Upper Paleolithic of the Central Russian Plain." Academic Press, New York. 539 p.

Stanford, D.
    1979   The Selby and Dutton Sites: Evidence for a Possible Pre-Clovis Occupation on the High Plains. I*n* "Pre-Llano Cultures of the Americas: Paradoxes and Possibilities" R.L. Humphrey, and D. Stanford, Eds.), pp. 101-123. Washington, D.C., Anthropological Society of Washington.

Stebbins, R.C.
    1985   "A Field Guide to Western Reptiles and Amphibians." Houghton Mifflin Company, Boston. 2633 p.

Steele, D.G., and Carlson, D.
    1984   Excavation and Taphonomy of Mammoth Remains from the Duewall-Newberry Site, Brazos County, Texas. *Abstracts: First International Conference on Bone Modification.* Carson City, Nevada. pp. 34-35.

Stock, C.
    1942   The fauna of Papago Springs Cave, Arizona, and a study of *Stockoceros*; with three new Antilocaprines from Nebraska and Arizona. *Bulletin of the American Museum of Natural History* **80**:143.
    1950   Bears from the Pleistocene Cave of Joscito, Nuevo Leon, Mexico. *Journal of Washington Academy of Science* **40**:317-21

Storer, J.E.
    1976   Mammals of the Hand Hills Formation, southern Alberta. *In* "Athlon: Essays in paleontology in honour of Loris Shano Russell." (C.S. Churcher, Ed.), pp. 186-209. *Royal Ontario Museum Life Sciences Miscellaneous Publications.* Toronto.

Strahler, A.N.
    1957   Quantitative analysis of watershed geomorphology. *American Geophysical Union Transactions* **38**:913-920.

Stricklin, F.

1961   Degradational stream deposits of the Brazos River, central
            Texas. *Geological Society of America Bulletin* **72**:19-35.
Sutcliffe, A.J.
1970   Spotted hyena: crusher, gnawer, digester and collector of
            bones. *Nature* **227**:1110-1113.
Swinehart, J.B., Souders, V.L., DeGraw, H.M., and Diffendal, R.F., Jr.
1985   Cenozoic paleogeography of western Nebraska. *In* "Cenozoic
            paleogeography of west-central United States" (S. S. Kaplan,
            Ed.), pp. 109-229. Denver, Rocky Mountain Section. Society
            of Economic Paleontologists and Mineralogists.
Taylor, D.W.
1960   Late Cenozoic molluscan faunas from the High Plains. *U.S.
            Geological Survey Professional Paper.* **337**:1-94.
1965   The study of Pleistocene nonmarine mollusks in North America.
            In "The Quaternary of the United States" (H.E. Wright and
            D.G. Frey, Eds.), pp. 597-611. Princeton University Press.
Tihen, J.A.
1962   A review of New World fossil bufonids. *American Midland
            Naturalist* **68**:1-50.
Todd, J.E.
1902   Hydrographic history of South Dakota. *Geological Society of
            America Bulletin* **13**:27-40.
Todd, L.D., and Frison, G.C.
1986   Taphonomic studies of the Colby Site mammoth bones. *In*
            (G.C. Frison, and L.C. Todd, Eds.), pp. 27-90. The Colby
            Mammoth Site. University of New Mexico Press. Albuquerque.
Toepfer, V.
1957   Die Mammutfunde von Pfaennerhall im Geiseltal.
            Veroeffentlichungen Landesmuseum Vorgeschichte, Halle. Heft
            16:1-58. Pls. I-XXIV.
Troxell, E.L.
1915   The vertebrate fossils of Rock Creek, Texas. *American Jour-
            nal of Science* **39**:613-638.
Turner, R.W.
1974   Mammals of the Black Hills of South Dakota and Wyoming.
            *University of Kansas Museum of Natural History Miscella-
            neous Publication* **60**:1-178.
Vereschagin, N.K.
1967   The Mammals of the Caucasus: A History of the Evolution
            of the Fauna (Translated by A. Lerman and B. Rabinovich).
            Jerusalem: Israel Program for Scientific Translation.

1977   Berelekh "Cemetery" of mammothes - Trudy
        Zoologicheskogo Instituta AN SSSR **72**:5-50 (Leningrad)
1982   The Kizel Cave as a trap for animals in the Middle Urals.
        Trudy Zoologicheskogo Instituta AN SSSR **111**:37-44
        (Leningrad).
Vereshchagin, N.K, and Tichonov, A.N.
    1986 A study of mammoth tusks. *Trudy Zool. Inst. USSR* **149**:3-14.
von den Driesch, A.
    1976   A Guide to the Measurement of Animal Bones from Archaeo-
            logical Sites. *Peabody Museum Bulletin* 1. Harvard.
Voorhies, M.R.
    1969   Taphonomy and Population Dynamics of an Early Pliocene
            Vertebrate Fauna, Knox County, Nebraska. *Contributions to
            Geology. Special Paper No. 1.* University of Wyoming,
            Laramie.
Voorhies, M.R., and Corner, R.G.
    1985   Small mammals with boreal affinities in late Pleistocene
            (Rancholabrean) deposits of eastern and central Nebraska.
            Institute for Tertiary-Quaternary Studies, Symposium Series
            1:125-142.
Walker, D. N.
    1982   Early Holocene vertebrate fauna. *In* "The Agate Basin site: a
            record of the Paleoindian occupation of the northwestern High
            Plains" (G.C. Frison and D.J. Stanford, Eds.), pp. 274-308.
            Academic Press, New York.
    1987   Late Pleistocene/Holocene environmental changes in Wyo-
            ming: the mammalian record. *In* "Late Quaternary Mammalian
            Biogeography and Environments of the Great Plains and Prai-
            ries" (R.W. Graham, H. Semken., and M.A. Graham, Eds.),
            Illinois State Museum Scientific Papers **22**:334-392. Spring-
            field.
Wanless, H.R.,
    1923   The stratigraphy of the White River beds of South Dakota.
            American Philosophical Society Proceedings **62**:190-269.
Ward, F.
    1922   The geology of a portion of the Badlands. *South Dakota
            Geological and Natural History Survey Bulletin* **11**:7-59.
Watts, W.A.

1983   Vegetational history of the eastern United States 25,000 to 10,000 years ago. *In* "Late-Quaternary environments of the United States" (H.E. Wright, Ed.), pp. 294-310. "The late Pleistocene." (S.C. Porter, Ed.), Minneapolis, University of Minnesota Press **1**.

Watts, W.A., and Bright, R.C.
1968   Pollen, seed, and mollusk analysis of a sediment core from Pickerel Lake, northeastern South Dakota. *Geological Society of America Bulletin* **79**:855-876.

Watts, W.A., and Wright, H.E.
1966   Late-Wisconsin pollen and seed analysis from the Nebraska Sandhills. *Ecology* **47**:202-210.

Webb, S.D.
1973   Pliocene pronghorns of Florida. *Journal of Mammalogy* **54**:203-221.

Webb, T., and Bryson, R.A.
1972   Late and postglacial climatic change in the northern Midwest, USA: Quantitative estimates derived from fossil pollen spectra by multivariate statistical analysis. *Quaternary Research* **2**: 70-115.

Wells, P.V.
1970   Postglacial vegetational history of the Great Plains. *Science* **167**:1574-1582.

Whitmore, F.C., Jr., Emery, K.O., Cooke, H.B.S., and Swift, D.J.P.
1967   Elephant teeth from the Atlantic Continental Shelf. *Science* **156**:1477-1481.

Wootton, J.T.
1987   The effects of body mass, phylogeny, habitat, and trophic level on mammalian age at first reproduction. *Evolution* **41**:732-749.

Wolcott, D.E.
1967   Geology of the Hot Springs Quadrangle, Fall River and Custer Counties, South Dakota. *U.S. Geological Survey Bulletin.* **1063-k**:427-442.

Wright, H.E.
1970   Vegetational history of the Central Plains. *In* "Pleistocene and Recent environments of the central Great Plains" (W. Dort and J.K. Jones, Eds.), pp. 157-172. University of Kansas Press, Lawrence,

Yates, T.L., and Schmidly, D.J.
1978   *Scalopus aquaticus. Mammalian Species* **105**:1-4.

410

Zingg, T.
1935   Beitraege zur schotteranalyse. *Schweizerische Mineralogische und Petrographische Mitteilungen* **15**:39-140.

Zegers, D.A.
1984   *Spermophilus elegans*. *Mammalian Species* **214**:1-7.

APPENDIX A

CONTRIBUTORS TO THIS VOLUME

CONTRIBUTORS TO THIS VOLUME

Dr. Larry D. Agenbroad
   Professor of Geology; Director, Quaternary Research Program, Northern
   Arizona University, Flagstaff, Arizona 86011.
   Dr. Agenbroad has been the principal investigator of the Hot Springs
   Mammoth Site, since 1974.
Finn T. Agenbroad
   Systems engineer, Dell Computer Corporation, Colorado Springs, Colorado,
   3335 Queen Annes Way, Colorado Springs, Colorado.
   He set up the initial Macintosh PageMaker format for this publication. He
   also served as crew member for several seasons at the Site.
Dr. Gennady Baryshnikov
   Zoological Institute, Russian Academy of Sciences, Universitetskaya nab.1,
   St. Petersburg, 199034 Russia.
   Dr. Baryshnikov was the visiting scientist for the 1992 field season. He is
   an expert on bears of Eurasia.
Maxine Campbell
   Secretary, Quaternary Studies Program, Northern Arizona University,
   Flagstaff, Arizona 86011.
   Maxine produced the final, camera-ready manuscript.
Dr. Nicholas J. Czaplewski
   Oklahoma Museum of Natural History, University of Oklahoma, Norman,
   Oklahoma 73019.
   Dr. Czaplewski served as a screen wash director for one season at the
   Mammoth Site. He collaborated with Jim Mead in identification of the
   microfauna.
Dr. Irena Dubrovo
   Paleontological Institute, Moscow, Russia.
   Dr. Dubrovo is an expert on Russian mammoths and other Pleistocene
   fauna.
Dr. Richard H. Hevly
   Associate Professor, Department of Biology, Northern Arizona University,
   Flagstaff, Arizona 86011.
   Dr. Hevly made the only successful pollen recoveries from the sinkhole
   sediments. His pollen data helps in the floral reconstruction of the
   paleoenvironment.
Pamela D. Kempton
   Department of Geosciences, Southern Methodist University, Dallas, Texas
   75275.

Pamela produced a Master of Science thesis on the terraces of the Fall River, South Dakota.

Dr. Robert L. Laury
Associate Professor Department of Geosciences, Southern Methodist University, Dallas, Texas 75275.
Dr. Laury undertook the study of the sedimentology aspects of the sinkhole fill.

Dr. Adrian Lister
Department of Zoology, College of London, England.
Research on mammoths in the British Isles and Europe; pelvic analyses for sexing mammoth remains.

Dr. Jim I. Mead
Associate Professor, Department of Geology; Associate Director, Quaternary Studies Program, Northern Arizona University, Flagstaff, Arizona 86011.
Dr. Mead served as assistant director and co-principal investigator at the mammoth Site. He also investigated the invertebrate and microvertebrate faunas from the Site.

Dick Mol
Member of Workgroup for Pleistocene Zoology. The Netherlands, Gudumholm 41, Hoofddorp 2133HG.
Extensive experience with *Mammuthus primigenius* from the North Sea, and other Pleistocene fauna of the European lowlands.

Dr. Louise Roth
Department of Zoology. Duke University Durham, South Carolina
Research on pygmy mammoth of California channel islands; growth in elephants; dental characteristics of *Elephas* and co-researcher on dentition of *M. primigenius*.

Dr. Jeheskel Shoshani
Elephant Interest Group, Bloomfield Hills, Michigan
Initiated and edits the publications of The Elephant Interest Group. Research in mastodon and mammoths. Currently researching in China.

Sandra Lash Shoshani
Former HSMS crew member, discoverer of the gland stone. Active in the Elephant Interest Group.

APPENDIX B

EARTHWATCH PARTICIPANTS

1976-1990

Ed L. Agnew	Texas City, TX
Dee Aiani	Chicago, IL
Shirley Aiken	Lake Forest, IL
Ken Aldrich	Conklin, MI
George A. Allen	St. Augustine, FL
Abraham Altman	New York, NY
Sarah S. Angelastro	Pennsauken, NJ
Lynn Aronoff	New York, NY
David Atkins	Newton, MA
Sue Barner	Vancouver, BC Canada
Barbara Barrish	Painsville, OH
Jackie Bash	Hopkinton, MA
Judith J. Battles	Sherman Oaks, CA
Scott Becker	Brown Deer, WI
Maurice Becker	Haslettm, MI
Ruth Berman	Flushing, NY
John W. Bernstein	Tenafly, NJ
Thomas Berry	Westminster, VT
Robert Berwick	New Canaan, CT
Gerda T. Beversluis	Prospect Park, NJ
Julian "Buck" Braswell	Miami, FL
Carolyn Brook	Santa Cruz, CA
Anita Brown	Live Oak, FL
Edward M. Brown	Live Oak, FL
R. Cotten Brown	Ft. Myers, FL
Thomas E. Brown	Live Oak, FL
Matt Butrick	Wadsworth, OH
Dennis E. Campbell	Lynnwood, WA
Pamela Campbell	Monticello, MN
Mary Carpenter	Abbotsford, WI
Alan Cartwright	Anchorage, AK
Daisy Cartwright	Anchorage, AK
Ronald Caruso	Boston, MA
Susan Catusi	Great Neck, NY
Francie Caudill	Manchester, MA
Anne Chapman	Denver CO
Cathie Charbonneau	Nevada, IA
David I. Chrestenson	Aurora, Il

Nancy Christman	Centerville, OH
Richard Coen	Laguna Beach, CA
Donna Cress	Burbank, CA
Glenn Cunningham	Brownfield, TX
John A. Dean	Seattle, WA
Donald DeWitt	Fairbanks, AL
Shirley Disend	Harrisburg, PA
Sid Disend	Harrisburg, PA
Gregory Dobbs	Charlestown, NH
Barbara Dowell	Yucaipa, CA
Ken Dowell	Yucaipa, CA
Csilla Duneczky	Westfield, NJ
Julia Dunsworth	Minneapolis, MN
Robert Durst	Casper, WY
Paul Edinger	Rosemead, CA
Sharyn M. Ehlers	Tiburon, CA
Hannah Eldridge	Valparaiso, IN
Lita Elvers	New York, NY
Walter Elvers	New York, NY
Richard Ernst	Massapequa Park, NY
Linda Fisher	Sacramento, CA
Bruce Flint	New York, NY
Juliann Fritchman	Renton, WA
Susan Furman	Fort Collins, CO
Donald Gannon	Shrewsbury, MA
Miriam Gayton	Lake Peakskill, NY
Andreas Georgi	Mt. Lakes, NJ
Bill Gibson	Heidelberg Middle School, NY APO
Scott Gordon	Monsey, NY
Jennifer Goyette	Potsdam, NY
Barbara Gromis	Collegeville, PA
Elizabeth Haight	Framingham, MA
Carol Hankins	Sunnyvale, CA
Tim Hetrick	DuBois, PA
Hal Hoberecht	Suisun, CA
Marc Hoberecht	Suisun, CA
Reynatta Hoberecht	Suisun, CA
Daniel Hofstadter	Tucson, AZ

Holly Hollstein	San Antonio, TX
Stephanie Hutter	New Canaan, CT
Michael Jenkins	Phoenix, AZ
Jim Jensen	Englewood, CO
Allan Jodrey	Beltsville, MD
Mildred Jodrey	Beltsville, MD
Frieda Johns	Cedar Falls, IA
Deborah Johnson	S. Pasadena, CA
Ralph Jones	Millville, NJ
Thirza Joost	Worcestor, MA
Phil King	Van Nuys, CA
Guy Kitchell	Ann Arbor, MI
Joshua Klein	Boston, MA
August Kroll	Seattle, WA
Vertis Lamb	Erie, PA
Sandra Lee Lash	West Bloomfield, MI
Terese Lawinski	New York, NY
Rebecca Laws	Flower Mound, TX
David Lepkojus	Many, AZ
Andrea Lindenmayer	Arlington, MA
Rachel Lipson	Grosse Point, MI
Betty Lockhart	Casper, WY
Lester Lorenz	Battle Creek, MI
Tom Lucia	Haverhill, MA
Donna Lukshides	Schwenksville, PA
Jeanne Lundquist	Lake Elmo, MN
Angela Maggi	Soldotna, AK
James Mahoney	Suffield, CT
Lucille Malka	Fair Lawn, NJ
Jon Marget	Washington, D.C.
Susan Marshall	Topeka, KA
Victoria Masotta	N. Andover, MA
William H. Maybaum	Philadelphia, PA
Robert McCarroll	Boulder, CO
Keith Morrill	Brookings, SD
Sharon Rose Moser	Fond du Lac, WI
Harry Muscovitz	Tenafly, NJ
Ruth Nahom	Paradise Valley, AZ

Hanna Nekvasil	Washington, D.C.
Teresa C. Nelson	Alliance, NE
Mary Nimrick	Aledo, IL
Nancy Nowlin	Austin, TX
Carol Olson	Tucson, AZ
Kenneth Olson	Tucson, AZ
Caroline Olynyke	Aurora, OH
John Outler	Atlanta, GA
Melissa Pelletier	Downey, CA
June Pellinen	Sacramento, CA
Beverly Pennington	Platt, SD
Christine Phelps	Greensboro, NC
Carol Piligian	Rochester, MI
Susan Ragland	Grand Junction, CO
Guy Renkert	Milton, MA
Donna Rensch	Angola, IN
Ione Rice	Torrance, CA
Wendell Ricketts	Clearwater, FL
Jacolyn Robbie	Colorado Springs, CO
Lib Roller	Nashville, TN
Hedwig Roripaugh	Mile City, MT
Rachel Ross	Kenai, AK
Maria Sancho	Phoenix AZ
Ray Sancho	Phoenix, AZ
Barbara Schmaelzle	Ringwood, NJ
Virginia Schroeder	Chicago, IL
Corinne M. Schultz	Ft. Myers, FL
Robert B. Schultz, M.D.	Ft. Myers, FL
Elizabeth Sears	Edmons, WA
David Seela	New Market, IA
Margaret Shepard	Edmore, MI
Margaret Shepard	Edmore, MI
Joe Slowinski	Kansas City, MO
Nancy Small	Columbus, OH
Janet Smith	Darlington, ID
Patricia Smith	Horsham, Sussex UK
Faith Spencer	New Orleans, LA
Frank Spingola	Lake Havasu City, AZ
Sharon Staats	Medford, NY

Billie Stephenson	Rockville, MD
Karen Ann Sturm	Sharon Springs, NY
Toni Jean Sulkowski	McMurray PA
Mary Taglieri	Honolulu, HI
Jane Tiers	St. Paul, MN
Jane Topliss	Wantage, Oxon UK
Jennie May Tucker	Jackson, MS
Barbara Tufty	Washington, D.C.
Paul Tyson	Los Angeles, CA
Earle Van Heyningen	Indianapolis, IN
Edward J. Vaughn	Lacine, WI
Elizabeth M. Wakelee	Menlo Park, CA
Heath Wakelee	Menlo Park, CA
Mary Josephine Wamser	Goleta, CA
David Weiss	Grafton, WI
Jacquelin Wert	Ft. Wayne, IN
Dorothy West	Whangarei, New Zealand
Patricia Westlake	Saint James, NY
Sally Wickersham	Mamaroneck, NY
Jerry Wilbur	Dragoon, AZ
Dale Wilson	South Euclid, OH
Stan Witmer	Naperville, IL

APPENDIX C

FIELD EXCAVATION CREW ROSTERS

1974-1990

Excavation Crews:

Salvage and Exploration Volunteer Crews

1974:   P. Anderson, D. Hanson, G. Hanson, D. Collogan, L.
        Agenbroad, B. Agenbroad, J. Mead, M. Jones, P.
        Corman, N. Ajeman, L. Scott, C. Landrey, K. Painter,
        G. Lichtenheld, R. Cedarface, M. Lewis, R. Lewis, G.
        Mason, M. Anderson, R. Cape, P. Olson, E. Cain, C.
        Ruskin.
1975:   L. Agenbroad, J. Mead, B. Dutrow, W. Gillman, M.
        McCafferty, D. Hanson, P. Olson, G. Duerksen, K.
        Woody

Funded Excavations

1976:   L. Agenbroad, J. Mead, R. Laury, P. Bjork, B. Dutrow,
        K. Olsson, C. Adcock, M. McCafferty, G. Allen, F.
        Edinger, J. Jensen, R. Jones, J. Marget, J. Outler, C.
        Brook, H. Nekvasil, J. Smith, S. Marshall, R. Caruso,
        A. Chapman, C. Duneszky, R. Lipson, S. Hutter, W.
        Maybaum, C. Olynyki, W. Ricketts, V. Schroeder, E.
        Vaughn, D. Wilson, M. Pelletier, A. Zucherman, R.
        Dumas
1977:   L. Agenbroad, J. Mead, R. Laury, B. Dutrow, G. Allen,
        J. Battles, J. Bernstein, H. Moscovitz, S. Moser, E.
        Height, J. Tucker, S. Ragland, D. Chrestenson, B. Flint,
        R. Brown, E. Brown, A. Brown, T. Brown, M. Jenkins,
        N. Nowlin, K. Sturm, E. Wakelee, H. Wakelee

1978: L. Agenbroad, J. Mead, R. Laury, B. Dutrow, E. Agnew,
       S. Angelastro, B. Barrish, D. Lukshides, J. Jundquist, T.
       Nelson, J. Tiers, B. Tufty, A. Altman, D. Atkins, G.
       Beversluis, D. Campbell, J. Dean, S. Ehlers, S. Gordon,
       J. Goyette, J. Klein, J. Robbie, E. Sears, M. Wamser
1979: L. Agenbroad, W. Agenbroad, B. Agenbroad, F.
       Agenbroad, J. Mead, R. Laury, B. Dutrow, F. Snocker,
       J. Bash, D. Cress, G. Dobbs, B. Gibson, A. Georgi, T.
       Hetrick, J. Klein, M. Shepard, J. Slowinski, D. Weiss,
       A. Altman, R. Berman, T. Berry, D. Johnson, S. Lash,
       K. Morrill, C. Schultz, R. Schultz, N. Small, T.
       Sulkowski
1983: L. Agenbroad, J. Mead, B. Barrish, F. Snocker, E.
       Mead, D. Meier, W. Agenbroad, F. Agenbroad, S.
       Aiken, T. Berry, G. Cunningham, J. Fritchman, J.
       Jensen, D. Lepkojus, B. Lockhart, T. Lucia, R. Nahom,
       G. Renkert, M. Shepard, F. Spencer, E. Van Heynigen,
       S. Wikersham, B. Magruder, S. Barner, S. Becker, M.
       Butrick, R. Coen, F. Caudill, S. Furman, I. Rice, R.
       Sancho, M. Sancho, B. Schmaelzle, M. Taglieri, J.
       Tucker, D. West
1986: L. Agenbroad, J. Mead, E. Mead, B. Barrish, F.
       Snocker, D. Aiani, M. Becker, D. Cartwright, A.
       Cartwright, A. Discend, S. Discend, J. Dunsworth, C.
       Hankins, A. Jodrey, M. Jodrey, M. Nimrick, D. Renseh,
       J. Braswell, S. Catusi, L. Elvers, W. Elvers, V. Masotta,
       C. Olson, K. Olson, C. Piligian, H. Roripaugh, F.
       Spingola, J. Wilbur
1987: L. Agenbroad, B. Barrish, F. Snocker, B. Cluer, K.
       Cluer, N. Czaplewski, J. Snider, C. Caywood, J. Bow-
       ers, P. Campbell, J. Mahoney, V. Miles, P. Schwartz, C.
       DeWoikin, T. Joost, L. Aronoff, R. Berwick, D.
       Gannon, H. Hoberecht, M. Hoberecht, R. Hoberecht, T.
       James, G. Kitchell, A. Linenmayer, L. Malka, J. Tucker,
       P. Tyson

1988: L. Agenbroad, B. Barrish, F. Snocker, B. Cluer, K. Cluer, A. Chrisman, J. Snider, P. Campbell, C. Charbonneau, R. Ernst, D. Hofstadter, T. Joost, V. Lamb, T. Lawinski, R. Laws, L. Lorenz, J. Mahoney, D. Seela, L. Aronoff, N. Christman, D. Dewitt, H. Eldridge, L. Fisher, M. Gayton, R. McCarroll, B. Bennington, S. Staats, J. Werts, P. Westlake

1989: L. Agenbroad, B. Barrish, F. Snocker, L. Luzzi, S. McKelvie, C. Allan, L. Aronoff, J. Clark, R. Durst, M. Wilson-Everett, T. Joost, J. Levie, M. Madden, T. Spencer, K. Vyfvinkel, D. Hofstader, M. Carpenter, D. Johnson, S. Kloss, C. Mikkelsen, J. Mikkelsen, R. Rhodes, E. Roller, S. Staats, R. Strom

1990: L. Agenbroad, J. Mead, B. Barrish, F. Snocker, D. Mol, L. Roth, L. Aronoff, R. Durst, M. Haaga, J. Haaga, N. Hallinan, C. Holstein, T. Joost, V. Lamb, J. Pellinen, K. Twiss, D. Walz, J. Walz, M. Carpenter, S. Eastman, B. Gallowway, E. Kingham, K. Lee, A. Lomne, M. Madden, B. Reinhardt, L. Roller, P. Whitman, S. Witmer

APPENDIX D

FOSSIL ELEPHANTS FROM THE

COMMONWEALTH OF INDEPENDENT STATES

I. DUBROVO

FOSSIL ELEPHANTS FROM THE COMMONWEALTH OF INDEPENDENT STATES

Irena A. Dubrovo

INTRODUCTION

Many remains of fossil Proboscidea are known from the territory formerly known as the Soviet Union and now comprising the Commonwealth of Independent States (CIS). They belong to several different taxa and have been found in sediments of Neogene and Quaternary ages.

The first known appearance of elephants in the study area has been documented from the Late Pliocene. Jaws and teeth of elephants known from sediments of that age in Moldova, on the coast of the Azov Sea, and in the Caucasus region were previously assigned to *Protelephas planifrons* (Falconer and Cautley 1846), *P.* cf. *planifrons*, or *P.* aff. *planifrons* (Burchak-Abramovich 1951; Gromova 1948; Pavlow 1910; Sherstukov 1954, 1958; and others). Re-examination of those specimens and published data concerning them has resulted in their referral to *Archidiskodon meridionalis meridionalis* (Nesti 1825) (Dubrovo 1964a). The subspecies *P. planifrons groznensis*, described from the Caucasus region by Sherstukov (1954), does not appear to be valid. The large, complete number of plates and the laminar frequency on the penultimate and last teeth of "*P. p. groznensis*" suggest that those teeth belong instead to *A. meridionalis*. Thus, the earliest south-Asian elephant, X*P. planifrons*, apparently did not occur in Europe or in the Asian part of the CIS.

Three genera of the subfamily Elephantinae, distributed in Eurasia, are known in the CIS. They belong to two phylogenetic lines, viz., the Archidiskodon-Mammuthus line and the Paleoloxodon elephant line. The first elephants known in the Late Pliocene in the southern regions of the CIS belonged to the genus *Archidiskodon*. The last form, *Mammuthus primigenius*, became extinct at the end of the Late Pleistocene, but in some places, such as Wrangel Island, the latest known specimens have been dated at about 6,000 yr B.P.

MATERIALS AND METHODS

In the present paper I have used the stratigraphic scheme that places the Neogene/Quaternary boundary at 1.65 million years (my) B.P. and recognizes Pleistocene (1.65-0.01 my) and Holocene (10,000 yr B.P.-present) subdivisions of the Quaternary. Early (1.65-0.8 my), Middle (0.8-0.13 my), and Late (0.13 my.-10,000 yr B.P.) chronostratigraphic subdivisions of the Pleistocene also are recognized (Table A-1).

The principal collections of fossil elephant remains from the CIS are housed at the Paleontological Institute of the Academy of Sciences of Russia (PIN) in Moscow and the Zoological Institute of the Academy of Sciences (ZIN) in St. Petersburg. There are also collections in museums in Kiev, Rostov/Don, and Yakutsk. Specimens used in the present summary are in those collections, various other museums in the CIS, and some other countries. Data from the literature also was used.

Use of correct methods of study are necessary to determine the exact systematic position of fossil elephant remains. Some dental characters, very important for systematic identification of elephants, can be altered in the process of normal tooth wear. Some of these characters can even be different on buccal and lingual sides of the same tooth or at its basal or apical part. All of the materials used in this study were examined using the same measurement procedures, diagnostic characters, etc., explained in detail in previous publications (Dubrovo 1960, 1981; Dubrovo and Jakubowski 1988). Diagnoses and descriptions of taxa in the present paper pertain only to forms described from the territory of the CIS.

SYSTEMATIC ACCOUNT

Order Proboscidea (Illiger 1811)
Family Elephantidae (Gray 1821)

Archidiskodon, Mammuthus, Phanagoroloxodon, and *Paleoloxodon.*

The genera *Archidiskodon* (Pohlig 1888) and *Mammuthus* (Brookes 1828) are known from the CIS and are of considerable interest both biologically and stratigraphically. Some workers (Aguirre 1969; Maglio 1973) hold the opinion that *Archidiskodon* is referable to *Mammuthus,* but these genera appear to be quite distinct on the basis of morphological differences in the skull, lower jaws and teeth, the postcranial skeleton, and the structure of the wrist. In the present study comparison of six specimens of *Archidiskodon* and 12 specimens of *Mammuthus* indicate that in these two genera there is a difference in the ratio of the width of the skull in the zygomatic and occipital regions, a different index of the width of the intermaxillary bones and skull length, and a difference in the index of height and length of the skull (Figure A-1).

As shown in Figure A-2, there are considerable differences in the form of the mandible in these genera. The lower jaw of *Archidiskodon* is longer and lower than that of *Mammuthus,* its anterior end forming a narrow, elongate, beak-like projection that is much longer than the short, stubby projection of the anterior end of the mandibular symphysis in *Mammuthus.* The mandible of *Mammuthus* is shorter and more robust, the ramus is of greater vertical diameter than that of *Archidiskodon,* and the posterior portion is broadly expanded, as opposed to the narrow and elongate posterior region in *Archidiskodon.* The proportions and detailed morphology of the molars of the latter genus also are different from those of *Mammuthus.*

Examination of specimens from Russia and Italy shows that in the postcranial skeleton the wrist of *Archidiskodon* has a distinct serial structure in the arrangement of the bones, whereas in *Mammuthus* there is an aserial arrangement (Dubrovo and Jakubowski 1988) (Fig-

Table D-1. Chronostratigraphic distribution of species of *Archidiskodon* and *Mammuthus* in the Commonwealth of Independent States. Abbreviations: Paleomag. pol. scale=Paleomagnetic polarity scale.

Age (m.y.)	Paleomag. pol. scale	Stratigraphic units		Faunistic complex	Taxon
0.01		Holocene			
	Brunnes	Pleistocene	Late	Upper Paleolithic	*M. primigenius* (late form)
0.13				Shkurlatov	*M. primigenius* (early form)
			Middle	Khasarian	*M. trogontherii chosaricus*
0.80				Tiraspolian	*M. trogontherii trogontherii*
	Matuyama		Early	Tamanian	*A. meridionalis tamanensis*
1.65		Pliocene	Late	Khaprovian	*A. meridionalis meridionalis*
				Skortsellan	*A. ex gr. rumanus*

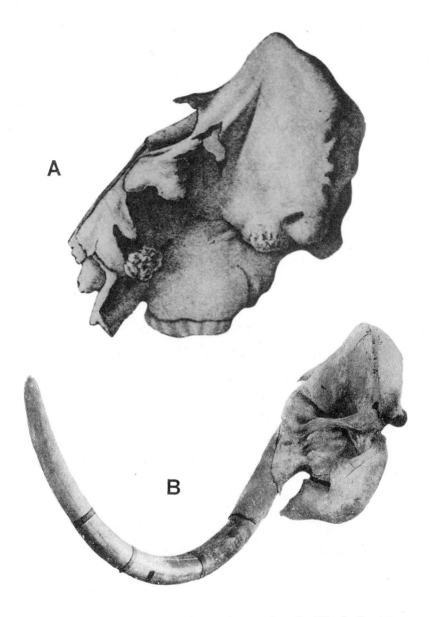

Figure D-1. (A) *Archdiskodon meridionalis meridionalis* (Westi). Lectotype skull, left lateral view. View Pliocene, Italy. (B) *Mammuthus primigenius* (Blum). Neotype skull, left lateral view. Late Pleistocene, Taimir Peninsula, Russia.

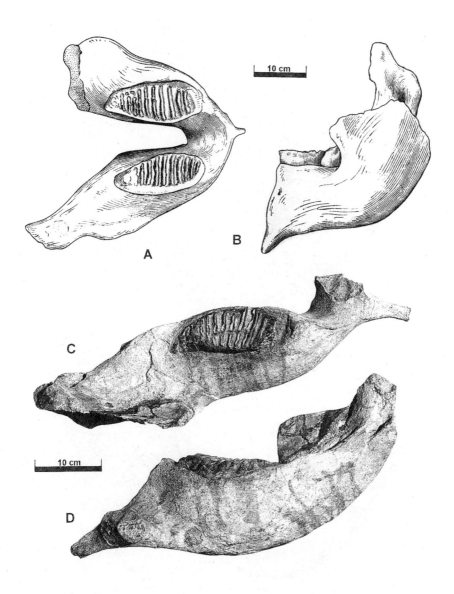

Figure D-2. (A-B) *Mammuthus trogontherii trogontherii* (Pohlig). Lower jaw.
Middle Pleistocene, Tiraspol, Moldova. [A] Occlusal view; [B] left lateral view.
(C-D) *Archidiskodon meridionalis tamanensis* Dubrovo. Right mandibular
ramus. Early Pleistocene, Port Kanton, Azov region, Russia. [C)] Occlusal view.
[D] Lingual view.

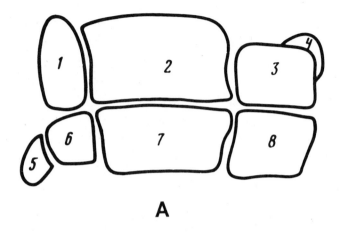

A

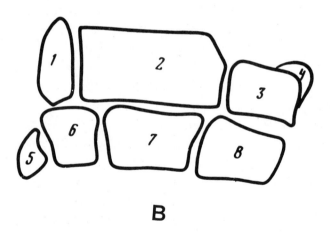

B

Figure D-3. Structure of the carpus in *Archidiskodon* and *Mammuthus*. (A) Serial type. *Archidiskodon meridionalis*, Early Pleistocene, Nogaisk, Russia. (B) Aserial type. *Mammuthus primigenius*, Late Pleistocene, Siberia, Russia. Explanation of figure: 1, scaphoid; 2, lunar; 3, cuneiform; 4, pisiform; 5, trapezium; 6, trapezoid; 7, magnum; 8, hamatum.

432

ure A-3). As determined from studies of carpal structures directly associated with dental remains, the lunar and magnum bones in *Archidiskodon* are of equal diameter transversely along their articular surface. In the carpus of *Mammuthus* the transverse diameter of the magnum is greatly reduced and does not equal that of the lunar, permitting the trapezoid to extend into the area of the anterior articular surface of the lunar. There are also differences in the form and proportions of the articular facets of some of the other carpal bones; e.g., the outline of the lower articular surface of the scaphoid is triangular in *Mammuthus* but is circular in *Archidiskodon* (Dubrovo and Jakubowski 1988).

In addition to osteological and dental features, these two genera exhibit differences in external characters that are used as indicators of generic distinction in the systematics of Recent mammals. *Archidiskodon* and *Mammuthus* were adapted to different biotypes and climatic conditions, so their appearance undoubtedly was not the same, the two forms differing in the character of their hair covering and probably in the size and shape of the external ears. The differences between them form stable complexes of characters that can be easily explained as functions of both the physiology and the ecology of these two biologically coordinate forms.

In Opinion 1661 of the International Commission on Zoological Nomenclature, "The generic name *Archidiskodon* (Pohlig 1888) . . ., previously a junior objective synonym of *Mammuthus* (Brookes 1828)," was "conserved as a consequence of approval by the Commission" and "is available for use by those who consider it to represent a genus or subgenus taxonomically distinct from *Mammuthus* (Anonymous 1991). Among the recent literature the name *Archidiskodon* has been employed by De Giuli *et al.* (1990) and Van Kolfschoten (1990).

The genus *Phanagoroloxodon* (Garutt) was described from the territory of the CIS on the basis of an incomplete skull (Garutt 1958), the exact locality and geological age of which was unknown. The teeth in the skull are the right M^1 and M^2 and part of the left M^2, all of which are badly damaged. However, two well preserved teeth that Garutt (1958) used to diagnose the dentition of *Phanagoroloxodon* are the paratype teeth of *Archidiskodon meridionalis tamanensis* from Upper Pliocene deposits of the Taman Peninsula. Furthermore, the type of fossilization of the holotype skull of *Phanagoroloxodon* is not known in fossil elephant remains from the CIS and is more like the type of preservation of material from the Maraga locality in Iran.

Some authors (e.g. Maglio 1973) have considered the genus *Palaeoloxodon* to be congeneric with *Elephas*, but there are several morphological features that suggest that the former taxon is a valid genus. The skull of palaeoloxodont elephants attains its greatest width in the front at the frontal edge of the premaxillaries and not posteriorly in the occipital or zygomatic region as in other genera. There is a frontoparietal crest on the skull of *Palaeoloxodon*, and the wide separation between the cranial types of *Palaeoloxodon* and *Elephas* has been mentioned by Osborn (1942). The morphology of the teeth is also distinct in *Palaeoloxodon*: they are very narrow and high-crowned and have the loxodont sinus. The carpal bone structure is also different in these two genera, being of aserial arrangement in *Palaeoloxodon* and serial in *Elephas*. Chinese authors (e.g. Zhang *et al.* 1983) have suggested that *Archdiskodon meridionalis* and *Protelaphas planifrons* should be included in the genus *Palaeoloxodon*, but specimens of all three taxa are distinguishable at the generic level.

On the basis of the considerations presented above, only the three proboscidean genera *Archidiskodon*, *Mammuthus*, and *Palaeoloxodon* are known from the territory of the CIS.

Archidiskodon (Pohlig 1888)

The genus *Archidiskodon* is represented in Europe by two species, *A. rumanus* (Stefanescu) and *A. meridionalis* (Nesti). The first taxon was based on very fragmentary remains from Rumania for which the diagnosis was not sufficient. *A. meridionalis* is represented by a considerable body of material, including skeletons, skulls, lower jaws, and teeth. The existence of *A. rumanus* on the territory of the CIS has only been assumed. *A. meridionalis* was widely distributed in that region in the Late Pliocene and Early Pleistocene. Most localities of archidiskodont elephants are in the southern regions of the European part of the CIS, such as Ukraine, territories near the Azov Sea, and the Caucasus region, but some remains have been found in the Asian part of the CIS. The northernmost locality for *A. meriodionalis* is in Viluisk district, Yakutia (Dubrovo 1990).

The richest localities of the Late Pliocene fauna of the CIS are Liventsovka and Khary near the city of Rostov/Don. In 1965 an elephant of the *Archidiskodon* complex was described as a new species, *A. gromovi* Garutt and Alexejeva, on the basis of specimens from the Liventsovka locality (Alexejeva and Garutt 1965). The validity of *A. gromovi* was questioned by V.I. Gromova (1965) and L.K. Gabunia and A.K. Vekua (1967). To determine the real taxonomic position of that form I made a thorough study of all data on *A. gromovi* and of stratotypical collections of *A. meridionalis* from Italy. The absence of differences in the skull structure and dentition of the elephant from Liventsovka and other localities of the same geological age in the CIS and those of typical *A. meridionalis* from Italy was established (Dubrovo 1977, 1985, 1989; Gabunia and Dubrovo 1989). None of the specimens of "*A. gromovi Y*" differed from those of typical *A. meridionalis*, thus indicating that "*A.*" "*gromovi*" is a synonym of the nominative species *A. meridionalis*. Three subspecies of *A. meridionalis* are known from the territories of the CIS. The earliest one is the nominative subspecies *A. meridionalis Y meridionalis* (Nesti), based on the holotype skull and teeth from Italy. Careful morphological studies of skulls and large series of penultimate and last teeth (Table A-2) from the Late Pliocene Liventsovka and Khapry localities and of the holotype and paratypes of *A. m. meridionalis* in Italian museums made it possible to establish that the elephant from Liventsovka is referable to the nominative subspecies of *A. meridionalis* (Dubrovo 1989). The occasional presence of constant premolars in *A.m.Y. meridionalis* is an atavistic character (Dubrovo 1985) that is known also in later elephants, such as

Mammuthus imperator and *M. trogontherii* (Friant 1941; Pontier and Anthony 1966).

Occurring in later horizons than *A. meridionalis meridionalis* is X*A. meridionalis taribanensis* Gabunia and Vekua, based on a nearly complete skeleton with a skull and teeth (Table 1) found in Taribana in the Caucasus region (Gabunia and Vekua 1963). No other specimens belonging to that subspecies are known. There are differences in the character of its skull and teeth (Gabunia and Vakua, 1963; Dubrovo 1977, 1989). None of its distinctions exceed the rank of subspecies, but they suggest that *A. m. taribanensis* is slightly more advanced than *A. m. meridionalis.*

The third subspecies of *A. meridionalis* is *A. meridionalis tamanensis* Dubrovo from the Early Pleistocene (Dubrovo 1964b). A skeleton, the skull of a female, and many teeth have been found. In addition to the specimens from the CIS, remains of this taxon have also been found in Spain, Israel, and Mongolia. This form demonstrates a clear, progressive change in morphological characters of molar teeth (Table A-2). A large series of more than 250 last and penultimate teeth of one population of elephants collected in Early Pleistocene beds on the shore of the Azov Sea near the village of Siniaya Balka on the Taman Peninsula in Krasnodar territory made it possible to conduct a thorough biometric study. The variational curves of all diagnostic characters are of a distinctly monovertex type (Dubrovo 1963a) that demonstrate that all of these teeth belong to a single taxon. The coefficient of distinction of *A. m. meridionalis* and *A. m. tamanensis* is the number of plates of M3 is 1.8, which is more than necessary (1.28) to indicate that they belong to a distinct subspecies. There are also morphological differences in the skulls of these two subspecies, as indicated by comparison of the skull of a female of *A. m. tamanensis* excavated at the Siniaya Balka locality with the skull of a female of *A. m. meridionalis* from Italy that was originally described as *"Elephas lyrodon"* (Weithofer 1889). The molars of the two subspecies also differ, *meridionalis* having a fewer number of plates, smaller lamellar frequency, thicker enamel, and a lower crown height.

Archidiskodon meridionalis tamanensis (Dubrovo 1964)

Holotype — The skull of a female with M^2 and M^3, Siniaya Balka village, Krasnodar territory, Taman Peninsula, Russia. Early Pleistocene. Collection of Paleontological Institute, Academy of Sciences of Russia, No. 1358-57.

Diagnosis — Length of: M3=225-317, M3=259-328; M^2=193-260, M2= 194-257. Full number of plates: M^3=12-17, M3=12-17; M^2=9-13, M2=0 10-13. Lamellar frequency accordingly 4.5-6.5/4-6 and 4.5-6.5/4-6.5. Enamel thickness: M^3=2.5-3.5, M2 =2-3.5.

Distribution and age — Eurasia (Spain, CIS, Israel, Mongolia). Early Pleistocene.

Description of holotype skull — It is low and very much elongated anterolaterally, and the distance from the condyles to the upper edge of the premaxillaries is almost equal to the height of the cranium from the tritor of the molars to the summit of the cranium. The summit of the cranium is low, without a median depression, and the occiput is of moderate width. The forehead is of medium length and is concave lengthwise. The nasal opening is wide and low. the premaxillaries are long and slightly broadened, and the tusks are very feebly curved.

The cranial measurements (in mm) are as follows:

Greatest length (summit to lower edge of premaxillaries)	1140
Length of forehead including nasal opening	593
Length of premaxillaries	643
Width across zygomatic arches	542
Width of occiput	608
Width of rostrum, upper	370
Width of rostrum, lower	422
Height of skull	738
Height of summit	475

Discussion — In all characters *A. meridionalis tamanensis* was the most advanced supspecies of *A. meridionalis*. It was one of the last archidiskodont elephants and was replaced by elephants of the genus *Mammuthus*.

Mammuthus (Brookes 1828)
Mammuthus trogontherii (Pohlig 1885)

The genus *Mammuthus* first appeared in the beginning of the Middle Pleistocene in the form of *M. trogontherii* (Pohlig), described from material from the Sussenborn locality in Germany. Pohlig (1888) did not designate a holotype for *M. trogontherii*, so Osborn (1942) proposed as the lectotype for that species two teeth, M^3 and M963 from Sussenborn. That designation was not correct, however, because a lectotype or a holotype must be based on specimens from one individual. Unrelated elements, such as the molars proposed by Osborn (1942) as the lectotype, cannot be utilized. Accordingly, I chose (Dubrovo 1963b) as the lectotype of M. *trogontherii* an M^3 that was the first one described by Pohlig (1888:193, fig. 79). That species is widely distributed in Europe and is known from Asia. Its inclusion in the genus *Mammuthus* is rejected by some scientists from the CIS, who assigned it to the genus *Archidiskodon*. However, the morphology of *trogontherii* precludes its acceptance in the genus *Archidiskodon*. The lower jaw of *trogontherii* is short and high. Its anterior end has as in *Mammuthus*, a noticeable symphysial process (Figure A-2a-b) but far less extensive than that of *Archidiskodon* (Figure -2c-d). *M. trogontherii* also has an aserial structure of the wrist bones, bypical of *Mammuthus*. The wrist in elephants of the genus *Archidiskodon* has an aserial structure.

Two subspecies of *M. trogontherii* have been named: the nominative subspecies *M. trogontherii trogontherii* (Pohlig), which includes the lectotype from Sussenborn (Dubrovo 1963b), and M. *trogontherii chosaricus* (Dubrovo 1966), described on the basis of material from the CIS.

Mammuthus trogontherii chosaricus (Dubrovo 1966)

Holotype — Skull and lower jaw with M3. Valley of Volga River near Cherny Yar village, Volgograd region, Russia. Middle Pleistocene. Collection of Paleontological Institute, Academy of Sciences of Russia, No. 4394.

Diagnosis — Length of: M3=310, M$_3$=225-370. Width of: M^3=89-108, M$_3$=74-98. Full number of plates: M^3=20-21, M$_3$=18-24; M$_2$= 14-15. Lamellar frequency: M$_3$=5.5-7; M$_2$=5.5-6.5. Enamel thickness: M$_3$=2-2.5; M$_2$=2-2.5

Distribution and age — Eurasia (Italy, Poland, the CIS, Mongolia, ?Japan). Middle Pleistocene.

Discussion — The morphological distinction between the two subspecies of M. *trogontherii* is based upoln differences in the number of molar plates, their frequency, enamel thickness, and crown width. All distinctions are transgressive. Elevation of *M. t. chosaricus* from subspecific to specific level has been suggested by some authors but is not substantiated. The morphological characters of *M. t. chosaricus* are somewhat more progressive than those of *M. t. trogontherii,* but the differences are only of subspecific value. Both of these subspecies were adapted to a steppe environment. The climate in the time of *chosaricus* was apparently cooler and the vegetation more coarse, but the differences in their environmental surroundings were not significant and their appearances may have been similar.

The nominative subspecies is typical for the earliest part of the Middle Pleistocene. It was widely distributed in Europe and is known from Asia. The richest localities for its remains are Sussenborn in Germany and Kolkotove Balka in Moldova.

At the beginning of the 20th century an elephant from the Kolkotova Balka locality was described as a distinct species, *Elaphas wusti,* by Pavlow (1910) (*Elephas s. lato*). There are no differences either in morphology or in the stratigraphic position of that elephant and *M. trogontherii* from Sussenborn (Dubrovo 1963b, 1971). Therefore, *E. wusti* is a synonym of *M. trogontherii*, that opinion having been verified by comprehensive examination of the rich assemblage of material from Sussenborn and Kolokotova Balka. In some geological and paleontological literature in the CIS the early Middle Pleistocene *M. trogontherii trogontherii* is occasionally called *Archidiskodon wusti, A. trogontherii wusti,* or *A. trogontherii,* but that elephant belongs to the genus *Mammuthus* and includes the lectotype of *M. trogontherii.* Accordingly, it must be named *Mammuthus trogontherii trogontherii* (Pohlig).

Mammuthus primigenius (Blumenbach 1799)

The most abundant and widely distributed species of Elephantidae on the territory of the CIS was the Wooly Mammoth (*M. primigenius*). Several subspecies have been described, but some are invalid and others are in need of reexamination. Most current authors in the CIS do not recognize any races of that species. Two forms of *M. primigenius* can be distinguished, an early, more primitive one and an advanced late form. The differences are fixed in details of tooth morphology, especially in lamellar frequency and enamel thickness. The late form of primigenius is highly adapted to an existence in severe climatic conditions and to coarse forage. Its teeth became very high-crowned and sometimes had as many as 30 plates, the lamellar frequency of which could be as many as 12, the enamel layers being very thin (1-1.5 mm).

In addition to skeletons and numerous isolated teeth and bones, some cadavers of the late form of *primigenius* are known from permafrost deposits of Siberia (Dubrovo 1990). Radiocarbon dating has been made on soft tissues and on the fodder mass from the stomachs of some M. *primigenius.* The dates for the Yuribey mammoth from West Siberia are 9600 ± 300 and 9730± 100 yr B.P., but the youngest known occurrence of fossil elephants on the territory of the CIS are the remains from Wrangel Island, which have been dated at about 6000 yr B.P.

Palaeoloxodon (Matsumoto)

Palaeoloxodont elephants seem to have been rather rare in the territories of the CIS. Their remains have been found in European and Asian parts of this commonwealth, but the material is rather poor. A skull with some fragments of the postcranial skeleton was excavated from terrace deposits of Middle Pleistocene age in Turkmenia, and some isolated teeth have been found at other localities. Based on remains from Turkmenia, the new form Hesp*eroloxodon turkmenicus* Dubrovo (1955) was described but was later referred to *Palaeoloxodon* (Dubrovo 1957). Teeth of that species are known from Turkmenia and Ukraine. It differs from other species of the genus in both cranial and dental morphology (Dubrovo 1960).

Palaeoloxodon turkmenicus (Dubrovo 1955)

Holotype — Skull with M3, fragmentary M3, atlas, and proximal part of femur belonging to an adult male. Kuday-Dag District, southwestern Turkmenistan. Middle Pleistocene Collection of Zoological and Paleontological Institutes, Academy of Sciences of Russia, No. 27052 and 885.

Diagnosis — Skull large with low frontoparietal crest situated rather close to the summit. Depression on the summit is weakly developed. Skull is medium-sized in occiput and in zygomatic arches. The forehead is wide and relatively short. The premaxillaries are very wide, but their divergence to the lower edge is relatively small. The tusks are straight and very massive and are approximately 3 m in length with a diameter of about 190 mm. The molars are relatively large, the length of M3 being 366 mm. The teeth are of average width and height (ratio of width/length of M^3 = 30.3%), and the index to the length is 71%. The number of plates of M^3 is 19, the lamellar frequency is 4-4.5, and the thickness of the enamel is 3-3.5 mm. The loxodont sinus is well developed on the lower teeth and weakly developed on the upper teeth.

Measurements (in mm) of the holotype skull:
Greatest length	1485
Length of forehead with nasal opening	585

Length of premaxillaries	905
Width of occiput	1114
Width across zygomatic arches	914
Width of premaxillaries (upper)	600
Width of premaxillaries (lower)	973
Height of skull	1016
Height of summit	590

Distribution and age — Eurasia (Ukraine, Turkmenistan). Middle Pleistocene.

A distinct species, P. *meridionaloides* (Gromova 1932), was based on an M3 from Nicolskoe village, Astrachan region, Russia, which had a very high crown (245 mm; height index 73.3%), a small number of plates (no more than 15), and a laminar frequency of 4.5-5. The validity of that taxon is questionable, but additional material is needed to settle that issue. The geological age of the holotype is Middle Pleistocene. Instead of *P. turkmenicus* and *P. meridionaloides,* the species *P. antiquus* (Falconer and Cautley 1847) and *P. germanicus* (Stefanescu, 1924) are known in the territory of the CIS. The first taxon was described from Armenia (Avakian and Alexejeva 1966), the latter from the Woronezh district. Some tooth fragments from Siberia were attributed to Paleoloxodon cf. *P.* namadi*cus* (Falconer and Cautley 1846) and to *P.* ex gr. *namadicus.*

Paleoloxodont elephants occurred in the territory of the CIS from the second part of the Middle Pleistocene into the Late Pleistocene.

STRATIGRAPHIC SIGNIFICANCE OF FOSSIL ELEPHANTS

The rapid evolution of elephants, the appearance in a short itme of new subspecies, species, and even genera and their clear morphological description make that group very important for the stratigraphy of the late Cenozoic and for long range geological correlatons (Dubrovo 1991). For those purposes it is necessary to define the exact geological age of each locality and of each proboscidean taxon and to correlate data from different parts of the world. However, such comparisons are difficult because the position of the Neogene-Quaternary line is controversial and is subject to variations in regional interpretations. Therefore, in some stratigraphic schemes the duration of the Pliocene and the Pleistocene and the subdivisions of the Quaternary are different. The boundary at 1.65 my B.P. was recommended by INQUA in 1982. The stratotype of that boundary is in Italy and was established by significant changes in widely distributed marine fauna.

With regard to the evolution of Elephantinae, the most significant boundaries can be placed at about 3 my (the appearance of *Elephas* sp. late in Eurasia) or at 0.8-0.7 my (the replacement of the genus *Archidiskodon* by the genus *Mammuthus*. The boundary at 1.65 my can be fixed only by the exchange of two subspecies of A. *meriodionalis*, but for the definition of the N/Q boundary the whole complex of paleobiological, geological, and chronostratigraphic factors must be taken into account. It is unrealistic to expect synchronous changes at a high taxonomic level for all groups. For some groups of organisms the N/Q boundary can be established only by replacements of species or subspecies, but the same boundary should be accepted throughout the world and with the same subdivisions.

Until November 1990 the stratographic scheme placing the N/Q boundary at 0.8-0.7 my was used in the USSR, at which time the Interdepartmental Stratigraphic Committee of the USSR resolved to mark the Neogene-Quaternary boundary at 1.61 my, as in Italy. The establishment of subdivisions for the Quaternary for the USSR was postponed until a later date.

Faunal assemblages have been recognized in the European part of the CIS for the different intervals of the Late Cenozoic (Alexejuva 1967; Gromova 1948; Vangenegeim and Zazhigin 1965), and each complex contains the appropriate taxa of Proboscidea. Some local faunistic complexes for the Asian part of the CIS that are analogous to the European ones are known, but they are not characteristic for large areas.

Six faunistic complexes of the Late Pliocene and the Pleistocene are recognized in the CIS and are quite important. Five of these include different elephants of the Archi*diskodon-Mammuthus* phylogenetic line. They are:

1. The late Pliocene Khaprovian faunistic complex, which included *A. meridionalis meridionalis.*

2-3. Two Early Pleistocene complexes:
   Earlier - Tamanian, with *A. meridionalis tamanenesis.*
   Later - Tiraspolian, with *M. trogontherii trogontherii.*

4. The middle Pleistocene Khasarian, which included *M. trogontherii chosaricus.*

5-6. Two Late Pleistocene complexes:
   Earlier - Shkulartov, with early form of *M. primigenius.*
   Later - Upper Paleolithic, with late form of *M. primigenius.*

The earliest—and poorest known—assemblage with elephants is the Skortselian complex (Alexejeva 1978), which, along with mastodonts, includes the first elephant, A. *rumanus,* or a form close to that species (Table 2).

Some authors have divided the Tamanian complex into two parts, Odessian and Tamanian, based upon the rodent faunas (Shevchenko 1965). Other workers (Topachevskiy *et al.* 1987) found no evidence in the evolution of Rodentia that indicated that the oldest part of the Tamanian complex could be distinguished as a separate (Odessian) faunistic complex. Elephant remains from the stratotypic locality of the Odessian complex, Zevachova Gora, belong to *A. meridionalis tamanensis (D*ubrovo 1964), the same subspecies of southern elephant as the elephant from the stratotypic locality of the Tamanian faunistic complex. The remains of elephants from other localities of that age (e.g., the locality at Psecups) can be identified only as *A. meridionalis.* Therefore, the Odessian faunistic complex is not substantiated sufficiently and consequently should not be recognized. Thus, the Tamanian complex is the oldest Pleistocene mammalian assemblage.

Trends involving the reduction of enamel thickness and the increase of hypsodonty and the number of tooth plates during the evolution of the *Archidiskodon-Mammuthus* phylogenetic line are very clear and have made fossil remains of proboscideans of that line very important for stratigraphic interpretations. Certain evolutionary changes in the *Paleoloxodon* line could also be mentioned, but the remains of animals of that genus are very rare and are mostly fragmentary. Consequently, paleoloxodont elephant remains are of limited stratigraphic value.

Paleoloxodont elephants are not known from Pliocene deposits on the territories of the CIS. A lower jaw from the Kriznanovka locality in the Odessian district was first published as *Peleoloxodon* cf. *P. ausonius* but has since been referred to the genus *Archidiskodon* (Dubrovo 1977). The earliest appearance of the genus *Peleoloxodon* is in the Early Pleistocene (Dubrovo 1977). The latest well-dated discovery was in the Veronezh district at the stratotype locality of the Shkurlatov faunistic complex, together with the remains of the early form of M. *primigenius* .

CONCLUSIONS

Summarizing all data on the taxonomic status of elephants from the Commonwealth of Independent States, three genera, six species, and five subspecies can be listed for that territory:

Archidiskodon meridionalis meridionalis (Westi)
Archidiskodon meridionalis taribanensis Gabunia and Vekua
Archidiskodon meridionalis tamanensis Dubrovo
Mammuthus trogontherii trogontherii (Pohlig)
Mammuthus trogontherii chosaricus Dubrovo
Mammuthus primigenius (Blumenbach)
Paleoloxodon antiquus (Falconer and Cauley)
Paleoloxodon turkmenicus (Dubrovo)
Paleoloxodon meridionaloides (Gromova)
Paleoloxodon germanicus (Stefanescu)

The well-appointed forms *Archdiskodon* ex gr. *rumanus* (Stefanescu) and *Paleoloxodon* ex gr. *namadicus* (Falconer and Cauley) also could be mentioned.

Most elephant taxa are characterized by quite complete and clear diagnoses, and their fossil remains can be defined. Their systematic and phylogcnetic links and their stratigraphic position have been established. Upper Cenezoic stratigraphic boundaries can be marked by the succession of proboscidean taxa (Table 2), and elephants of the *Archidiskodon-Mammuthus* phylogenetic line are very significant for Upper Pliocene and Pleistocene stratigraphic correlation. The nominative species of *Archidiskodon meridionalis* is characteristic of the Late Pliocene, but in the Early Pleistocene it was replaced by more advanced subspecies of that form. Their descendant, *Mammuthus trogontherii*, was characteristic for the Middle Pleistocene but was replaced by *M. primigenius* in the Late Pleistocene. By the middle of the Holocene, the last elephants on the territory of the CIS had become extinct.

ACKNOWLEDGEMENTS

I express my thanks to Albert E. Sanders for his assistance with the English wording of the manuscript and to Larry D. Agenbroad for his aid in the publication of this paper.

(Editors note) Dr. Dubrovo's M1=M4; M2=M5; M3=M6; as used in the earlier portions of the manuscript.

REFERENCES CITED

Aquirre, E.
   1969   Evolutionary history of the elephants. *Science*
          164(3886):1366-1376.
Alexejuva, L.I.
   1967   Moldavian mammalian faunistic complex. In: "Paleon
          tology, geology, and mineral resources of Moldova."
          Kishinev, Issul **2**:111-115. (In Russian.)
   1978   Fauna intermediate between Moldavian and Khaprovian
          complexes (according to the data from Southwest of the
          European part of the USSR. In: "Late Cenozoic fauna of
          Dnestr-Prut watershed." *Kishinev*, 47-55. (In Russian.)

Alexejeva, L.I., and Garutt, V.E.

 1965   New data on the evolution of *Archidiskodon*. *Bulletin of
        Commission for the study of the Quaternary* **30**:161-166.
        Moscow. (In Russian.)

Anonymous

 1991   Opinion 1661 *Mammuthus* Brookes, 1828 (Mammalia,
        Proboscidea): conserved, and *Elephas primigenius*
        Blumenbach, 1799 designated as the type species. *Bulle
        tin of Zoological Nomenclature* **48(3)**:279-280.

Avakian, L.A., and Alexejeva, L.I.

 1966   The first discovery of Paleoloxodon elephant in Arme-
        nian SSR. Izvestia, Academy Nauk USSR **19(1-2)**:1-9.
        (In Russian.)

De Giuli, C., F. Masini, and Torre, D.

 1990   The latest Villafranchian faunas in Italy. The Birro Nord
        local fauna (Apricena, Gargano). *Quartärpaläontologie*
        8:29-34.

Dubrovo, I.A.

 1955   New data on morphology and distribution of ancient el
        ephant (Hesperoloxodon). *Reports, Academy Nauk USSR*
        101(4):759-762. (In Russian.)

 1957   The genera systematic of subfamily Elephantinae Gray
        (Elephants). Vertebrata Palasiatica **1(3)**:223-232. (In Rus-
        sian.)

 1960   Ancient Proboscidea of the USSR. *Transactions of the
        Paleontological Institute, Academy Nauk USSR* **85**:1-78.
        (In Russian.)

 1963a New data on the Taman faunal complex of vertebrates.
        Bulletin of Moscow Naturalist's Society **6**:94-99. (In Rus-
        sian.)

 1963b On the systematics of *"Elephas wusti."* *Paleontological
        Journal, Academy Nauk USSR* **4(95)**:95-102. (In Rus-
        sian.)

 1964a On the existence of *Protelephas planifrons* (Falc. and
        Cautl.) on the territory of the USSR. *Proceedings of the*

Georgian Academy of Sciences **34(3)**:599-603. (In Russian.)

1964b *Archidiskodon* of the USSR. *Paleontological Journal, Academy Nauk USSR* **3**:82-94. (In Russian.)

1966 On systematic position of fossil elephant from the Khazarsky faunistic complex. Bulletin of Commission for Study of the Quaternary **32**:63-74. Moscow. (In Russian.)

1971 The order Proboscidea. In: "Pleistocene Tiraspolya." *Kishinev* 92-108. (In Russian.)

1975 Mammuthus trogontheri trogontherii (Pohlig) aus dem Pleistozan von Tiraspol. *Quartarpalaontologie* **1**:125-156.

1977 A history of elephants of the Archidiskodon-Mammuthus phylogenetic line on the territory of the USSR. *Journal of the Paleontological Society of India* **20**:33-40.

1981 Die fossilen Elephanten Japan. *Quartärpaläontologie* **4**:49-84.

1985 Problems of the systematics of fossil elephants. *Acta Zoologica Fennica* **170**:241-245.

1989 The systematic position of Khaprovian elephant. *Pale ontological Journal, Academy Nauk USSR* **1**:78-87. (In Russian.)

1990 The Pleistocene elephants of Siberia. In: Agenbroad, L.D., J.I. Mead, and L.W. Nelson, editors, "Megafauna and Man: Discovery of America's Heartland." *The Mammoth Site of Hot Springs, South Dakota, Inc. Scientific Papers* **1**:1-8.

1991 Stratigraphic significance of fossil Elaphantinae and the boundary between the Neogene and Quaternary systems. *Geological Series, Academy Nauk USSR* **10**:9-16.

Dubrovo, I.A., and Jakubowski, G.

1988 Morphology of carpus of the paleoloxodont elephants and its significance for taxonomy. *Prace Muzeum Ziemi* **40**:65-96.

Friant, M.A.
1941   A propos du développement de molaires de l'Elephas
        meridionalis Nesti. *Annales SociéteéGéologique Nord*
        79(2):113-128.
Gabunia, L.K., and Dubrovo, I.A.
1989   Systmatics and stratigraphic importance of genus
        Archidiskodon (Mammalia, Proboscidea). *Bulletin of
        Moscow Naturalist's Society* **65(3)**:75-82. (In Russian.)
Gabunia, L.K., and Vekua, A.K.
1963   Fossil elephant from Taribana. Tbilisi. Pp. 1-68. (In
        Russian.)
1967   On new find of southern elephant remains in the southern
        Caucasus. In: *Quaternary fauna of Georgia and its
        geohistorical significance.* Pp. 101-103. (In Russian.)
Garrut, V.E.
1958   Phanagoroloxodon mammontoideus gen. et sp. nov. and
        the ways of the phylogeny in the family Elephantidae.
        Zoological Journal **37(10)**:1541-1554. Leningrad. (In
        Russian.)
Gromova, V.I.
1932   The new materials on the Quaternary fauna of volga re
        gion and the history of mammals of East Europe and North
        Asia. *Bulletin of Commission for Study of the Quater
        nary* **2**:69-184. (In Russian.)
1948   Paleontological and archaeological substantiation of the
        stratigraphy of the Quaternary continental deposits in the
        territory of the USSR. *Transactions of the Geological
        Institute of Moscow* **64(17)**:1-521.
1965   Brief review of the Quaternary mammals in Europe. Mos
        cow. Pp. 1-141. (In Russian.)
Maglio, V.J.
1973   Origin and evolution of the Elephantidae. Transactions
        of the American Philosophical Society **63(3)**:1-149.
Osborn, H.F.
1942   *Proboscidea, a monograph of the discovery, evolution,*

and extinction of the mastodonts and elephants of the world. 2 vols. The American Museum Press, New York. Pp. 1-1675.

Pavlow, M.
    1910   Les éléphants fossilies de la Russie. *Nouvelaux Mémoires Sociétié Impériale des Naturalistes* **17(2)**:1-56.

Pohlig, G.
    1888   Dentition and Kraniologie des Elephas antiquus Falk. mit Beitragen uber Elephas primigenius Blum. und Elephas meridionalis Nesti, II. *Nova Acta Leopold Carolina* **53(1)**:1-279.

Pontier, G., and Anthony, R.
    1966   Presence d'une premolaire chez *l'Elephas imperator* Leidy. *Conte Rendu Academie Science* **196**:1686-1987.

Sherstukov, N.M.
    1954   Description of the fossil elephantine remains found in the Checheno-Inguch Autonomous Soviet Socialist Repub lic. *Transactions of Natural History Museum.* Grozniy. **8**:227-261. (In Russian.)
    1958   On a new find of a fossil jaw of Protelephas planifrons in the Checheno-Inguch ASSR, Caucasus, Asia. *Vertebrata Palasiatica* **2(4)**:254-258. (In Russian.)

Shevchenko, A.I.
    1965   The key complexes of the Pliocene and Lower Antropogene of southwest part of Russian lowland. In: *Stratigraphic significance of Antropogene small mammal fauna.* Moscow. Pp. 7-57. (In Russian.)

Topotchevskiy, V.A., Skoric A.F., and Rekovetz, L.I.
    1987   *Rodents from Upper Neogene and Lower Pleistocene de posits of Chadzhibey liman.* Kiev. Pp. 1-207. (In Rus- sian.)

Van Kolfschoten, T.
    1990   The early Biharian mammal faunas from Bavel and Dorst- Sural. Quartarpalaontologie **8**:265-272.

Vangengiem, E.A., and Zazhigin, V.S.

1965   Some results of the study of Antropogene mammal fauna of west Siberia. In: *Basic problems of study of the Qua ternary Period. Moscow.* Pp. 201-210. (In Russian.)

Zhang, Yuping, and Guanfu Zong

1983   Genus *Paleoloxodon* of China. *Vertebrata Palasiatica* **71(4)**:304-312.

INDEX

278, 279, 281, 283, 357, 360
Mammuthus trogontherii   236, 248, 269
Mandible   162, 175, 176, 182, 215, 241, 243, 255, 256, 257, 259, 260, 263, 265, 295, 300, 304, 308, 314, 315, 319, 321, 327, 349
Martin, P.   30, 117, 131, 153, 242, 251, 372
Mastodon   161, 191, 287, 371
Maxilla (maxillary)   138, 140, 181, 182, 183, 186, 188, 239, 241, 244, 245, 270, 272, 295, 309, 319, 321
Mead, J.   5, 13, 21, 24, 67, 117, 127, 136, 149, 150, 178, 181, 188, 213, 283, 287, 306, 307, 309, 345, 346, 358, 363, 370
Megafauna   24, 28, 59, 61, 64, 67, 350, 364
Metacarpal   224, 225, 229, 230, 243, 245, 247, 250
Metatarsal   138, 224, 225, 230, 233, 234, 235, 241, 247, 251
Mexico   355
Microtus   144, 145, 149
Mirror Lake, SD   39, 62, 63, 64
Missouri River   22, 119, 130, 279
Mol, D.   215, 224, 247, 251, 257, 267, 269, 276
Molars   145, 265, 272, 273, 295, 309, 315, 327, 328, 330, 348, 349
Moss, C.   163, 178, 213
Murray Springs, AZ   23
Mustela   145, 307

N

National Geographic Society   67, 135, 375, 377
Natural Trap Cave, WY   119, 352
Nebraska   4, 23, 103, 130, 133, 146, 147, 240, 241, 247, 248, 251, 375
Neotoma   143, 149
Niobrara River   130
North America   10, 117, 127, 128, 147, 158, 159, 169, 235, 236,

242, 247, 251, 269, 270, 279, 281, 306, 315, 323, 333, 345, 348, 357, 376
North Sea   224, 247, 248

O

Occipital condyle   239, 259, 276, 309, 312, 319, 333
Odocoileus 157
Osborn, H.   21, 56, 158, 159, 281

P

Palaeoloxodon   434, 440, 441
Paleoindian   4, 131, 243
Panthera   350, 352
Pelvis   205, 208, 212, 213, 235, 240, 244, 262, 263, 292, 299, 300, 303, 304, 309, 341
Permafrost   208, 359
Peromyscus   142, 143
Phenacomys   144, 146, 147
Physa   125, 127, 129
Picea   120, 123, 132
Pickerel Lake, SD   119, 129
Pinus   120, 123, 131, 132
Pisidium   125, 127
Pleistocene   21, 24, 66, 69, 105, 106, 110, 117, 133, 134, 136, 138, 140, 142, 144, 146, 147, 148, 149, 150, 153, 159, 163, 213, 215, 224, 236, 242, 244, 247, 248, 250, 251, 269, 281, 290, 295, 306, 307, 308, 309, 312, 315, 327, 328, 333, 348, 350, 352, 355, 357, 358, 372
Poaceae   123, 132
Pollen   24, 58, 117, 120, 121, 123, 125, 127, 128, 129, 130, 132, 133, 134, 136, 149, 150, 306
Polygonaceae   123
Populus   123
Potamogeton   123, 128
Protelephas   426, 447, 450
Pupilla   125, 127

Q

Quaternary   29, 33, 65, 68, 70, 111,
   139, 270, 372, 375, 377, 378,
   426, 427, 443, 447, 448, 449
Quercus   123

R

Radius (radii)   145, 204, 235, 240,
   241, 243, 245, 257, 259, 260,
   261, 262, 263, 265, 292, 300,
   303, 304, 307
Rosaceae   123
Rosebud, SD   119, 130
Roth, V.   181, 182, 186, 253, 255,
   265, 266, 269

S

Salix   123, 127, 128
Saunders, J.   23, 181, 182, 183, 186,
   191, 214, 283, 284, 287
Saxifragacea   123
Scalopus   137, 146
Scapula   5, 198, 200, 216, 218, 239,
   240, 241, 243, 245, 257, 259,
   260, 261, 262, 263, 292, 299,
   300, 303, 304
Scavenger   289, 290, 303, 304, 349,
   350, 352, 355, 356, 357, 358, 370
Sex
   determination   200, 205, 209, 214
   dimorphism   163, 198, 208, 356
Shipman, P.   284
Shoshani, J.   181, 182, 186, 255, 359
Shoshani, S.   359
Siberia   208, 212, 235, 248, 355, 357,
   359
Sikes, S.   230, 359, 364, 365
Smilodon   352
Soffer, O.   191
South America   322
South Dakota   4, 5, 10, 16, 20, 24,
   29, 39, 62, 63, 67, 68, 70, 103,
   105, 110, 117, 118, 119, 120,
   128, 129, 130, 133, 135, 136,
   137, 140, 141, 142, 143, 146,

148, 150, 152, 153, 207, 215,
   220, 224, 236, 242, 245, 247,
   251, 269, 279, 283, 303, 306,
   349, 359, 376, 377, 379
Soviet   426, 450
Spermophilus   134, 138, 139, 140,
   146
Spiral fracture   290, 292
Stagnicola   128
Steppe-grassland   132, 134, 136, 149,
   150, 306, 371
Stockoceros 155
Sylvilagus   138

T

Taphonomy   136, 208, 283, 284, 356
Tappen, ND   119, 130
Taxidea   308
Taxonomy   158, 159, 281
Teeth (tooth)   4, 27, 138, 139, 140,
   141, 142, 143, 144, 145, 176,
   178, 180, 181, 182, 183, 186,
   188, 253, 265, 266, 269, 270,
   272, 273, 274, 276, 304, 319,
   321, 322, 327, 328, 330, 333, 349
Teratorn   352, 358
Thalarctos   319, 348, 349, 352
Thomomys   142
Tibia   138, 139, 140, 207, 222, 234,
   235, 240, 241, 243, 245, 248,
   249, 257, 259, 260, 261, 262,
   264, 292, 300, 303, 304, 309,
   341, 345
Trampling   292, 357, 370
Tremarctos   315, 322, 327, 328, 330,
   331, 333, 338, 354, 358
Trolinger Spring   191
Tundra   127, 131, 132, 134
Tusk   8, 191, 198, 200, 208, 209,
   213, 237, 240, 244, 287, 292,
   295, 304, 305, 360

U

Ulmus   123, 128
Ulna   140, 204, 235, 240, 241, 243,